D1066424

Rethinking Fisheries Management

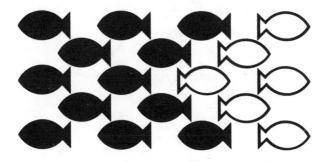

Proceedings from the
Tenth Annual Conference
Held June 1-4, 1986
Center for Ocean Management Studies
The University of Rhode Island

Jon G. Sutinen
Lynne Carter Hanson
Editors

Library of Congress Cataloging-in-Publication Data

Rethinking fisheries management.

  1. Fishery management--Congresses. I. Sutinen, Jon G.
II. Hanson, Lynne Carter, 1950-   . III. University
of Rhode Island. Center for Ocean Management Studies.
SH328.R48 1986   333.95'615   86-26866
ISBN 0-938095-01-3

Published in 1986 by
Center for Ocean Management Studies
University of Rhode Island
Kingston, Rhode Island 02881

Printed in the United States of America.

CONTENTS

Preface   *vii*

Acknowledgements   *ix*

PART ONE   Critical Assessment of the Current
Fisheries Management System   1
LEWIS M. ALEXANDER

1   The NOAA Fishery Management Study   3
BRUCE W. NORMAN

2   The Present System: What's Right and Wrong
The OMB Perspective on Fisheries Management   7
CAROL BALLEW
Critical Assessment of the Current Fisheries Management System   9
WILLIAM G. GORDON
Critique from a Council Viewpoint   14
DOUGLAS G. MARSHALL
What Fishermen Think About Fishery Management   18
BARBARA DUER STEVENSON
An Assessment of the Current System from a
Commercial Perspective   21
RICHARD E. GUTTING, JR.

PART TWO   Comparative Analysis of
Resource Management Approaches   45
LYNNE CARTER HANSON

3   An Overview of Fishery Management: Lessons From Other
Resource Management Fields   47
THOMAS E. BIGFORD

4   Resource Management Strategies
Approaches Utilized to Manage the Fishing Industry in
Atlantic Canada   57
BEN FERGUSON
Fisheries Management in Japan   62
HIROYUKI TAKAGI
Fisheries Management in the EEC   65
RICHARD R. BANKS
Natural Resource Targeting: Opportunities for Fisheries and Forestry   75
RICHARD P. GALE
Management of the Oil and Gas Resources
of the Outer Continental Shelf   87
GERALD D. RHODES

PART THREE   Alternative Strategies and Arrangements   **111**
DENNIS W. NIXON

5   Increasing the Role of State and Local Governments in
Fisheries Management
The Federal Government Perspective   113
RICHARD H. SCHAEFER
Prospects and Potential Problems of a Greater Role for the
State of Alaska   117
GUY THORNBURGH
The State of Massachusetts and Increased
Fisheries Management Responsibilities   120
PHILIP COATES
Increasing the Role of Texas in U.S. Fisheries Management   127
GARY C. MATLOCK

PART FOUR   Enforcement   **133**
JON G. SUTINEN

6   Fisheries Law Enforcement: An Incentive Systems Perspective   135
TIMOTHY M. HENNESSEY
DAVID W. KAISER

7   Improvement in Fisheries Enforcement:
How Do We Get There From Here?   145
JOHN L. DENTLER

8   A Simple Model for Fisheries Enforcement   149
THOMAS A. NIES

PART FIVE   Research Needs   **157**
KENNETH SHERMAN

9   Fisheries Research Strategies for the 1990s   159
KENNETH SHERMAN

10   A New England Fishery Management Council Perspective   167
GUY D. MARCHESSAULT

11   Rethinking Research for Fishery and Ecosystem Management   179
ALEC D. MacCALL

PART SIX   **Privatizing the Fisheries**   **197**
KENELM W. COONS

12   Fisheries Management: Another Option   199
S. FRED SINGER

13   Parsing Privatization Proposals   205
DANIEL A. REIFSNYDER

14   Views on the Issue of Privatizing
Myth of Privatization   211
JAMES D. O'MALLEY
If the Shoe Doesn't Fit, Stretch It   214
RICHARD B. ALLEN
Privatization Schemes: Opportunity and Controversy   219
WALTER T. PEREYRA

PART SEVEN   **Conference Summary**   **227**
JON G. SUTINEN

List of Registrants   231

The Center for Ocean Management Studies was created in the fall of 1976 for the purpose of promoting effective coastal and ocean management. The Center identifies ocean management issues, holds workshops and conferences to discuss these issues, and develops recommendations and research programs to resolve them.

PREFACE

The United States entered a new era of fisheries management when the Magnuson Fishery Management and Conservation Act (MFCMA) was signed into law in 1976. Prior to the act, approaches to fisheries management were haphazard and management and conservation efforts weakened by inadequate enforcement and divided authority. The act was intended to overcome these shortcomings by creating a new and unique system for protecting marine fishery resources from excessive exploitation.

After nearly ten years of experience with the MFCMA, and with re-authorization of the act to be considered soon by congress, it is clearly useful to take stock of the federal fisheries management system. The tenth annual COMS conference was designed to do exactly that. Specifically, the conference sought to critically examine the methods and results of fisheries management under the MFCMA and to identify how the current system can be improved.

To this end, the conference was structured around six basic questions:

- What are the principal strengths and weaknesses of fisheries management under the MFCMA?

- How should the role of the private sector in fisheries management be expanded?

- What are the prospects and problems of increasing the states' role in fisheries management?

- What can we learn from the federal experience with management of other natural resources?

- Which management strategies employed by other countries should be used in U.S. fisheries? and

- What kinds of enforcement and research will be needed to support alternative approaches to fisheries management?

The authors of the papers and panel discussants were asked to address the above questions. Their answers are often rich in insight and controversial. Some of their recommendations are radical, others practical. On the whole the contents of this volume should help us prepare more effective and beneficial approaches to fisheries management for the next ten years.

I would like to thank COMS and its staff, especially Lynne Carter Hanson and Carol Dryfoos Hunter, for their extraordinary support in organizing the conference and producing this volume. Since they grappled with all of the crises, the experiences for me were actually pleasurable.

JON G. SUTINEN
Conference Chairman
Associate Professor
Department of Resource Economics
University of Rhode Island
Kingston, Rhode Island

*   *   *   *   *   *   *   *   *

Please Note: These proceedings do not include the transcribed discussions as in past proceedings. The participants were invited to comment on any session. The few remarks included here were the only ones received in writing.

ACKNOWLEDGEMENTS

I am really pleased to be writing acknowledgements for our tenth annual conference. There are many people who have been supportive to COMS over this ten-year period. I would like to specifically thank two of them for making ten years of COMS possible--John Knauss and Lewis Alexander. Without their longtime and continuing guidance to the Center, we would not have been able to make the contribution to marine policy that we hope we have made. Our most sincere thanks.

When one considers the tremendous amount of planning, preparation, and follow-through that goes into any meeting and its resulting publication, it is no wonder that I have a great many people to thank for their efforts. I would like to begin with the planning committee. My special thanks go to them for their efforts in planning the program, identifying speakers, and participating as session chairs: Jon Sutinen, Conference Chairman and Associate Professor of Resource Economics at the University of Rhode Island; Lewis Alexander, Director of COMS and Professor of Geography and Marine Affairs at the University of Rhode Island; Joel Dirlam, Professor Emeritus of Economics and Resource Economics at the University of Rhode Island; Dennis Nixon, Assistant Professor and Coordinator of the Marine Affairs Program at the University of Rhode Island; Kenelm Coons, Director of the New England Fisheries Development Foundation; and Kenneth Sherman, Director of the Narragansett Laboratory, National Marine Fisheries Service, NOAA.

I would like to thank our speakers and participants. Without them there would be no words to put into the proceedings. I would especially like to commend Doug Marshall and Dick Schaefer for so graciously filling in for two speakers who could not make the meeting at the last moment. For any meeting the funding sources are truly critical. To our funders--National Oceanic and Atmospheric Administration: National Marine Fisheries Service and Sea Grant, my grateful thanks.

My office staff always deserves my thanks for their support and sometimes extraordinary efforts to accomplish our varied tasks with true professionalism. Carol Dryfoos Hunter, COMS Coordinator, is always a valuable right hand and especially when producing proceedings; her efforts at copy editing and coordination of the publication process have made our short turn-around time possible. Artie Venturini, COMS Secretary, painstakingly typed these proceedings. My thanks to them both. My final thanks go to my student drivers who were graduate students in the Marine Affairs Program.

LYNNE CARTER HANSON
Executive Director
Center for Ocean Management Studies
University of Rhode Island
Kingston, Rhode Island

PART ONE

Critical Assessment of the Current

Fisheries Management System

In this opening session of the conference we present an overview of the existing fisheries management system in the United States, including both an assessment of present-day management objectives, and a look at current arrangements in terms of their overall strengths and weaknesses. If we are going to rethink fisheries management, there is a lot in the system which should obviously be retained; there are also aspects which should be modified, or perhaps changed completely, but as the papers presented here will demonstrate, any major changes must be considered within the context of what is politically feasible.

Assessments of fisheries management systems are an ongoing process, as needs and opportunities change, and as new problems arise in the light of experience. But this is a particularly significant year, both because it marks the tenth anniversary of the enactment of the Magnuson Fishery Conservation and Management Act of 1976, and because a panel of experts, working for NOAA, is in the process of assessing the results of ten years of management efforts in the U.S. We shall hear in our first presentation about the results of a draft report the panel has prepared. We shall also hear the views on current fisheries management from representatives of the federal government, the Regional Fisheries Management Councils, the fishermen themselves, and the processors. This session should set the stage for subsequent considerations of what should be done next.

LEWIS M. ALEXANDER
Director
Center for Ocean Management Studies
University of Rhode Island
Kingston, Rhode Island

CHAPTER 1

The NOAA Fishery Management Study

BRUCE W. NORMAN
Staff Director
Fishery Management Study
National Oceanic and Atmospheric Administration
Washington, D.C.

In February, 1986, Dr. Anthony Calio, Administrator, National Oceanic and Atmospheric Administration (NOAA), commissioned a study on the way we manage fisheries in the United States. The reason for the study is the need to reauthorize the Magnuson Fishery Conservation and Management Act of 1976 (MFCMA). Dr. Calio's overall approach was to reauthorize the act for two years (FY 1986 and 1987) and undertake two studies—one to examine and improve the NOAA/Council relationship under the MFCMA and the other to seek out better ways to manage fisheries *in toto*. His objective in the latter study was to see if there were innovative concepts, institutional structures, or management strategies that would reduce the federal regulatory burden and cost to the general taxpayers while conserving the nation's fishery resources. He also wanted ideas that transcended politics—ideas that would survive political change and the economic reality of reduced federal spending.

He called on 11 individuals and asked them for their views within 90 days. The result was the NOAA Fishery Management Study. Public comment on this study and the NOAA/Council task group report, the recent American Fisheries Society report and the proceedings of this conference will be used to put together a management plan for NOAA's fishery management program. We expect that plan to be ready in late 1986 to provide the basis for the FY 1988 budget and reauthorization of the MFCMA.

IMPETUS AND ISSUES

I think I can safely predict that the study will be significant but not particularly radical. The study contributors are aware of what's feasible and were not inclined to spend time debating whether the MFCMA and federal role in fishery management should be scrapped. This was a source of some frustration to me as staff since, while Dr. Calio did not have a particular institutional arrangement in mind, I knew he wanted a range of alternatives to the present system, some of which would entail more effective management at lower cost. The Gramm-Rudman-Hollings Act is not the excuse or the impetus for this study—the impetus is simply a desire for good management of the resource and the taxpayers' money.

A Critique

The study sets out the basic convictions of the contributors and reviews the pluses and minuses of the current system. Chief among the pluses is the regional approach with state, federal and public participation. Chief among the minuses is that overfishing persists in some fisheries. The study addresses a variety of specific topics and some basic concepts, the pivotal one being optimum yield. The topics are some of those most of you would list if asked to review fishery management—highly migratory species, scientific information and statistics, fees and licensing, limited entry, "Americanization," enforcement, and habitat. The study also addresses, in general, the issue of priorities among existing fishery programs.

In some respects, the study replowed the ground covered by the NOAA/Council task group, but succeeded in considering a large number of alternatives. These were grouped into those with all-federal involvement, those with no federal involvement and those with a mixture of state, federal and private involvement. Dr. Calio asked the contributors to look from the outside in, rather than from the inside out. This is extremely difficult to do when you have lived with a system for almost ten years. If most of us were asked to do a comparable review of the Constitution, we might have the same problem—the inclination is to tinker. Still, these individuals have come up with some significant tinkering, even within the existing mixed system. They considered the alternatives and preferred the state/federal/private approach to management.

Optimum Yield

As I said, the concept of optimum yield (OY) is pivotal to the study. Optimum Yield is a magnificent compromise and was intended as such. It is the essence of the current system and gives free play to politics in fishery management. Optimum yield really only papers over competition between commercial and recreational interests and among different users within these interests. In the competition among fishermen for a piece of the resource, the resource itself may not get the priority it needs to assure long-run productivity. Conservation of the resource should have priority over allocation pressures among users.

Like politics in Congress, the short-term is dominant in the existing fishery management system and drives everything including science. Science is being focused on fishery management problems, but the system seems to specify those problems on a near-term basis. I am unaware of any plans that are specifically tied to a stock rebuilding program except Pacific salmon and surf clams. This is perhaps understandable when enforcement in some fisheries is so difficult.

Enforcement

Enforcement has two aspects: what we normally think of as enforcement, which is a matter of how best to detect violations and to exact penalties; and a more subtle notion—the ability to get accurate data from the fishery. I do not wish to link these two elements too closely—sources of data are confidential and, as a matter of policy, data are not a source for law enforcement. But the commonality is that data may be *required* from fishermen and penalties exist for false reporting. Law and policy aside, we are dependent on cooperation from fishermen and processors for our fishery-dependent data. I am working this all back to the issue of short-term management—without a reliable data base and research it is difficult to consider managing for the long-term. The fishery has to be micro-managed and even then, we can't be assured that overfishing is not occurring. Some feel (and I am one) that preventing overfishing is the prime directive of the act. I would not be giving much away to say that the issue of scientific information and statistics was a major concern of the contributors to the study.

Optimum Yield and Habitat

The link to optimum yield should be obvious. The basis of OY is maximum sustainable yield (MSY) or some suitable biological measure of productivity. An assessment of the status of stocks requires both fishery-independent and fishery-dependent data. If the fishery-dependent data is flawed, we don't have a firm grasp on the basis for taking into account social, economic, and ecological factors.

Habitat is a natural topic in this regard since without some threshold level of spawning, feeding and nursery grounds, the productivity of our marine areas will plummet. Habitat has two sides: the science of fishery resource dependence on habitat; and the management of coastal areas. Fishery managers must be concerned with habitat conservation or their efforts will be wasted in the long run; their concern has to be given great weight in decisions about converting habitat to other uses.

Decision-making

Science is a hard nut. No scientist is willing to say, in most cases, that we know enough to make definitive statements about naturally variable phenomena, but they do sometimes stick their necks out. At some point we have to make decisions. We can't wait for the definitive statement, nor can we ignore less-than-certain scientific analyses. The decisions may prove wrong, even when based on the best available data, but at some point you have to decide between conservation of a natural resource and the short-term welfare of all the participants in a fishery—at least under the current system of common property fishery resources.

Common Property V. Private Property

Common property is another one of those basic concepts that needs careful review if we are to rethink fishery management. Limited entry has either passionate supporters or passionate opponents. One reason for this polarization is that limited entry is a blanket term covering a variety of techniques, some of which have failed to control effort in the long run and others of which are untried. Despite the long history of limited entry, it still remains an uncertain solution to the U.S. problem of too many fishermen pursuing too few fish. The simple varieties of limited entry that have been tried and found wanting have failed for the same reason common property fails—limiting the number of vessels, for instance, only creates common property on a smaller scale; the vessels still remaining continue to compete for the fish. The incentive to conserve the resource is still not there. The greatest promise is offered by changing common property into some form of private property so that fishermen perceive the resource as an asset to be managed, rather than a free good they need to take before someone else does.

Licenses and Fees

This leads me to the topic of fees and licenses. While fish are treated as common property, they really belong to the people of the United States. At present, the people, in the form of taxpayers, spend a large amount of money to manage a resource that is free to any domestic user. The larger public deserves an answer to the question of who should pay for fishery management.

Licenses bring me back to the topic of scientific information and statistics. To this day, we cannot say with great confidence how many fishermen—commercial or recreational—there really are. Nor do we have a good handle on total removals from the resource. Fees, limited entry, and licenses can be related, but the real issue with licenses is their role in data collection. For a licensing system to assist in data collection, reporting requirements need to be enforced. An interesting discovery that the study participants made for themselves was the apparent large difference between the east coast and the west coast when it comes to licensing and reporting.

CONCLUSION

I hope I have conveyed that each of these topics is fundamentally related to the others. To review the way we manage fisheries is much more than a time-and-motion study of the process. To leave out habitat, to leave out fundamental research, to leave out the basic responsibility of the individuals involved is to ignore major parts of the fishery system. One reason for managing fisheries and attending to them as systems is so that our people can take full advantage—now and in the future—of the resource available to them.

The responsibility of government is by whatever means, to make sure the resource is available and usable, or as the act states it, that "there be a multiplicity of options available with respect to future uses of these resources." Science and good management should make the resource available; concern for habitat can make it usable. But usability has another aspect and this is encompassed within the term "Americanization." Government has a responsibility here too, but only to assure that our industry is competing fairly internationally and has the climate it needs to thrive domestically. The responsibility for taking advantage of the resource and the markets is industry's. The most optimistic trend in fisheries today is that industry is rising to the challenge—in squid, in sablefish and even Alaskan pollock.

I have touched on most of the issues addressed by the fishery management study in the hope that this conference will help us go a step farther. As I indicated earlier, this conference is timely and its proceedings will be used as we formulate a management plan including proposals for reauthorizing the MFCMA, and for budget decisions for FY 1988 and beyond. The theme of this conference is "rethinking" fishery management. To fulfill that theme, I hope we can keep in mind Dr. Calio's admonition to the study: let's do our rethinking from the outside in, rather than from the inside out.

CHAPTER 2

The Present System:

What's Right and Wrong

THE OMB PERSPECTIVE ON FISHERIES MANAGEMENT

CAROL BALLEW
Budget Examiner
Office of Management and Budget
Washington, D.C.

BACKGROUND

Thank you for inviting me to participate in your conference on these very important and timely issues. I have been involved with the National Oceanic and Atmospheric Administration's (NOAA) Fisheries programs for a little more than a year now, and I am certain that your discussions and deliberations will be of great benefit to me as I go about my work as the budget examiner for NOAA. In the past year I've been able to visit a number of National Marine Fisheries Service (NMFS) sites in the Southeast, the Northwest, and Alaska, as well as attend fishery management council meetings and meet with representatives of most of the councils. I am here mostly to learn from you so I'll keep my remarks brief.

Primarily, I want you to know what the Office of Management and Budget (OMB) concerns are in relation to fisheries management and the actions that OMB takes in the process of addressing those concerns. First of all, for those of you who may not be quite as familiar as others, the Office of Management and Budget is part of the Executive Office of the President and serves as staff to the President. I am not here as an administration spokesperson, however. I am a career civil servant working for OMB. I have been with OMB as a budget examiner for almost six years, so I have served under two administrations. During that time I have worked on a number of programs, not just NOAA—all the way from the Small Business Administration, to the Panama Canal Commission, to the Federal Maritime Commission, and the Economic Development Administration. As you can see, examiners are expected to have a set of general skills that can be applied to various program areas.

OMB FUNCTIONS

The Office of Management and Budget has three major functions with which you would be concerned. There is the management side which deals primarily with concerns about organizational efficiency and productivity. This includes the implementation of A-76 (OMB circular, "Performance of Commercial Activities") with which most of you are familiar, review of management plans and initiatives across the federal government, and financial management improvements. There is the Office of Information and Regulatory Affairs (OIRA) which handles the regulatory analysis and implements Executive Order 12291 that gives OMB the responsibility for assessing the impact of regulations. The OIRA of course is the lead office for OMB with the fishery management councils and fishery management plans. There are also the Offices of Federal Procurement Policy and Statistical Policy. The really important part of OMB, however, is the budget side. We put together the President's Budget that goes to Congress. We monitor the considerations of that budget on the Hill and then we monitor the implementation of appropriations. We conduct policy analysis as it relates to the particular program areas in which we work and provide advice to policy officials so that they can make informed decisions.

This administration has several themes that relate to the issue this conference will be addressing. The administration is looking at the very basic question of "why" from the ground up. In other words, we have been doing this or that year after year and now let's take a good look at why we do it at all. Does the federal government have a role? If so, how much of a role? The appropriate federal role vis-a-vis state and local government and the private sector is a major theme for this administration. Obviously you are aware that dealing with a burgeoning deficit is an administration priority. Therefore, ways to reduce costs to the general taxpayer and/or increase revenue is a priority. Over-extension of the federal role into the private sector and into the lives of individuals has been a concern that this administration has been trying to address by reducing regulations or eliminating mandatory or unnecessary reporting requirements and regulations. Another major theme has been that of privatizing, or if you would, reducing or eliminating the assumption by the federal government of roles and activities that are more appropriately performed by the private sector. In other words, getting the federal government out of the business of competing with the private sector. Under this administration particularly, we, and I am referring to we as staff, have been challenged to question and rethink what the federal role is in all areas. This includes fishery management.

THE FISHERIES MANAGEMENT STUDY

The OMB has been interested in rethinking and relooking at the issue of fisheries management at least since 1982. In 1982, OMB asked the Department of Commerce (DOC) and the National Oceanic and Atmospheric Administration (NOAA) to undertake the fishery management study which included an assessment of the current system and identification of alternatives. The concerns that prompted this request were: that the resource be managed wisely and efficiently where necessary; that burdensome regulations be reduced and unnecessary regulations eliminated; that the government not subsidize inefficient operations and interfere as little as necessary in private business decisions; and that the cost of federal management be reduced. That study effort was a long time in coming about, but it is now underway. The study panel's advice should be available by summer, 1986 to NOAA and the DOC and ultimately to OMB. The administration will review the panel's findings and we, meaning the DOC, NOAA, NMFS, and OMB, will work together to develop the administration's policy. That, of course, will be after consideration of public comment and public debate. The administration will pursue implementation of needed legislation with the Congress.

OMB AND FISHERIES MANAGEMENT

In a related action, the OMB provided guidance to NOAA and DOC earlier this year to the effect that where management of a fishery is necessary, the councils are encouraged to consider alternative measures to the current methods, including limited entry and marketable catch quota systems. We do recognize that alternate measures might not be appropriate in all fisheries and that some measures are more appropriate to a particular fishery than others. OMB's interest in fisheries management takes several forms: review and comment on the fishery management plans and related regulations, as well as development of the President's budget request for the NMFS, but also for the Coast Guard and the State Department, since they each play a role in fisheries management. We also review and clear legislation that is in support of the President's budget and the administration policy and develop policy options and recommendations for consideration by administration officials.

The OMB is often accused of closed-mindedness and inflexibility. I suggest that that depends on where you stand on the issue under consideration. As staff, we try to expose policy officials to all alternatives, to the advantages and disadvantages of each, as well as our judgement of what makes the most sense analytically and programmatically. And, as is usually the case, good arguments can be made on all sides. Hopefully, we bring all that to light so that an informed decision results. We are also often accused of having a very limited vocabulary which consists primarily of "why" and "no." As a taxpayer, I think that you can appreciate that there is someone there saying those sorts of things and asking the hard questions.

CRITICAL ASSESSMENT OF THE
CURRENT FISHERIES MANAGEMENT SYSTEM

WILLIAM G. GORDON
Assistant Administrator for Fisheries
National Oceanic and Atmospheric Administration
Washington, D.C.

INTRODUCTION

Some of you may have seen the sign on the wall at the Point Judith Fishermen's Cooperative nearby which says, "Even a fish would stay out of trouble if it kept its mouth shut." Obviously, fish don't and we don't; and while we're not necessarily in trouble, we do need to rethink our present system—a system meant to benefit both fish and fishermen.

There are many perspectives from which to rethink, as the diversity of this panel suggests. Each perspective shapes our thought and our motivation for the task. My perspective is that of a federal fishery manager. I have said many times before that the primary role of the federal government in fishery management is to act as "steward" of the resource. Today, I would add "advocate" for the resource. Let me tell you why, as I respond to your request to "critically assess" our current system.

CONTEXT

From whatever perspective, a critical assessment should be placed in context—that is, "compared to what?" There is an evolutionary and continuous rethinking process at work. The Magnuson Fishery Conservation and Management Act of 1976 (MFCMA) emerged from strong and specific historical, political, environmental, and economic pressures. The consensus was that there was need for fishery management. The act's language was responsive to that need. During its ten-year existence, the MFCMA has been "rethought" significantly as these early pressures matured. Initially, the act's encompassing purpose was conservation and management, of which a corollary objective was to bring foreign fishing under control as a means to that end. The chief benefit would be the development of a climate encouraging economic growth in the domestic fishing industry. Through a series of amendments over the years, the primary purpose of conservation and management became economic growth. These changes were snapshots of political attitudes, an evolutionary bootstrapping of the initial objectives.

The same thing has happened to the concept of optimum yield (OY). Optimum yield was the product of management theories which had been based alternately on science and politics dating back to the 1600s. The concept encapsulated a conservation level of catch as modified by the interests of the participants in the domestic fishery. In theory, OY integrated plan objectives and balanced the various interests comprising the regional and national welfare, affirming that what's good for the fish can be good for the fisherman. Ideally—and I believe rightfully so—the act placed the U.S. fishing industry in decision-making partnership with the federal government as steward of the nation's fishery resources. In practice, OY has increasingly served as an arena for user competition for short-term advantage, which has too often demonstrated the reverse—that what's good for the fisherman at the moment is often bad for the fish.

CRITERIA

We usually measure success of the current fishery management system in terms of the goals of the act, health of the resource, number of federal management plans developed, trade balances, or metric tons of fish caught, processed, marketed or consumed. Today, I want to join the theorists for a moment, and look at success from a totally different perspective. To what extent are the act's concepts and processes being absorbed into our social and economic system? Dr. George Gallup suggested some years ago that new ideas are accepted slowly, subject to the following "resistance" factors:

- How complex is the idea;

- How it differs from accustomed patterns;

- How it competes with prevailing ideas;

- Whether its usefulness can be demonstrated or proven;

- How well it meets a felt need;

- How strong are the vested interests that may block change; and

- How often is the public reminded of the new idea.

ASSESSMENT

It doesn't take higher math to draw some inescapable conclusions about resistance to the current management system under these criteria.

1. It is complex. Legal complexity alone fills volumes of 3-ring binders--complexity of process, of information and data need, and of regulations; the layering of decisional responsibility and diffusion of accountability; relationship with other applicable law, and the multiplicity of government jurisdictions.

2. It differs from major accustomed patterns such as: traditions of individualism; free enterprise; and resistance to control on individual behavior and free access to a common property resource. Competing viewpoints often exist in community values (ports, regions, cultures).

3. Competition of perspectives is demonstrated through: the polarities of decisional style, language, semantics between bureaucrat and fisherman/processor; tensions between U.S. and foreign interests; the federal government v. the states; different gear types and fish uses; and the multiple uses of the ocean.

4. Ask a fisherman (or OMB or the Internal Revenue Service) whether all aspects of the system are justified or subject to proof. Besides his boat, a fisherman's true property right currently resides only in his knowledge of the ocean--small wonder he is unwilling to share it. Ask a scientist about "best available information."

5. Felt needs are in the eye of the beholder. With passage of the MFCMA, the U.S. harvester expected unrestricted access, freed from foreign competition. The fact that uncontrolled domestic fisheries could also deplete the resource and/or reduce economic return was forgotten or ignored. Competition to the domestic processor from joint ventures was unanticipated.

6. The strength of vested interests is abundantly apparent. Ask a gillnetter about longlines. Ask a trawler about pots. Ask a shoreside processor about joint ventures. Ask a sportsfisherman about a commercial fisherman. Attend a council hearing.

7. Fishery management decisions affect government, and all elements of the commercial and recreational industry—harvester, head-boat operator, processor, tackle manufacturer, shipper, marketer, motel operator, beer distributor, and consumer, among others. They touch each element in a different time and place and in a different way. Thus, reminders of the "new idea" are difficult to transmit across

this diversity and usually are acknowledged only when there is threat of adverse impact; blame is then easily placed on the current "system."

What we find, then, is that the current system is too *complex* to work well; that fisheries management often seeks changes that are too *radical* to work well; that not everyone *wants* fisheries management to work well; that fisheries management often works *better in theory* than in practice; that users compete against each other to create a system that must work *for all* of them; that fisheries management *has not often met real needs;* and that as a result, people *like to blame* the system.

EXAMPLES

Let me give you two examples—one having to do with fishermen, the other with fish.

First, many people like to think that it is the federal government that keeps fishery management from working well, citing the burden of rules and regulations placed on the users of the fisheries. If we look closer, however, we find that the burden of rules and regulations is usually inversely proportional to the ability of competing user groups to work together to determine who should catch how much of a given allowable catch, and when, where, and for what purpose. When the users of the resource cannot agree among themselves on the who's, how's, and what for's, we find they trade agreement for regulation.

Lack of agreement can lead to flagrant violation of the rules by those who didn't agree with them in the first place. The situation goes downhill from there. The result generally is that the resource suffers first, then the fisherman, then the processing worker, then the consumer through scarcity and higher prices. User groups need to work together to reach common goals and compatible strategies.

Second, we very often do not know enough about a resource to know what fishery management practice is good and what is bad. We know that fishing pressure decreases at least the short-term abundance of the fish population. We are not always sure of the extent of change. Fishery resources often run in cycles. Fishing activities can intensify a declining cycle or retard an increasing cycle. Funding is simply not adequate for the scientific research to allow resource abundance to be accurately predicted. Who is to provide the information essential for effective resource management for all its beneficiaries? Should this be the major federal role? Is the public willing to support the effort? How has the public interest been defined?

The *point* is that a change of attitude is hard to come by, whether it be of user group or government entity. Dr. Gallup's resistance factors need time to be acted upon, counterbalanced, or reduced by experience and evolving perceptions. We have already seen changes in the MFCMA that reflect certain kinds of changes. I expect the debate here and the reports of Dr. Calio's "internal" and "external" evaluation groups will contribute significantly to the evolutionary process.

TRENDS

The most recently published report of the Council on Environmental Quality (CEQ) identifies two important trends in the evolutionary process. One is the extent to which the current regulatory control over environmental quality and natural resources has moved our nation strongly in the direction of a "planned" economy. In principle, all "bordercrossings" between man and the environment are now guarded.

A second trend—in part a reaction to the managed economy approach—has been an increased awareness of the market as an alternative means of reconciling conflicting values, while preserving resource and environmental amenities. According to CEQ, there has been a growing realization that environmental problems largely arise because of the prevalence of "common property" resources. Un-owned resources are more likely to be over-exploited than resources privately owned and managed. Since a private owner directly benefits from the preservation and maintenance of such resources, he may have greater incentive to act as a responsible steward.

The Council on Environmental Quality spoke not of fish, but of air, water, wildlife, archeology, forests, and wilderness. Whether self-interest is a reliable protector of conservation values should certainly be examined and tested under appropriate circumstances. As Garret Hardin noted 20 years ago in describing the tragedy of the commons, the morality of an act is a function of the state of the system (society's values) at the time it is performed. If we believe CEQ's assertion that no other national goal retains such strong public support from such a broad base of the population as environmental conservation, perhaps there is hope for fish. I think you will agree that for that hope to become reality, our job is to act as steward of the fish resources—to be their advocate, protector, and defender.

CONCLUSION

The MFCMA brought historical imperatives and industry hopes together in 1976, but, with hindsight, it seems that the chances for success of the system shouldn't have looked quite so good at the beginning. In evaluating it ten years later, we need to look at which of those resistance factors could actually have been successfully resolved in only ten years. As we rethink this system of fishery management—or in constructing a new one—it might be well to keep them in mind. Certainly, centuries of evolving fishery management theory and practice have not brought significant improvement in the condition of the stocks or the economic condition of the industry. Nor, on the whole, has ten years under the MFCMA. The system is approaching a crossroads. Will it be the "feds," the states, the users of the resource, or the existing—or some other—combination which will assume the responsiblity for setting and implementing a future course?

Whatever the judgment of Congress on reauthorization and amendment of the MFCMA in 1987, the outlook is that more will have to be done with less, and better. The role of government is changing as priorities are reexamined in light of diminishing federal resources. All levels of democratic government share, to one degree or another, three major responsibilities: protecting the public interest; acting as steward (advocate) for the people's resources; and resolving conflict. That pretty well describes the basic functions of fishery management. Marine resources are part of the true wealth of the nation. How well they survive is an indication of how seriously we take these responsibilities. Perhaps the time has come for the users to take up a larger share.

The successes and failures of ten years under the MFCMA demonstrate that there are no guarantees in the fish business, only opportunities. It is good that we have had these ten years. Most fishermen are adept at taking advantage of opportunities. Around the nation, many did and so prospered over periods within those ten years. Many processors did also. Now we can assess some of the economic impacts of the good years and the bad years and why things happened. I ask the question, however, did mother nature take advantage of the opportunities? Nevertheless, the experiences of these ten years should guide us toward a more realistic baseline assessment of attitudes as we look to the next ten.

CRITIQUE FROM A COUNCIL VIEWPOINT

DOUGLAS G. MARSHALL
Executive Director
New England Fishery Management Council
Saugus, Massachusetts

A critique of the present fishery management system from a council perspective is my given topic, but what I will say in no way represents the views of the New England Fisheries Management Council, only my own perspective.

BUDGET CONCERNS

The question of fishery management and the system that we have in the United States today seems to involve several issues, not the least of which is the one that Carol Ballew is particularly concerned with, that is money. We spend quite a lot of money on fishery management. Looking at the budget of the National Marine Fisheries Service (NMFS) over the past three or four years, you will see that it ranges from approximately $150 to $160 million per year. This is for all fishery resource programs that are operated by NMFS, including some State grants and a number of other items in addition to NMFS' own activities and the operations of the Fishery Management Councils. That doesn't sound like a lot of money in terms of the total federal government budget but, on the other hand, it is significant. I'm not very good at remembering numbers, but I believe that the ex-vessel value of the commercial fisheries under regulation by the New England/mid-Atlantic Council plans, excluding fisheries which are not regulated and some for which I don't have the numbers, bring in approximately $1 million a day or $365 million a year. If you compare the budget expended for management of the previously-mentioned marine programs to that sum, it is substantial.

It should be clear that not all the money that is spent on fishery resource programs is spent directly on management, per se. In fact, a great deal of it is not. It has been very popular (at least in some quarters) in the past several years, to have the NMFS budget justified on the basis of the Magnuson Fishery Conservation and Management Act of 1976 (MFCMA). If you look at some of the NMFS documents related to their program of Management by Objectives, you will find that NMFS claims it spent as much dealing with the lobster management plan as the New England Council spends running its whole operation in any particular year.

I think there has been a tendency to say, "Well, we need this budget because we are doing all these things that relate to fishery management." However, you need to look at not only the management issues but at all the other things that NMFS is spending money on. I quite agree with Carol Ballew that what you have to do in dealing with these concerns is not assume that because we have been doing something a certain way, that it is the right way or the way we should continue to do it. We need to step back and ask first, "Is this activity worth doing?" If it isn't then we should stop doing it. If it is worth doing, we need to ask whether the federal government should be doing it or whether it should be someone else's responsibility?

Personally, I am not convinced that all of the money that is spent by the federal government is well spent. I don't say this as somebody sniping from the outside. I spent 20-odd years as a federal bureaucrat myself. I think that all of us who have been involved have to admit that there are times and places when money is freely spent that might very well have been better off left in the treasury. We are not going to see the good old days again, where any amount of money that is desired is forthcoming. There are some ways to save money within the existing system if we want to do it. I'll get to some of those a little bit later. But, when we talk about fishery management we have to step back and address some of the fundamental questions that Bill Gordon alluded to in his remarks. Why do we manage the fisheries? What is it we are really trying to accomplish? I don't think we all have the same point of view.

HOW MUCH IS TOO MUCH MANAGEMENT?

First of all, we may try to do too much in managing fisheries. There are a lot of problems in the world that are amenable to neat solutions and there are a lot of problems in the world that don't have any good solutions, neat or otherwise. You just cope with the problems as best you can and go along. It is incredibly difficult to closely estimate the number of fish in a fishery. There may be isolated cases where that works, where fisheries are very species specific. But even then you have enormous natural fluctuations in stock size. Nobody knows quite why. There is a current example—the haddock stocks by common agreement are not in very good shape and yet this year we have a bumper crop of young haddock coming up from a relatively small spawning stock. Those things happen. Sometimes when you have a big spawning stock you don't have much recruitment. So, I think to try to put numbers on fisheries by and large is a losing game, particularly in a case where you have a fishery that includes a number of species.

I think the New England Council has done the right thing in plans that it has generated in the past several years. That is, not to put out hard numbers that represent annual quotas or optimum yields but rather to take the approach of trying to take care of the resource by assuring that enough fish stay in the ocean until they are of a sufficiently mature size to spawn and assure a continuing supply of fish. Now, what this implies is that there are going to be years when everybody can make a lot of money and there are going to be other years when hardly anybody will make any money. Some people will probably go broke. I don't know of any business in the United States where that is not the case. There are people who go broke in any business and I don't know why the fisheries business should be any different from any of the others. In the fish business there are no guarantees but there are a lot of opportunities. There is a certain amount of risk taking and I think that is the way the world ought to work.

One of the things I should say right up front is that in spite of flaws in the MFCMA and in spite of some serious problems in the fishery management council system, I think it is fundamentally a good system. I don't think it is perfect and I would not at all suggest that there should not be some changes made, but I really believe that the idea of bringing people in the industry and people who are interested parties into the process of managing fisheries is a good one.

I fully agree with the Office of Management and Budget's (OMB) view and the view of the current administration that the fewer regulations we have the better. I don't think we are terribly good at managing but I think we are pretty good at regulating. Frankly, I think that what we really ought to focus on is regulating the people who are involved in fisheries to protect juvenile fish and let the resource go up and down with the natural fluctuations that are there.

HABITAT CONCERNS

I am personally alarmed at what is happening to the environment in the United States and, in fact, to the environment worldwide. Therefore, I have a lot of interest in questions of habitat protection and habitat enhancement. However, when NMFS set up its habitat policy, I do not think it was very realistic for the councils to adopt this policy and incorporate habitat considerations into their management plans. Most of the people who serve on fishery management councils are not scientists. They are mostly business people and recreational fishermen and are not really competent to get into the details of habitat issues. There are a lot of other people around who are already doing habitat work and it ought to be left to them to do it. I do not have any problem with NMFS being involved with habitat issues. It is a perfectly legitimate role for the National Marine Fishery Service. It is even more of a legitimate role for the various state governments up and down the coast. But I don't think the fisheries management councils per se should have any responsibilities in the area of habitat even though council members may be concerned or interested.

AREAS OF CHANGE

I would like to see some changes made in the system and I will tell you what some of them are. First of all, the boundaries that were drawn when the councils were organized may have made sense at the time; however, in retrospect they don't make as much sense as they seemed to initially. I believe that there should be one council that extends from Cape Hatteras to Canada instead of two and part of another. The concern has been expressed that that would result in an unwieldy and exceedingly large council. The member selection would have to be done differently and I would suggest that the state director and one obligatory member from among three nominated by the Governor of each state from Maine to Carolina and appointed by the Secretary of Commerce, would result in a nice compact little group.

Looking at the problems associated with the council system, I think the plan development process that we go through is basically a sound one. We have industry advisors, we have scientific advisors, both from the states and from academic institutions who serve to give the councils advice. We have council members who represent a variety of groups of people—they are businessmen, active fishermen, and representatives of recreational interests. They bring a lot of good information and good advice into the process. They don't always agree. There are some very bitter quarrels and wrangling that go on. We have public hearings, we have committee meetings, we have council meetings. If fishermen do not get involved in the process and then discover at the end that they did not come out as well as they would have liked to, they really have only themselves to blame because the system is there and it provides ample opportunities to affect the outcome.

Where I think the present system breaks down is in the review process. After we have gone through all the developmental process and have received all of the comments, suggestions and advice, listened to arguments pro and con, heard the scientists and the user groups, then the plan goes forward to Washington where the process of review is almost more complicated than the process of development. What it really boils down to, quite candidly, is a great many people who *haven't* been involved in the process second guessing all the people who *have* been involved in the process.

I would like to see the review process shortened dramatically. To assure that the concerns of the federal government with respect to Executive Order 12291, the Paperwork Reduction Act, Regulatory Flexibility Act, Administrative Practices Act, and all the rest of the alphabet soup, are not done harm to, I would like to see more involvement than we now have in the plan development process by representatives of the federal government. We have the Regional Director of the National Fisheries Service as a voting member of our council. We have a State Department officer, a Coast Guard officer, a Fish and Wildlife Service officer and, a representative of the Atlantic States Marine Fisheries Commission (ASMFC). These latter don't vote on the council. I would like to see both the Center Director and the Regional Director have a vote on the council. Quite frankly, I would be willing to give Fish and Wildlife Service, the Coast Guard and Department of State votes on the council as well. I would also be delighted to have someone from OMB involved in the process, although that seems less likely.

I think the things that the reviewers go through in Washington are, in fact, the same things that the council goes through in the process of development the plan. When you go through the process you have a different view of it and you have a lot of understanding of the nuances that don't show up in the final product no matter how carefully the plan is drafted, or how well prepared the regulatory impact statements and reviews may be. If you have higher level of federal involvement then when the plan is finished the review process should be a very simple one. The basic question that should be asked is, "Is this *grossly* inconsistent with national standards in the act or with the executive order or any of these other applicable laws?" I say grossly because you will never have perfect compatibility between any two documents that you can generate in any given law. The other question should be, "Did the Council go through the process of seeking public input from all the interested parties?" This covers everyone from the National Wildlife Federation to the National Fisheries Institute and any of the other organized groups that have an interest in fisheries and marine affairs.

The other thing that I would do with my "Super Council," that would go from Cape Hatteras to Canada, is to ask each Governor to nominate a representative of a conservation or environmental group and to nominate a representative of a consumer organization group. Out of those nominees, I would have the Secretary of Commerce pick a couple of consumer representatives and perhaps three conservation organization representatives. You would end up with a council of about 35 people who vote. Everyone on the council should be a voting member.

If you compare this "Super Council" with the existing New England and mid-Atlantic councils, you should save approximately ten person days per meeting day of the two councils. You could probably also save about six council staff positions. There would probably be a small but not significant increase in travel costs.

I disagree with Bill Gordon that the MFCMA is so many pages of gobbledygook. I think part of the problem with the act is that we have interpreted it to death. It is a fairly straightforward, simple document and if we spent a little bit less time fiddling with the guidelines we might be further ahead than we are. I have, here in my hand, a new set of NMFS guidelines on regulatory analyses of fishery management actions. If you read what is demanded in the regulatory analyses, it seems that where the required actions really belong is in the process of *developing* fishery management plans--not in writing regulatory analysis. Once you identify the problem, prepare a description of utilization patterns, and define management objectives, then you need to identify and describe management alternatives. An analysis must then be performed in terms of which one achieves the objectives and provides the greatest number of benefits--and God knows what that means. Finally, a process must be developed which is designed to review and monitor the operations of the plan and its impacts on fishery management.

I don't have any trouble with these specifics, but the analysis that is required to be included as part of fishery management plans really ought to be done during the process of developing the management plans themselves. Having gone through all of this, it is fine to say, "Here it is, it's available, we did it." But then to have that analysis itself all reviewed seems to me like repeating the whole process again and then trying to second guess the decisions that were originally made.

We often hear that the councils are very political and that this is somehow not a very good thing. I think it *is* a good thing. I think the issues that are involved in question of managing fisheries are as much political issues as they are economic or scientific. I don't deny that there are scientific resource questions, but on the other hand, I think we are really managing fisheries because we want fish out there for people to catch. We want fish out there for recreational harvesters and we want fish out there for the commercial fishing industry. Those are legitimate concerns. However, the idea of trying to manage fisheries to preserve certain levels of this stock or that stock or this species or that species, is at best a kind of scientific guessing game. I don't think that that is what we ought to be spending our money on. If we can assure the continued availability of the fishery resource and then let the fishermen compete freely for that resource under adequately conservationist regulations, then we will have done, I think, the most we can expect to accomplish.

WHAT FISHERMEN THINK ABOUT FISHERY MANAGEMENT

BARBARA DUER STEVENSON
Boat Owner
Otonka, Inc.
Dagsboro, Delaware

MANAGEMENT: WHAT KIND AND AT WHAT COST?

When I was trying to decide what to say about fishermen and fishery management, I went around to many fishermen and asked them what they thought of fishery management. Universally, their answer was, "You don't use those kind of words, do you?" This answer left me with not much more to say. But, in my personal experience—having been on the mid-Atlantic Fishery Management Council for six years and owning two trawlers—I find that "You don't use those kind of words..." applies to something quite different now than it did ten years ago. Ten years ago it meant that we don't want any kind of management, we don't need management, and we will never benefit from management, period.

Now when one asks a fisherman how he's doing he says, "You've got to do something about those people in North Carolina catching small fluke." When you ask a surf clammer what's wrong they say, "Well, we've got to change the size limit." If you ask if he wants to drop the size limit altogether he says, "No, no, no, we need a size limit; we just want to change it." I get the feeling that many of the fishermen have decided that management is needed; but, what kind and at what cost are difficult questions to them.

Fishermen are having a lot of trouble interfacing with the system. One of the major problems fishermen have—and this is their problem not the system's problem—is they don't want to be bothered with the meetings, papers, and discussion that involvement with management entails. They just want to know what they are supposed to do and for that to be something they agree with.

This problem of the amount of time necessary to be a participant in fishery management can be provided for in a fishery's regulations, as for instance, in the surf clam fishery. Currently a vessel can only fish one day every two weeks which leaves fishermen 13 days for meetings and management activities for every day fished. Obviously, most fishermen would prefer some other system.

Fishermen are not quite sure what to expect out of management. Some say, "Well, if management is good maybe a whole lot of management is great. Solve all of our problems and we will all be rich and there will be plenty of fish to catch." Other fishermen will desire the least management possible. Fishermen that think all their problems will be solved are quickly disappointed in the system because: 1) when they want their problem solved, they want it done today (fishermen don't understand that it takes two years for a plan to be written and a year for it to be reviewed, etc.); and 2) because fishery management cannot solve all of their problems under the most ideal of circumstances.

Another problem fishermen have, when they start talking to managers, is that they realize managers don't understand their individual fishery in the same way they do. While managers may understand broad spectrums and general situations, fishermen are so involved in their own fishery that they cannot understand how someone can manage when they do not understand the basics of an individual fishery. For instance, several years ago I found out that Woods Hole (N.E. Fisheries Center) thought there was only one trawl fishery in the mid-Atlantic which caught X amount of this and X amount of that. Actually, there are several fisheries for different species operating at once. If one worked to manage that area, the management measures that would go along with what the Woods Hole people thought would be very different from what would be practical from the fisherman's viewpoint.

Fishermen have problems with management when there is too much change. It takes time for fishermen to accommodate themselves to regulations and time to figure out what they are going to do about them—obey or devise avoidance mechanisms. As it is now, things change before the fishermen have become comfortable with a particular set of regulations.

REGULATORY PROBLEMS

Uneven levels of enforcement of regulations and difficult to enforce regulations cause fishermen varying problems. First, regulations that look good on paper and that managers like because they can check off x, y, and z, may not work in real life. Fishermen either think this is wonderful because they can get around them, or they think it is terrible because the regulations will not have their intended results. This type of regulation generally hurts the "honest" fishermen while leaving the others unaffected.

Second, regulations that could work, given a certain level of enforcement, don't work because that level of enforcement is not available. Of course, fishermen react to this the same way as to unworkable regulations. This gets extremely frustrating to those fishermen who had hoped to get some benefit from management. Even these fishermen cannot continue abiding by the regulations as more and more people disregard them. I think a good example of this is in the surf clam fishery. Originally when the surf clammers thought their hours, days, and other regulations were going to be intensely enforced, most people abided by them. But, as time went on and people cheated and did not get caught, more and more fishermen began cheating because if they did not they would not get their share. There had developed a high level of cheating before strong enforcement actions began.

Third, regulations that are socially unacceptable stand little chance of being abided by. If fishermen in general don't believe that a regulation is good, they will cheat; they will then cheat more as a game than as a necessity. These types of regulations do no one any good—the resource does not receive the protection envisioned, the fishermen stand the chance of being caught, and the managers look bad to both the fishermen and those overseeing their management efforts.

Fishermen do not have long time horizons. When a fisherman is caught and it takes a year to get a notice that the system even knows he was caught and then another year to get some kind of fine and then the case can go on for many appeals, the impact of having actually caught someone is significantly reduced. In several fisheries, there are cases where the regulations had changed twice between a violation and the court appearance and what a fisherman had been caught doing was now legal. So, fishermen aren't sure whether they should really worry about being caught. They would much prefer a system that is swift and sure.

The lack of local control concerns fishermen interested in management—they think a system has been agreed on, they go back fishing, and the plan goes to Washington. The plan is turned down. Fishermen are no longer sure when a proposed system is set. Plans recently have been turned down because they are too lenient and because they are too tough.

The biggest problem with current management is the lack of predictability. If a fisherman has a problem and comes to the council or NMFS, no one can predict how long it will take for a plan to develop and for something to be done about his problem. They can't predict the level of enforcement to be applied so they don't know whether to go along with it or whether to cheat. They can't predict how long a particular measure will be in effect.

Fishermen also complain that if managers really want to do something to help the fisheries they will help develop the underutilized and wasted species we have on this coast. Off the New England coast now the underutilized and wasted species more than equal the amount of non-industrial fish landed.

SUMMARY

Fishermen now suspect that management might possibly be needed and might even be beneficial; but, currently the process too often only produces frustrations and problems.

AN ASSESSMENT OF THE CURRENT SYSTEM
FROM A COMMERCIAL PERSPECTIVE

RICHARD E. GUTTING, JR.
Vice President
Governmental Relations
National Fisheries Institute
Washington, D.C.

Overfishing prompted Congress to change our fishery management system ten years ago.[1] The U.S. jurisdiction was extended to include over 2 million square miles of ocean, and the federal government thrust itself into the formidable task of realigning U.S. fishery relations with other countries and managing dozens of offshore fisheries.[2] Congress explained that this was necessary to "prevent overfishing, to rebuild overfished stocks, to insure conservation, and to realize the full potential of the nations's fishery resources."[3]

My task is to assess this system from the perspective of the commercial seafood industry. This industry is made up of the chain of companies moving fish out of the water to the dinner plates of the consumer. Attitudes and opinions about fishery management vary widely among individual companies depending on their position along this chain and their geographical location.[4] Some complain that the system is fundamentally flawed and should be scrapped. Others are convinced that only minor adjustments are needed. One belief is shared—a conviction that the current system is less than perfect.

Policy discussions abound with talk about the respective roles of various public officials. Very little is said about the health of the fishery resources and the thousands of companies that depend upon them. It is time to get back to basics and ask whether we are better off today than we were ten years ago before the present system was set up.

This question, from the perspective of the commercial industry, can be broken down into several related issues:

1. Has production increased?;
2. Are the resources in better shape?;
3. Have production costs been reduced?;
4. Have investment risks been reduced?;
5. Has product quality been helped? and
6. Have prices suffered?

Another way to look at it is to ask whether the benefits achieved under the present system outweigh its costs.

This paper attempts to answer these questions. The views expressed are my own and do not necessarily reflect those of the National Fisheries Institute.

THE PRESENT SYSTEM

Americans do not eat a lot of fish, nor do they eat fish in any great variety. In recent years, however, they have been increasing their consumption of fish and cutting back on their consumption of meat. Many experts believe this change is due to concerns over health and nutrition rather than price, since the price of fish has increased relative to meat and poultry. The demand for better quality and more variety is also growing and retail stores, supermarkets, and restaurants are gearing up to meet this demand.

Americans spent $16 billion for fish and seafood last year, or about four percent of their food purchases.[5] Per capita consumption has been increasing about 1.2 percent per year.[6] Last year it increased six percent and now averages 14.5 pounds.[7] Because of population growth, total demand is growing at about two to three percent annually.[8]

Supplies to meet this growing demand come from hundreds of fish stocks managed by states, the federal government, various international organizations, and many foreign governments.

The States

The states manage those stocks which account for the bulk of our domestic production.[9]

State governments serve as harvest regulators, data collectors, habitat protectors, researchers and stock enhancers. How they carry out these different roles varies widely from state to state. State legislatures often delegate management issues to commissions but frequently retain politically sensitive issues to themselves. Some ask a state agency to take on these responsibilities, while others pass decision-making on to cities, towns and counties. In recent years, a few coastal states have reorganized to broaden the regulatory powers of their marine programs. Decision-making, however, often is cumbersome and time-consuming. And it almost always is influenced by political pressure groups.

Enforcement and monitoring activities also vary widely. In some states, specific law enforcement units are responsible for marine fisheries, while in other states law enforcement officials have a wide range of duties. State penalties differ significantly and so do manpower, equipment, and other law enforcement capabilities.

Each year the states produce a blizzard of administrative rulings, regulations and laws. The diversity and volume of these restrictions are so great that no one can keep track of them all.

Often times state restrictions are requested, even demanded, by fishermen and processors, or by some competing group which happens to have political strength at the time. Some discriminate against nonresidents. Others impose restrictions which conflict with those of other states. These practices, in part, prompted Congress to prohibit discrimination and insist on consistency in the federal system.

Three interstate marine fishery commissions have tried to bring more consistency to state rules since the 1940s. These commissions, however, are limited to making recommendations and so far, with one exception, the coastal states have been unwilling to vest them with regulatory authority.[10] As a result, the commissions are not able to take quick and decisive action when the stocks get into trouble.

Congress has encouraged interstate cooperation in the past through various grant programs.[11] Funding, however, has been scarce recently and Congress has begun to resort to the threat of preemption to force state action.[12]

The Federal System

The second largest part of our domestic production comes from federal waters.[13]
Establishing the 200-mile zone ten years ago and putting the foreign fleets under fishing quotas were done quickly and at little cost. Within only a few months the Secretary of Commerce had developed and implemented 16 preliminary plans to regulate foreign harvests. While most of these plans have been superceded by fishery management plans, seven are still in effect.

The system for managing foreign harvests includes an elaborate, and often times mysterious, process for allocating fish to the foreign fleets. Sixteen nations have participated in this process receiving permission to harvest over 17 million metric tons (mt) and the right to operate foreign factory vessels in U.S. fisheries.[14] In return they have paid about $200 million in fees and fines.[15]

The regulation of foreign fishing over the years has generated a lot of controversy and a series of legislative changes. In the center of this controversy is the idea that the U.S. industry should somehow get priority access to the resources over the foreign fleets. The foreign fleets are only supposed to get the leftovers, or "surplus" fish that are available after the needs of the U.S. industry are subtracted from the available yield. This statutory equation for calculating the "total allowable level of foreign fishing," however, *provides no real priority on the fishing grounds or in the marketplace.* Over the years, therefore, fishery managers have attempted to use various strategies to give the domestic industry a priority including:

1. The "fish and chips" policy;

2. Legislative phase-out schedules for foreign harvesting and/or processing;

3. Reducing the "optimum yields" to eliminate foreign harvesting and/or processing; and

4. Giving priority access to fishing grounds or markets through time and area restrictions in fishery management plans.

Under the "fish and chips" policy, allocations of "surplus" fish are supposed to be made in exchange for foreign trade concessions or purchases. Allocations, however, are made in a highly political environment. Efforts to obtain foreign concessions have been frustrated on several occasions by the linkage of allocations to whaling in the so-called Pelly/Packwood Amendment as well by the "catch-all" criterion, or "basket clause," in the Magnuson Fishery and Conservation and Management Act of 1976 (MFCMA) which says that any matter deemed to be "appropriate" an be considered in allocating fish. As a result, allocations have been much more dependent upon historical shares of the catch, various national defense issues, and whaling concerns, than any interest in developing U.S. fisheries.

The other strategies to give the U.S. industry a real priority have been opposed at various times by federal officials and a few industry groups with an economic interest in helping the foreign fleets. No single strategy has emerged with a solid political consensus behind it.

Central to the federal system for regulating domestic harvests is a regional council process of checks and balances. This process was designed by Congress ten years ago to ensure that regional interests were not ignored by federal bureaucrats, and that the various interest groups would have multiple points of access into decision-making. The idea was that fish should be allocated by a user-group consensus, and not by some fish "czar."

The councils, however, are ill suited to manage fisheries. They have very limited staffs and budgets. Council members meet periodically only to be deluged with esoteric scientific data and self-serving rhetoric from the competing user groups. Like many committees, they often bog down because of philosophical disputes, personality conflicts or hidden agendas.

Many council members are private citizens with an immediate economic stake in the regulations they vote on. These special interests can slant council decisions, lead to delaying tactics, or result in cosmetic solutions.

Most importantly, no one has clear authority in the council system, nor is anyone fully accountable for the results. Instead, authority is shared among the councils and the Secretaries of Commerce and State. The result is constant political tugging and pulling.

These political tensions are exacerbated by a lack of policy direction. Congress never really explained what the councils were supposed to do beyond stopping the "overfishing" of the foreign fleets. The national priorities with regard to domestic harvesting, in particular, were left unclear. Was the objective to: increase our food supply; provide for coastal employment; maintain a "way of life;" or "save" the fish from fishermen? Congress didn't say. Instead, it asked the councils to decide on a fishery-by-fishery basis.

This lack of policy direction makes the council appointment process all that more important to the various groups seeking access to the resources. Appointments have become increasingly political with charges and countercharges of bias and favoritism, and various interest groups jockeying for position. Given the political turmoil and turnovers in council seats, it's a wonder that anything gets accomplished.

Efforts by the councils to set fishery-by-fishery goals have met with limited success. Early plans failed to identify any objectives. Later efforts produced laundry lists of "mom-and-apple-pie" objectives with no clear priorities. Only recently have a few councils begun to tackle priorities.

Some improvements have been made in the council system from a bureaucratic standpoint. Initially, the councils were going to prepare 75 different fishery management plans.[16] Many of these, however, were either consolidated or dropped because they were not needed. Some plans now are more flexible, so seasonal and routine adjustments can be made more quickly. And the process has been shortened, although it still can take several years to complete and implement a plan.

Council performance has been uneven. Some councils moved quickly and have improved their procedures and understanding of the fisheries over time. The management of fisheries by these councils is settling down into an annual cycle of review and adjustment. Actions are scheduled in advance and people usually have notice of what will be considered. Other councils got off to a slow start and still seem to be off balance. These councils have accomplished very little, if anything, of value to the commercial industry.

So far, 26 fisheries have come under federal regulation and more are scheduled for management in the future. For the past three years, regulatory activity has been growing at an annual rate of eight to ten percent. Last year 211 regulatory actions were published in the *Federal Register*.[17]

Both the state and federal systems use the political process to allocate fish among domestic users. Conflicts over who should get the fish seem to be increasing. Examples include disputes between fishermen using fixed fixed gear and mobile gear, commercial and recreational fishermen, and fishermen and processors over the operation of foreign factory vessels. These disputes are often fought out with little useful biological or economic information available to help resolve them. The end result is that the process is becoming more and more expensive as growing numbers of lobbyists and lawyers argue with each other.

In head-to-head confrontations over the resources, the smaller but more numerous vessels (whether recreational or commercial) almost always win over the larger but fewer vessels. That's good politics. The person lost in this political two-step is the consumer, and ultimately the commercial industry. Consumers are not really represented on the councils and their interest in quality products *at reasonable prices* is frequently overlooked in the debates among fishermen over who should get the resources.

Turf battles erupt periodically among the councils. These disputes involve conflicts over council boundaries, who should have the lead in managing fisheries, what the planning priorities should be, and a wide range of issues over how fisheries should be regulated.[18] When several councils have authority over a fishery, management activity can grind to a halt. The classical example of this is the billfish plan which was begun in March 1977 and still isn't even at the draft plan stage.

Tensions between the state and federal systems also remain unresolved. Federal authority does not extend to state waters unless a fishery is "predominately" in federal waters and some state action is found to be detrimental to federal management. During the past ten years, "turf battles" have flared up between various state and federal officials with different ideas about who should get the fish, or how much should be harvested. Sometimes formal confrontations have occurred in the courts. Most often, however, disputes are fought out "off the record" as plans are developed.[19]

Jurisdictional tensions exist with Mexico and Canada as well. Shortly after U.S. jurisdiction was extended, an agreement was signed between U.S. and Mexico for the phaseout of U.S. shrimping in Mexican waters. Mexico, in return, was promised allocations of Alaska groundfish. Since then no management agreements have been reached even though the two nations share several major fisheries, including those for shrimp, anchovy, tuna, and groundfish. The need to manage these fisheries in cooperation with each other has not been compelling enough for either side to acquiesce to the demands of the other. Instead, our fishery relations have been marked by trade embargoes, vessel seizures and conflicting juridical claims. Even fishery research must be conducted on a scientist-to-scientist basis.

Similar conflicts exist with Canada, particularly on the east coast. Our inability to achieve a satisfactory management scheme for Atlantic fisheries in the late 1970s led to international litigation and the delineation of a maritime boundary by the International Court of Justice in 1984. Different biological, economic, and social perspectives have led to a series of controversies involving virtually every major commercial fishery shared by the two countries. In the meantime, many of the fishery resources in the Gulf of Maine have declined to very low levels.

Our west coast fishery relations with Canada have met with some success. An agreement was reached on salmon management ending many years of negotiation. Also, agreements regarding the management of halibut, albacore tuna, and high seas salmon fishing have been maintained and strengthened.

The International System

The remaining part of our domestic production comes from waters beyond U.S. jurisdiction.[20]

Several international commissions manage some of these fisheries under various treaties including ones for tuna, halibut, and salmon. U.S. involvement in these organizations is dominated by veteran bureaucrats, an occasional interested member of Congress, and selected representatives of the industry who often wield considerable power in determining the U.S. position.

A major flaw in these arrangements is that fishing restrictions can be formulated during a commission meeting at a geographically-remote location without prior notice. These restrictions, in turn, can be binding on the federal government later on when regulations are issued.

U.S. officials have sometimes acted hastily during commission meetings setting off a storm of political controversy. This was particularly true of a 1982 decision to end commercial fishing for Atlantic bluefin tuna.   This decision was based on a highly-suspect U.S. stock assessment which had been released at the last moment without adequate public or peer review.[21]

Management of tuna, in particular, has been complicated by the United States' refusal to recognize the authority of coastal nations to manage tuna on an unilateral basis.   This policy is implemented through import embargoes and compensation programs for vessel seizures.

The U.S. fishery management system also supports the efforts of foreign officials who manage those fisheries which produce products exported to the United States. These products come from over 100 countries.   However, in terms of their value, about half come from just six countries: Canada, Mexico, Japan, Iceland, Denmark and Norway.   While the U.S. plays no direct role in the fishery management systems of these nations, several federal laws provide U.S. penalties for violations of foreign fishery regulations.[22]   On occasion, federal officials divert substantial resources from domestic programs to this activity.   In 1984, for example, over 300 cases were brought against U.S. shrimpers for alleged violations of Mexican law.

Other Restraints

State, federal, and international fishery management programs rely almost entirely on regulating harvests.   They virtually ignore the other human activities which impact the productivity of fish stocks.   Fishery managers, for example, do not regulate waste disposal, the damming of rivers, or wetland development.   Instead, they are limited to making recommendations and, if that fails, mitigating habitat losses with hatcheries, artificial reefs, fish ladders, etc.   While the laws which govern these non-fishing activities frequently refer to fishery resources, they are procedural in nature and contain no binding standards.[23]   Instead, the burden is on those wanting to conserve fisheries to show that activities other than harvesting have an adverse impact.

The ability of managers to maintain or increase fishery production also is limited by the Marine Mammal Protection Act and the Endangered Species Act.[24]   Marine mammals, for example, consume vast amounts of fish and shellfish.   They also infect fish with parasites making them more costly or difficult to use.   Yet the taking of marine mammals to increase the food supply is prohibited.   Only where it can be proved to a judge that a marine mammal population is above its "optimum population" level can harvesting be allowed.

The protection of marine mammals also has priority in the allocation of U.S. fish to foreign fleets. If an action of a foreign government "diminishes the effectiveness" of an international conservation program for marine mammals, U.S. law requires that it lose its access to U.S. fisheries irrespective of any harm to the U.S. fishing industry.

So the system is not perfect.   The difficult question is whether it is working.

ARE WE BETTER OFF?

In the congressional debates leading up to the passage of the MFCMA, it was argued that, if foreign fishing was ended and domestic harvests were regulated, the depleted fishery stocks would rebuild and catches would increase.   This increased catch, in turn, would produce increased employment and economic wealth. Also, with increased supplies there would be downward pressure on prices thereby encouraging increased consumption and benefits to the consumer. The new system, in short, was a magic solution.

In the decade before 1975, U.S. landings had increased about two percent per year (by volume). The National Marine Fisheries Service, however, reported that 21 major commercial stocks were "depleted," another 10 were in "imminent danger of depletion," and that an additional 24 were under "intensive use."[25] The U.S. Comptroller General assessed the overall situation this way:

> Some of our important species have been depleted or are threatened with depletion. In some instances domestic fishermen have crowded into the high-value fisheries. As a result, there are more fishermen and gear than can be used efficiently in these fisheries. In contrast, too little fishing has been directed to species which, though underutilized by our fishermen, are taken in large quantities by foreign fishermen.[26]

The U.S. Office of Technological Assessment came to similar conclusions.[27]

Ten years later the national statistics suggest that U.S. fisheries are healthy and prospering. Production is up significantly, and the U.S. share of the world catch has increased.[28] Production shifts in the U.S. Exclusive Economic Zone are especially dramatic. Table 1 shows the total catch in this zone including the so-called "joint venture" catches which were sold to foreign processing vessels.

Foreign fishing has been discontinued for cod, haddock, yellowtail flounder, sea herring, butterfish, squid, Pacific shrimp, king and tanner crab, and black cod. While total production (domestic and foreign) from the zone has declined, U.S. production

Table 1

Production From The EEZ
(in thousands of mt)

Year	U.S. Landings	Joint Ventures	Foreign	Total
1975	663		2,700*	3,363
1976	730		2,300*	3,030
1977	753		1,699	2,452
1978	664		1,754	2,418
1979	805	11	1,650	2,466
1980	858	62	1,628	2,548
1981	928	140	1,655	2,723
1982	802	255	1,415	2,472
1983	721	435	1,313	2,469
1984	683	665	1,353	2,701
1985	761	911	1,164	2,836

* Official records for foreign catch do not exist for 1975 and 1976. These amounts were estimated by NMFS officials during Congressional testimony.

has increased 152 percent! Production from state waters during this same period rose 62 percent, while production from waters beyond U.S. jurisdiction fell 13 percent. Overall U.S. production increased 72 percent.[29]

U.S. landings of edible products show significant annual growth immediately after the MFMCA was passed followed by a substantial decline, and then a leveling off (see Table 2).

Table 2

U.S. Landings

Period	Average Change
1966-1976	+ 2.1 %
1976-1980	+ 13.4 %
1980-1982	- 5.1 %
1982-1985	——

Average prices paid to fishermen have followed the general trends in the national economy. Real prices (in inflation-adjusted dollars) increased from 1970 to 1973, then decreased through 1975. They increased again between 1975 and 1979 and then turned down along with the economy in the early 1980s.

Landings, however, do not tell you about the changes in the fishing effort that went into the catch, or the changes in stock conditions.

Information on fishing effort is sketchy. The national statistics suggest that each year during the past decade an average of about 6,300 additional fishermen and 2,400 craft entered the U.S. fisheries. During this period, the number of larger vessels (over 5 tons) grew more than twice as fast as smaller boats.

Investment activity has had its ups and downs. Prior to the mid-1970s, the industry was mostly self-financing. New vessels and plants were bought with profits generated by the industry. Japanese companies, however, invested heavily in existing U.S. companies on the west coast during the late 1960s and early 1970s, in anticipation of the U.S. extending its fishery jurisdiction and to maintain their access to U.S. supplies. Some European and Canadian companies also had invested in U.S. companies to gain better access to the U.S. market.

Passage of the MFCMA and the promise of huge profits prompted a surge in domestic investment in both vessels and plants in the mid-1970s. Fishermen who had been deckhands or skippers long enough to be considered experienced found it easy to obtain financing with a minimal investment. A number of outside investors also bought vessels looking for tax breaks and capital gains. Annual requests for government financing assistance went up ten times between 1975 and 1979. Financing also was accelerated by some banks but most especially by the Production Credit Associations.

The combination of a few years of production gains, real price increases, and easy credit led to rapid expansion. Interest rates, however, kept climbing and many companies became over extended. As one fish stock after another got into trouble and the national economy slumped in the late 1970s, investment slowed.

The industry since then has diversified and consolidated. Interest rates and fuel prices have fallen along with the value of the dollar. As a result, investment is increasing again with the building of factory/trawlers and additional processing facilities.

Accurate indicators of productivity are not available. An extremely simple estimation of productivity can be derived by dividing landings by the recorded number of fishermen and craft in 1975 and 1985. This calculation shows that landings per fisherman increased from 13.7 to 16.3 mt and that landings per craft increased from 22.4 to 29.5 mt, or a gain in productivity of about 19 percent for fisherman, and 31 percent for craft.[30]

This quick glance at the government's statistics could lead you to think that tremendous progress has been made. A closer look at what has happened to the major fisheries, however, shows that serious problems exist.

The Atlantic Coast

Commercial production from state and federal waters along the Atlantic coast is up 17 percent since 1975, due mostly to increased landings of menhaden and blue crab from state waters. Production from federal waters surged ahead 60 percent in the late 1970s, then declined. Government scientists say that most traditional offshore fisheries today are no longer producing at their full potential. The 1984 decision of the International Court of Justice which awarded Canada a portion of Georges Bank also hurt production. Foreign fishing, however, has been cut back. As a result, several non-traditional fisheries, such as those for squid, mackerel and hake, are in relatively good shape.

The National Marine Fisheries Service (NMFS) scientists tell us that there may have been some significant shifts in the Northeastern ecosystem. In the early 1970s, for example, herring, mackerel and silver hake were the dominant species. Today, these are no longer the dominant species. Why the shift occurred is unclear. Nevertheless, continued heavy fishing pressure on traditional species may have helped other less sought after species to gain an upper hand. A 1985 government report summed it up this way:

> Estimates of total biomass peaked at 8.0 million mt in 1968 and then declined to only 1.9 million mt in 1975...Since 1980, estimates have fluctuated about an average of 3.3. million mt...with declines in some groundfish stocks in 1984.[31]

Many of the offshore fisheries along the Atlantic coast have suffered the past ten years while only a few have made gains. Management of the *New England groundfish* fishery, for example, began on an emergency basis in 1977 with depleted fishery stocks and a depressed industry. The council's objectives were to rebuild the stocks and then maintain them at higher levels. The council's initial strategy was to allocate species to individual vessel groups, and then spread out the landings during the year using quarterly quotas and vessel trip limits.

At several points, the weekly allocations were too small to justify the expense of a trip, so some vessels stayed out for longer periods to pick up two allocations. Longer periods at sea meant that vessels sometimes operated in unsafe weather conditions and delivered product with a shorter shelf life.

Officials struggled to balance the short-term welfare of the fishermen against the long-term need to rebuild the stocks. Each time quotas were exceeded, the industry protested and emergency adjustments were made. The fishery almost never closed.

At one point, widespread violations of trip limits and other restrictions threatened anarchy. Hundreds of citations were issued and attitudes hardened into a "them and us" mentality on both sides.

The council's initial strategy was discontinued in 1982 in favor of an "interim plan." This plan closed spawning areas and imposed gear and minimum size restrictions until a more comprehensive plan could be worked out. This plan was submitted last year but was disapproved in January because it failed to "prevent overfishing." Instead, the Secretary recommended that an "effort control and quota system" be developed.

Throughout this period, a few strong yearclasses recruited to the fishery but were fished out and the stocks went down. Haddock and yellowtail flounder are now "depleted" and cod is listed as "fully utilized."[32] Excerpts from a recent government report tell the story:

> The haddock fishery provides a good example of the effects of overfishing and the loss to the nation due to uncontrolled fishing mortality...Overfishing in (1965 and 1966) caused a rapid decline in abundance to very low levels by the early 1970s...The catches since 1966 have averaged only 16,000 metric tons; a potential loss of 32,000 metric tons per year for the last nineteen years...we have had a good yearclass in 1975 and again in 1985. Under careful management such opportunities could rebuild the stock to some degree.

> Catches increased steadily on the cod stock from 1976 to the early 1980s until these stocks, too, were overfished and the catches have now declined in the past two-three years...The current level of abundance of cod in the Georges Bank area is the lowest ever observed and will continue to decline in 1986.

> Yellowtail flounder...have been so overfished in recent years that we now consider this stock to be exhibiting recruitment failure...The yearclasses since 1980 have been very poor and the abundance index is now at the lowest point in the time series which began in 1963.[33]

The scarcity of fish has put the squeeze on both harvesters and processors. Production is down significantly despite major increases in effort. As a result:

> ....landings-per-vessel and revenue-per-vessel have, with minor fluctuations, shown a downward trend over the period marked by the implementation of the MFCMA in 1977, have been diluted to a large extent by the growth in the fleet.[34]

The sea scallop fishery also has suffered declines. Government scientists concluded that the stock on Georges Bank was "depleted" in the early 1970s because it was "being overfished" and that scallops from all areas were being harvested at much smaller than the size producing the maximum meat yield.[35]

Scallop prices went up in 1975 and vessels began to enter the fishery. The number of "days fished" escalated and overall production climbed.[36] State regulations had little effect because most sea scallops were caught beyond state waters except in Maine.

The offshore fishery did not come under federal regulation until 1982 when the council imposed a minimum average meat count/shell height restriction. This restriction was adjusted a year later to 35 meats per pound and a shell height of 3 3/8 inches. A 1985 amendment would establish a minimum size standard but may not be implemented.

By 1985, catches of sea scallops were the lowest since 1974. The stock is listed now as "depleted" and the catch per unit of effort has declined to the lowest levels ever recorded.[37]

The offshore stock of *Atlantic herring* on Georges Bank has suffered a worse fate. This stock exceeded one million mt in 1967 but was overfished prior to 1975. When the MFCMA came into effect, the Secretary of Commerce prepared a plan which allowed for a domestic harvest of 12,000 mt and a foreign harvest of 21,000 mt. The State of Maine sued arguing that these levels were too high but lost. The stock, however, collapsed in 1977 and remains commercially extinct.[38]

The nearshore stock of herring in the Gulf of Maine is in better shape. Harvests of this stock are regulated by the states and have increased with the succession of strong yearclasses. Because of declines in export markets, a significant proportion of the adult population is not being used for human consumption.

More progress has been made in rebuilding the *surf clam* beds which were depleted in the 1960s and early 1970s. In the mid 1970s the industry was heavily overcapitalized with fishing power that far exceeded annual production levels. The fishery had followed a "boom and bust" cycle every seven years or so. The efforts of officials at that time to limit harvests using state authority were frustrated due to a lack of interstate cooperation.

When the fishery came under council management in 1977, an annual quota was adopted to address the biological need of the fishery to rebuild. The overcapitalization problem led to the adoption of a moratorium on the new entry of vessels. The other provisions were designed to spread the catch out over the year to prevent the periodic closing of processing plants.

At first, fishing was limited to a few days a week, then only a few hours a week, then only a few hours every other week. These restrictions discouraged the practice of exploratory fishing which had led to the discovery by the industry of new beds in the past. Vessels also went to sea in adverse weather conditions rather than lose their chance to fish. When the danger to vessel safety was recognized, the plan was adjusted to allow "make up days" for bad weather.

In 1981, a shift occurred in the market creating a demand for smaller clams. This led the council to impose a minimum size restriction which led to a series of emotional confrontations caused by uneven enforcement by federal officials. Size restrictions also have caused high discarding of small clams and a tremendous amount of waste. The fishery continues to be heavily overcapitalized adding significant production costs.

Surf clam landings declined to a low point in 1979 but have been on the rise since then. Part of this increase is due to the expansion of the fishery to the Georges Bank in 1984. Strong 1976 and 1977 yearclasses have recruited to the fishery and it is now in relatively good shape.[39] The catch per unit of effort has risen since 1980 and the NMFS scientists say that there are resources available to sustain the fishery into the 1990s.[40]

The *mackerel* fishery, which is shared with Canada, also has recovered and the U.S. catch is beginning to rise from the low point reached in 1974. Catch per unit of effort also is up.

Foreign fishing for mackerel in U.S. waters came under regulation in 1977 while regulation of domestic harvests began in 1980. Harvest levels are set depending on the level of spawning stock biomass. The stock at this point could sustain significantly higher U.S. harvests.[41] Low prices and the high value of the dollar have held production down in recent years. The fishery, however, may now be ready for full U.S. development.

The management of the *Atlantic butterfish* fishery in federal waters began in 1977 with the purpose of promoting U.S. development. At this time there was a significant market in Japan for butterfish which was being supplied by Japanese vessels operating in the U.S. fishery. The mid-Atlantic council reasoned that, if the optimum yield was lowered, foreign fishing would be reduced and Japanese buyers might offer U.S. producers an export price which would allow them to develop the fishery. Federal officials, however, dragged their feet and refused to go along with this idea. After a political scuffle, they approved the council's strategy.

The strategy worked. After a slow start, U.S. exporters improved the quality of their products and U.S. production climbed. By 1984, offshore foreign operations had ended. This hard-won development, however, was threatened on several occasions by various state officials who gave foreign factory vessels permission to operate in state waters despite the protests of the council that the U.S. industry had the capacity in the region to fully exploit all the available butterfish.

Because butterfish have a short life span (about four years) and a high mortality, fishing effort has concentrated on one-and two-year-old fish. Discards of younger fish have been high at times and could adversely impact the productivity of the stock.

The council also has attempted to help the U.S. industry to develop the *loligo and illex squid* fishery. These stocks are particularly variable because of their short life span (one to two years). Historically, the foreign fleets had the first opportunity to harvest squid as they recruited to the offshore fishery during the winter. U.S. fishermen got the leftovers later in the year when they migrated into nearshore areas. Because the initial management plan was based on a calendar year, the foreign fleets actually received priority access to the fishing grounds and markets. This meant that U.S.-produced products were exported after the foreign production had arrived in Europe.

The council went to great lengths to apply the "fish and chips" policy in allocating fish to the foreign fleets and approving offshore purchases of squid by foreign factory vessels. Arguments flew back and forth about supply, demand, prices, value-added benefits, and conflicts of interest. At one point the council even seemed to be arranging individual sales among companies. While these efforts generated substantial controversy, the U.S. industry did gear up, and the foreign allocations declined. At this point there should no longer be a foreign fishery.

The Atlantic states seem to have had more success than the councils in the management of traditional fisheries. The largest of these is the fishery for *Atlantic menhaden*. It's an enormous fishery characterized by highly efficient harvesting and processing operations. Vessels and plants are managed by vertically integrated companies and produce meal and oil. The fishery has been regulated by the states although an interstate plan was adopted by the Atlantic States Marine Fisheries Commission in 1981.

The stock was listed as "depleted" in 1975 but is in better shape today. As a result, production has expanded 30 percent and the stock is back at the level it was during the peak production years of 1953-1962.[42]

Menhaden fishermen, however, are steadily losing access to the nearshore fishing grounds in state waters. Several states have restricted harvesting because of conflicts with recreational fishermen and coastal development. Also, several plants have had to close and vessels have been tied up because of a drop in the market. As a result, fishing effort has shifted to the southern states.

Inshore landings of *American lobster* account for over 80 percent of the catch, so the states have had the primary management responsibility. Their efforts have been coordinated through the interstate commission. All but one state now imposes a 3 3/16 inch size limit. The offshore fishery came under council management in 1983.

Landings from both inshore and offshore areas remained relatively stable between 1965 and 1975 averaging about 11,100 mt. A 1976 government report, however, concluded that the stocks were "seriously overfished, resulting in depletion throughout its inshore range."[43]

Since the mid-1970s, inshore catches have increased over 40 percent to the 16,000-17,000 level while the offshore catch has declined.[44] Government scientists say that the biomass appears to have declined and that the "great bulk of landings result from catching lobsters which have just molted into the legal size range."[45] Efforts are underway to convince the coastal states to increase the minimum size limit to allow more female lobsters to reproduce before being caught.

The *northern shrimp* fishery is the only fishery directly regulated by an interstate commission. Under this arrangement, three coastal states enforce the commission's regulations regarding mesh size and seasonal closures. Landings peaked at 28,000 mts in 1969, averaged 11,000 mts in the early 1970s and then collapsed to 400 mt in 1977. Landings in the past few years, however, have increased somewhat.[46]

The traditional *oyster* grounds from the Chesapeake Bay northward have been the most productive areas in the past. Overfishing and disease outbreaks, however, have reduced landings. Beds are also vulnerable to being buried by sediment. Today, the most productive grounds are found in the Gulf of Mexico. Landings since 1975 in the Atlantic show a downward trend from about 28 million pounds in the 1960s and early 1970s.[47]

The *blue crab* fishery, which is under state management in 13 states, is the dominant U.S. crab fishery. Landings have increased in the past ten years and the fishery appears, at least momentarily, to be stable. Landings in 1985 were 190.5 million pounds valued at $53.6 million.

Gulf of Mexico

Commercial landings in the gulf have increased 52 percent during the past ten years due to increased production from the nearshore fisheries. State regulation is especially important since the major fisheries are mostly in state waters. Conserving the estuarine areas also is important since almost all major species spend a part of their lives in the marshes and shallow-water areas. Council activity has focused more on economic and gear-conflict issues than on maintaining stock levels.

Conflicts between commercial and recreational fishermen are especially severe in the Gulf of Mexico and South Atlantic. These disputes are fought out in both the councils and the state legislatures.

The Gulf of Mexico *shrimp* fishery is largely in state waters. While stocks fluctuate each year, there is no evidence that changes are due to fishing. Environmental factors appear to determine annual productivity levels. Federal efforts to control harvests, therefore, are aimed more at maximizing economic returns and controlling the bycatch of other species.

Ten years ago the stocks were listed as being in "imminent danger" and a government report noted:[48]

> Shrimp landings over the last eleven years or so have been essentially constant. The catch per unit of effort has decreased, which indicates more intensive effort for the relatively constant level of the shrimp biomass.

For the past ten years, management responsiblility has been shared by the states and the gulf council. State regulations vary. Texas regulations, for example, aim at producing larger shrimp, of greater value, which are caught by the larger offshore vessels. Louisiana regulations, on the other hand, foster shrimping in nearshore waters by smaller craft.

Annual production the past ten years has fluctuated between 194 and 384 million pounds. Scientists describe the fishery today as being under "intensive use" and say that the maximum biological yield is being harvested.[49]

High shrimp production years tend to attract new vessels to the fishery. This added capacity plus the displacement of about 400 vessels from Mexican waters in the late 1970s have reduced the share per vessel. Landings per craft, in terms of volume, fell 31 percent between 1970 and 1980 and fell another 11 percent between 1980 and 1983.[50] A recent government report cited evidence that:

> ...the capacity expanded in response to higher prices, and this expanded capacity has reduced the catch per craft, raised the cost per pound harvested, and, despite the rising value of the catch per craft, reduced net revenues per craft.[51]

Actions of the council have been helpful in resolving gear conflicts between shrimpers and *stone crab* fishermen who were running high in the late 1970s and the newspapers reported that the two groups were shooting at each other. The council and the state were able to work out a plan which divided the grounds between the two groups.

Gulf menhaden management is coordinated by the Gulf States Marine Fisheries Commission, with individual states enacting harvesting rules and the NMFS doing stock assessment work. The fishery was listed as "intensive use" in 1975.[52]

Gulf landings show an upward trend since 1975. Last year 1.9 billion pounds were landed valued at $67.5 million which is slightly below the record catches of 1984 and 1983.[53] The size of the fleet and average vessel crew size have declined the past two years, but productivity has improved.

The *mackerel* fisheries are highly contentious and complex. Battles among recreational and commercial fishermen are often heated and emotional, particularly with respect to highly efficient gear such as purse seines. Management is complicated by different state and federal management philosophies and biological questions over the discreteness of the stocks.

So far, management efforts have not produced significant benefits. Commercial catches of Spanish mackerel in the gulf, for example, were relatively stable in the early 1970s averaging about 7.3 million pounds per year. After the 1976/77 season, however, landings dropped to the 2.5-million-pound level. Commercial landings in the Atlantic went up almost threefold in the mid-1970s and then started to decline steadily.

Federal management began in 1983 with a plan calling for annual harvests of 27 million pounds for Spanish mackerel and 37 million pounds for king mackerel. A series of subsequent stock assessments, however, convinced many scientists that the stocks were being overfished. A regulatory tug-of-war ensued and continues today with recreational interests arguing for state management only and commercial interests supporting regional solutions.

User-group battles over *redfish* are similar. The interstate commission had completed a profile of the redfish fishery in 1980. At that time it was primarily a sport fishery with most harvesting conducted in state waters. Texas and Alabama had closed their fisheries to large-scale commercial fishing and sport fishermen were putting political pressure on state legislatures to have the fish declared a gamefish. Creative marketing, however, opened up a national market for redfish and commercial landings began to increase.

Restrictions in state waters prompted commercial vessels to fish in federal waters and by 1984 harvests offshore on the larger spawning fish were beginning to escalate rapidly. This shift prompted efforts to get the council to draft a plan to control the offshore harvests. These efforts were blocked, however, by council members who wanted the states to maintain the lead through landing restrictions.

Little is known about the status of the stocks. Concern over the trends, however, prompted Congressman John Breaux to introduce legislation in an effort to force federal action.[54]

Pacific Coast

During the past ten years landings in California, Oregon, and Washington have declined by 59 percent (by volume) because of significant declines in tuna and anchovy landings.

In the mid-1970s shrimp and salmon were having their best back-to-back years. Other fisheries, such as those for tuna, anchovy, crab, and groundfish, were doing well. The Soviets and the Poles had established an offshore midwater trawl fishery for Pacific whiting but there was little domestic production from this fishery.

One of the most pressing management problems on the Pacific coast in 1975 was to reverse the decline in chinook and coho *salmon* runs which were fished in state, federal, and Canadian waters by a wide diversity of user groups. The fishery had been under extensive management by the states. License limitation programs, for example, were put into place by Alaska in 1973, Washington in 1974, and California and Oregon in 1979. Stocks were listed as "intensive use (depleted)" in 1975 and the fishery had been the subject of protracted litigation regarding native American fishing rights.[55]

The Pacific council took on the formidable task of regulating the offshore harvests in 1978 to help achieve the spawning escapements needed to enhance production. Allocation of the harvests among the users was constrained by the federal courts and was accomplished indirectly through detailed rules regarding seasons, gear, size of fish, and fishing areas. Later on, a so-called "framework" plan was designed, at least in theory, to allow for rapid adjustments. While political tensions seem to be subsiding, confrontations continue to occur particularly with the states of Oregon and California over the need to close the fishery at certain times.

During the past decade, more than one salmon official has thrown up his hands in despair. Efforts to regulate the harvests continue to be plagued by the conflicting desires of the many different user groups, the migration of salmon across political boundaries, habitat destruction, growing populations of marine mammals which prey on the fish and the numerous different salmon species, stocks, and runs which intermingle in the fishery. Production, in the meantime, has increased from 64.5 million pounds in 1975 to 75.3 million pounds last year.[56]

The changes which have occurred in the *Pacific groundfish* fishery the past ten years follow a classic pattern. The traditional fishery in the mid-1970s was small and targeted on the Pacific ocean perch (which had been decimated by foreign fleets during the 1960s), sole, cod, and rockfish. Products were sold fresh and were caught mostly with bottom gear.

Trouble began when the shrimp fishery increased rapidly in the early 1970s, peaked in 1978 and then collapsed bringing widespread economic distress and the need to diversify along the coast.

The shrimpers and traditional groundfish vessels lacked the fishing power needed for the Pacific whiting fishery. Through vessel conversions and new construction, however, a number of U.S. vessels began to deliver whiting to foreign factory vessels.

These more powerful vessels also turned their attention to widow rockfish. Landings of rockfish took off in 1981, then collapsed.

With several traditional fisheries depressed, attention continues to focus on whiting which has a total allowable catch level approaching 300,000 mt. Whiting, however, has not found a market nitch. Technical difficulties in handling and processing, plus low market prices, have prevented any major U.S. expansion into this fishery. With limited resources available, some of the bigger vessels have moved northward into the Alaska fisheries.

Throughout this period, the council struggled to manage groundfish with an exceedingly complex multispecies arrangement which required extensive data that were not readily available.

The other major fishery on the Pacific coast is the one in California for *anchovy*. For years the California legislature ignored the advice of fishery scientists that a large-scale reduction fishery be permitted. In 1965, however, the state commission allowed a quota which was later increased. The biomass was at its peak of 4.7 million tons in 1965. Despite the warnings of scientists, it fell sharply to 1.3 million tons in 1978.[57]

Council management began in 1978. At the time, the widespread use of anchovies for live bait by both recreational and commercial fishermen was politically and economically more significant that their use as meal and oil. Since then, the market shifted and the reduction fishery has all but disappeared. U.S. landings have fallen from a record 329.4 million pounds in 1975 (five to eight percent for bait) to 14.6 million pounds (88 percent for bait).[58]

There is no U.S./Mexico agreement for the management of anchovy even though the central subpopulation is shared with Mexico. When Mexico expanded its fishery jurisdiction, it established a major processing operation for anchovy and purchased a fleet of new U.S.-built purse seiners. Annual production climbed rapidly to around 200,000 tons.

Alaska

During the past decade landings in Alaska have risen 167 percent. Salmon, halibut, herring, crab, and shrimp have been the traditional mainstays. Sharply declining crab and shrimp stocks, however, have forced the industry to diversify into groundfish.

Management disputes in the North Pacific are truly heroic in scale. On one side is the state which traditionally gives local communities priority access to the stocks nearby. This policy, which is supported by many nearshore fishermen, has led the state to adopt various regulatory schemes over the years based upon exclusive area registration and limited entry.

On the other side of this struggle are those fishermen with mobile gear and the ability to switch from one fishery to another. These fishermen want to keep the fisheries open so that vessels can adjust to constantly changing biological and economic conditions. This "open ocean" group includes several fleets based in Alaska and the Pacific Northwest. Both viewpoints are represented on the council, although the Alaska viewpoint dominates.

The restoration of Alaska's *salmon* runs is one of the dramatic success stories of the past decade. Catches have climbed from an annual catch of 29 million fish in the five-year period before U.S. jurisdiction was extended to annual harvests of more than 100 million fish in recent years.

Why this threefold increase occurred is unclear. State managers have certainly gained a better understanding of escapement needs. The state also has been active in habitat restoration and hatchery production. Perhaps even more important has been the several years of favorable ocean conditions. Finally, international agreements which moved the Japanese high seas salmon fleet westward must also have helped.

The fishery for *halibut* also has made gains. Catch limits for this fishery are recommended by an international commission to the U.S. and Canada. Domestic management is the responsibility of the State of Alaska and the North Pacific Fishery Management Council. The fishery was listed as "depleted" in 1975.[59] The stocks at this point appear to be in good shape in all areas, particularly in the Gulf of Alaska. As a result, the allowable catch levels have gone up.

The real battle over halibut concerns economics and by-catch. As the state closed entry into other traditional Alaska fisheries and the price for halibut increased, the number of vessels in the fishery escalated and fishing seasons shortened dramatically into a "Fishing Derby." Improved technology, such as the circle hook, also improved catch rates. There were many complaints about quality because of the large volume of fish that had to be processed in a short time period. By 1980, there was concern that the traditional longline fishery was degenerating into a very short fishery of little economic value. Some feared that it might become an incidental fishery to the trawl fisheries for other species.

Following enactment of the North Pacific Halibut Act of 1983, the council obtained authority to impose a three-year moratorium on new entry. This effort was bitterly opposed, particularly by fishermen from the central and western ports who viewed halibut as their only hope of surviving the hard times caused by the depressed fisheries for crab and shrimp. As a result, limited entry was abandoned. Instead, halibut seasons were staggered and shortened to avoid gluts and spread out the deliveries of fresh fish.

Production from the *herring* fishery has risen dramatically since 1975 from about 26 million pounds in 1975 to over 123 million pounds in 1985.[60] A small inshore roe fishery got underway in 1977 and grew so rapidly that by 1980 the traditional foreign offshore fishery was shut down. The rapid growth of the roe fishery also prompted the state to issue a series of regulations designed to allocate fish between local residents and "outsiders." More recently, some U.S. fishermen have attempted to open up an offshore winter fishery to use the herring for food purposes.

Both the crab and shrimp fisheries have suffered major reversals. The state set up area quotas and size limits for *king crab* in the 1960s. By the mid-1970s the fishery had been fully developed by U.S. vessels and was listed as being under "intensive use." It came under council management in 1977. Later on, a "framework" plan was approved which adopts state management restrictions provided they are consistent with federal standards.

King crab is one of the world's most hazardous fisheries. Winds in excess of 125 knots can come up suddenly along with bitter cold and heavy icing. Fishery management restrictions, however, required vessels to operate in short seasons and encouraged vessels to carry as many pots as possible to maximize their catch. More recently, however, vessel safety needs have been recognized and changes have been made to the regulatory system.

While the king crab fishery got underway, the *tanner crab* fishery got little attention from the domestic industry. In the late 1960s, however, the king crab stocks went into a temporary decline and interest picked up. By the mid-1970s, tanner crab were being caught by both U.S. and foreign vessels.

The council turned its attention to fully developing the fishery in 1978 when it set the optimum yield for tanner crab at a level significantly below its estimated maximum sustainable yield. Its strategy was to reduce the foreign supply and block the Japanese from undercutting prices on the world market. Federal officials at first disapproved this idea saying that the council lacked proof that this strategy would work. They later agreed, however, to go along. This strategy worked and was continued until foreign fishing ended in 1982.

Despite extensive research and harvest regulations, both the king and tanner crab stocks dropped significantly in 1981 and are producing at very low levels. Exactly why the resources went down is unknown. The fisheries, however, were listed as "depleted" in 1984.[61]

The *shrimp* fishery also has declined. In 1975 it was under state management and listed as being under "intensive use." Since then, annual landings have fallen from a record 129 million pounds to under 20 million pounds. The stock has been very depressed since 1979 and recoveries are not expected in the near future.

Why the shrimp stock went down is unclear. Some researchers suggest heavy predation by cod and pollock, while others point to an increase in ocean temperatures. There continues to be a suspicion, however, that the historical fluctuations in stock abundance are unrelated to fishing.

With resource setbacks in crab and shrimp, U.S. fishermen turned their efforts to *groundfish* (pollock, Pacific cod, flounders, Atka mackerel, and rockfish). The pollock fishery in the late 1970s was one of the largest single-species fisheries in the world. High seas fleets from the Soviet Union, Japan, and Korea were taking about 1.1 million mt from the waters off Alaska alone. United States landings were negligible. Pacific cod was the target species for Japanese longliners but began to claim a greater share of the foreign trawl catch as the 1970s went on.

This foreign catch of cod, and a sevenfold increase in the cod biomass prompted U.S. vessels to target on cod. A series of technological improvements were made in U.S. operations including the cod-end transfer technique, load sensors, blow-out panels, polyproplene nets, new trawl doors and electronics. When offshore sales to foreign factory vessels began in the late 1970s, U.S. catches of cod jumped to over 30 million pounds.

United States interest in pollock picked up in the early 1980s when Japan, Poland, and West Germany began buying product offshore. The Koreans at this time also increased their purchases. A very large pollock roe fishery began in Shelikof Strait in 1981.

A number of forces had converged to accelerate these developments. Congress had amended the MFCMA to clarify that those countries helping the U.S. industry would be given preference in the allocation process, and U.S. officials were putting heavy political pressure on the foreign buyers. The U.S. industry had banded together to promote these actions, and to negotiate a series of agreements with their Japanese counterparts which called for increased sales. Throughout this period, fishery managers played a key role in putting pressure on the foreign fleets to buy U.S. product.

The groundfish fisheries are growing so rapidly at this point that gear conflicts and excessive competition are causing serious problems. Black cod seasons are beginning to look like fishing derbies. The joint venture operations in the Shelikof fishery were forced to fish on a "first-come-first-served" basis this year and could not time their operations to coincide with the peak mature roe seasons. More importantly, a series of gear conflicts between the U.S. trawlers and fixed-gear fishermen threaten to unravel future plans for growth.

HAS IT BEEN WORTH IT?

Production

Production from most of the high-valued offshore fisheries is declining. While overall U.S. production in federal waters is up, much of this increase is from low-valued species which had previously been harvested by the foreign fleets. Fishery managers have failed to rebuild and maintain many of the traditional fisheries which prompted Congress to act in the mid-1970s. They have, however, fostered the expansion of U.S. fleets into those fisheries formerly dominated by foreign vessels.

In the inshore fisheries, the major shifts have been the dramatic restoration of Alaska's salmon runs, the steady increase of menhaden landings and the decline of California's anchovy fishery. The role the management system played in these changes, however, is unclear.

Stocks

Changes in the marine environment unrelated to fishing may account for several of the dramatic ups and downs in stock levels which have occurred on all three coasts. Perhaps the balance among species shifted, or there was some long-term change in water temperature. Exactly what happened and why it happened are unclear.

Putting the foreign fleets under quotas did help a few offshore stocks to rebuild. These stocks are probably in better shape than they would have been if they had remained under international management. Market forces, however, also played a role in reducing fishing pressure on some of these stocks.

Council efforts to rebuild those traditional stocks which were under domestic fishing pressure, however, have failed to produce significant results. Many of these fisheries are depleted and producing far below their potential. Some have collapsed, or have declined significantly. Only the surf clam fishery has made significant gains, although the fishery is grossly overcapitalized with vessels remaining idle most of the time.

Pollution and environmental damage have had no measurable effect on large-scale commercial fisheries except for nearshore shellfish beds. Some local effects have been severe but they have been limited to individual bays, rivers, and harbors. Damage from oil spills has not materialized. Their effects, if any, on offshore fisheries have been negligible. Even their impact on inshore stocks appears to be transitory.

Production Costs

Fishing pressure has increased significantly. As several high-valued stocks declined, U.S. fleets have had to remain idle for longer periods of time each year, or have turned to lower-valued stocks which had been harvested by the foreign fleets.

The fishing quotas being imposed by the present management system have tended to lead to overcapitalization and a race to catch the resources. When the product was brought to shore in a rush, product quality suffered along with the industry's ability to market fresh products. This, in turn, has led to increased regulation to spread the catch out over the year. These regulations further limit vessel efficiency and spread production among a larger number of vessels than otherwise are needed. In some instances they promote increased discards.

Government intrusion in the marketplace has increased dramatically. More and more restrictions have been imposed including permit and license requirements, landing taxes, limited-entry schemes, quotas, gear restrictions, harvesting moratoria, and the like. Many of these restrictions have tended to make the commercial producers less efficient, and less able to adjust to changing biological or market conditions.

The catch per unit of effort in many fisheries has declined despite significant improvements in fishing technology. Production costs are up dramatically. But the data aren't available to make any firm conclusions. Norton, Miller and Kenny proposed an industry "health index" two years ago to overcome the lack of cost and productivity information. This index measures changes in prices and costs between 1965 and 1983 for eight fisheries. They found that the economic "health" of the majority of fishing fleets they studied had declined.[62]

Fishery management restrictions are moving onshore and into the market place. The councils, for example, have recently proposed banning imports of American lobster, spiny lobster, New England groundfish and swordfish from various foreign fisheries in which they could be harvested legally under foreign law. This trend invites retaliation and threatens substantial disruption of the market.

Investment Risks

Regulating the foreign fleets and giving a "priority" to domestic vessels did reduce investment risks. As domestic fisheries become more crowded, however, pressure increased on the stocks and some may have become more unstable. Crowding also has caused gear conflicts and the need for extensive regulation. Since much of this regulation is based upon pressure-group decision-making and no clear policies have been established, investment risks in some fisheries have increased significantly. This seems to be occurring in more and more fisheries.

One strategy to reduce risks is to operate larger multipurpose vessels that can move from fishery to fishery when stocks get into trouble. This strategy, however, is being frustrated by fishery managers who are responding to the political pressures generated by the operators of smaller vessels who want to maintain employment, lifestyles or quality recreational experiences.

Many fisheries continue to follow a "boom and bust" cycle in which nobody wins. There have been a few attempts to break this cycle by limiting the number of vessels or otherwise controlling the inputs of a fishery. These schemes, however, have been very controversial and are often seen as being unfair. They frequently have stifled innovation and technological improvements and have not eliminated the "race" for the fish which exists in most U.S. fisheries today.

Product Quality

The fishery management system has done little to improve product quality. In fact, regulatory quotas and the "race for the resources" has hurt product quality in several fisheries.

Costs V. Benefits

Excess capacity, higher discard rates, increased investment risks, uneven landings, poor product quality and vessel safety all translate into costs which are passed on to the consumer. The system has not been very successful when measured against the producer's interest in maximizing profit, or against he industry's interest in providing value to the consumer, i.e., quality at reasonable prices.

Prior to the MFCMA the federal government was spending millions of dollars for fishery management. This investment, however, did not prevent the depletion of the stocks or the tremendous build-up of domestic fishing effort.

The present federal program employs 131 council members, 86 council staff, over 1,000 federal bureaucrats, plus many thousands of man-hours of U.S. Coast Guard time each year. The cost to the taxpayers last year was about $223 million. The program, however, generated about $40 to 45 million in revenue through foreign fishing fees, so it had a net cost of about $180 million.[63] This net cost translates into about $0.05 per pound of fish produced from federal waters in 1985.

The federal government also spent about one million dollars last year to support the work of several international fishery organizations. How many additional millions of dollars were spent by the states is not known.

CONCLUSION

When you think about it, mother nature and the marketplace seem to dictate what happens and not the management system. Perhaps the regulation of harvests is not the major factor we think it is. Perhaps the fishery managers just did too little, too late to make any real difference. Or perhaps, too much, too soon.

One thing is clear. The government is spending a lot of money to sort out who should get the fish, and how much should be caught. I'm not convinced that the consumers and the taxpayers are getting their money's worth.

NOTES AND REFERENCES

[1]   16 U.S.C. 1801-1882.

[2]   Office of Technology Assessment, Establishing a 200-mile Fisheries Zone, p. 24 (1977).

[3]   Section 2 (46 U.S.C. 1802).

[4]   A quick look at where these fish companies get their supply explains why. Only about 42 percent come from fisheries in federal waters. 52 percent comes from state waters, and another 6 percent from fisheries under international management. A full 64 percent of edible products are imported. See, *Fisheries of the United States, 1985* (April 1986) (hereinafter Fisheries), pp.11 and 66.

[5]   Calculated using the Value Added Table in *Fisheries of the United States, 1981* (April 1982) and the landings and import data for 1985 in *Fisheries*, pp.11 and 66.

[6]   *Fisheries*, p. 78

[7]   *Fisheries*, p. 78

[8]   *Fisheries*, p. 78

[9]   *Fisheries* p. 11. Fifty-two percent by volume and 50 percent by value in 1985. In terms of value, the fish caught within state waters were worth over $200 million more than those caught by U.S. fishermen in federal waters. At the time the Magnuson Act was passed 59 percent of U.S. production (by volume) came from state waters, 18 percent came from federal waters and 23 percent came from waters beyond U.S. jurisdiction (beyond 12 miles). Ten years later production from federal waters has increased in relative importance while that from state and international areas has decreased in relative significance. U.S. dependence on foreign production, however, also has increased because U.S. supplies have been unable to keep up with demand.

[10] The exception is the northern shrimp fishery managed by the Atlantic States Marine Fisheries Commission.

[11] PL 88-309 and 89-304.

[12] Atlantic Striped Bass Conservation act of 1984. Also, the Magnuson Act, Atlantic Tunas Conservation Act and Pacific Salmon Treaty Act.

[13] Forty two percent by volume and 42 percent by value in 1985. *Fisheries*, p. 11.

[14] *Fisheries*, p. 95.

[15] Unpublished NMFS data.

[16] Department of Commerce Press Release dated February 24, 1977.

[17] *Fisheries*, p. 90.

[18] Boundary disputes arose between the Gulf and South Atlantic councils and the Pacific and North Pacific councils.

[19] Examples include disputes with the states of Florida, Oregon and Hawaii.

[20] *Fisheries*, p. 11. Six percent by volume and eight percent by value in 1985.

[21] David Hoover, "A case Against International Management of Highly Migratory Marine fishery Resources: The Atlantic Bluefin Tuna," *Environmental Affairs Law Review* (1983), Vol.11, pp. 11-61.

[22] See, e.g., The Lacey Act Amendments of 1981.

[23] See, e.g., the National Environmental Policy Act (42 U.S.C. 4321), the Fish and Wildlife Coordination Act (16 U.S.C. 661), and the Northwest Electric Power Planning and Conservation Act (16 U.S.C. 839).

[24] 16 U.S.C. 1361-1407.

[25] "A Preliminary Listing of Marine Fishery Resources Which Are Depleted, In Imminent Danger Of Depletion, Or Under Intensive Use," *A Legislative History of the fishery Conservation and Management Act of 1976*, Committee On Commerce (October, 1976, pp. 1149-1152. See also, U.S. Department of Commerce, *A Marine Fisheries Program for the Nation* (July, 1976), p.7.

[26] U.S. General Accounting Office, The U.S. Fishing Industry—Present Condition and Future of Marine Fisheries (1976), pp.113-114.

[27] OTA, p.3.

[28] OECD, *International Trade in Fish Products: Effects of the 200-Mile Limit* (1982).

[29] *Fisheries*, p.11.

³⁰ *Fisheries,* pp.11 and 84.

³¹ Status of the Fishery Resources Off the Northeastern United States for 1985 (DOC August 1985), p. 25.

³² Roland Finch, "Fishery Management Under The Magnuson Act," *Marine Policy* (July 1985), p. 174.

³³ Anthony, Memorandum to Joseph W. Angelovic Regarding "Status of the Stocks—New England Groundfish—1986" dated February 14, 1986.

³⁴ NOAA, p.11.

³⁵ GAO, p. 221.

³⁶ NMFS, "Report on the Status of the Atlantic Sea Scallop Fishery" (Jan. 1986).

³⁷ Ibid., See also, Finch, p.174.

³⁸ *Fisheries,* p.1.

³⁹ Finch, p.174.

⁴⁰ NOAA, p.125.

⁴¹ NOAA, pp.90-93.

⁴² See Note 25.

⁴³ NOAA, p.118-120

⁴⁴ Ibid.

⁴⁵ Ibid.

⁴⁶ NOAA, p.121-123.

⁴⁷ *Fisheries,* p.2.

⁴⁸ See Note 25.

⁴⁹ Finch, p.174.

⁵⁰ International Trade Commission, Conditions of Competition Affecting the U.S. Gulf and South Atlantic shrimp Industry (Aug. 1985) (USITC Publication 1738)

⁵¹ Ibid.

⁵² See Note 25.

⁵³ *Fisheries,* p.1.

⁵⁴ H.R. 4690.

55 See Note 25.

56 *Fisheries*, p.1.

57 *Fisheries*, p.1.

58 Ibid.

59 See Note 25.

60 *Fisheries*, p.1.

61 Finch, p.174.

62 V. J. Norton, M. M. Miller, and E. Kenny, "Indexing the Economic Health of the U.S. fishing Industry's Harvesting Sector," *Eight Annual Seminar of the Center for Oceans and Law and Policy*, 1984 (University of Virginia).

63 Foreign Fishing Schedule (51 Fed. Reg. 202 and 50 Fed. Reg. 41533).

PART TWO

Comparative Analysis of

Resource Management Approaches

As was mentioned in our opening session there are a number of reasons why we are examining the question of fisheries management. Even though the National Marine Fisheries Service has the primary Federal responsibility for the management of marine fishery resources in the 3-200 mile fishery zone, they do not own the resource. That is, the fisheries are common property—owned by no one or belong to everyone.

Governments have been dealing with the management of common property resources for as long as there have been governments. They have developed a wide range of management techniques to deal with those resource management issues. Common property resources include not only marine fisheries, but also forestry, water, oil and gas, minerals and air to name just a few. Methods that have been used to manage these resources usually include some form of access limitation, quotas, or economic incentives.

This session will examine the methods developed and used in other resources and by other governments in fisheries resources to promote more efficient and wise management of those resources. I have asked the speakers to describe the administrative, regulatory, or management methods that are in place or have evolved to manage this variety of resources. We are looking for lessons that can be learned from these experiences that may be applied to the management of U.S. marine fisheries.

We will begin with an overview presentation of a study conducted by NOAA on this subject of techniques used in other resource management schemes. We will call upon our international friends to present management methods used in the management of marine fisheries in Canada, Japan and the UK/EEC. Following those presentations we will then discuss in more detail two examples of other managed resources: forestry and oil and gas.

LYNNE CARTER HANSON
*Executive Director
Center for Ocean Management Studies
University of Rhode Island
Kingston, Rhode Island*

CHAPTER 3

An Overview of Fishery Management:

Lessons from Other

Resource Management Fields

THOMAS E. BIGFORD
Chief
Habitat Conservation Branch
Management Division
National Marine Fisheries Service
National Oceanic and Atmospheric Administration
Gloucester, Massachusetts

INTRODUCTION

The time is right to consider alternative approaches for managing our marine fisheries. Trends show that the health of many fish stocks and the economic viability of many commercial and recreational sectors are tenuous; stock and fishery pressures are increasing, and measures of catch are declining. In response to these trends, the National Oceanic and Atmospheric Administration (NOAA) and its National Marine Fisheries Service (NMFS) initiated a study in 1984 to analyze management approaches used in other natural resource fields.[1] As compared to fisheries, the other fields use innovative and aggressive resource allocation tools which provide excellent blueprints for change in fishery management. The report examines management approaches in those other fields and identifies potential applications of any relevant experiences to fisheries. These findings provide background on management strategies used by agencies with jurisdiction over a scarce resource. Any interpretations or applications must be made by managers in each fishery.

The overview was originally intended to be rather narrow, focusing on three resource fields that seemed most applicable to the fishing industry. However, the project quickly expanded, mostly since recent history indicates that the fishing industry, from managers to harvesters to retailers, has much to learn from other resource fields. Hence, the study was expanded to eight fields, including U.S. and foreign fisheries, timber, water, minerals, rangeland, telecommunications, migratory birds, air pollution, and park concessions. Not all are natural resources but each offers insights to common property management.

APPLICATION OF FINDINGS TO THE PROBLEMS IN FISHERIES

Governments manage natural resources using many combinations of access rights, leasing systems, and economic incentives. Not all strategies will work in all cases; but, if applied with care, the benefits and pitfalls of different practices should be instructive when attempting innovation in fishery management. This section examines common management alternatives used to establish marketable rights or economical incentives for common property resources. The four basic management alternatives are: overall approach; initial allocation of rights; transferability of rights; and duration of the rights. Each alternative is discussed below.

The Overall Approach

Although not mutually exclusive, the four general approaches to resource management are: limits on input factors; direct control of output; tax programs (fees or royalties); and areal rights.

- Limits on Input Factors

The most common approach to managing fisheries is to limit the total number of some input factor, e.g., vessels, fishermen, units of gear, or time fishing. The term "limited entry" generally refers to a limit on the number of vessels permitted in a fishery, but the economic consequences of limiting "effort" by restricting the total number of fishermen, gear, or time fishing are similar. Furthermore, limiting one factor of production often creates an incentive to compensate elsewhere to at least maintain the same production capabilities. This technology creep is evident with electronic gear in the fishing industry, with improved space technology in telecommunications, and in many other resource fields.

- Direct Control of Output

Controlling total fishery output with limits on individual production is discussed in fishery literature under terms such as "individual fishermen's quotas" and "stock certificates." Each control is a limit on the amount of fish available for harvest to an individual vessel or fisherman for a given time period; the sum of individual quotas or certificates usually does not exceed the total yield from the stock at that time. The quota philosophy has been used by the U.S. Environmental Protection Agency to establish marketable rights to certain air pollutants. The timber industry imposes bid quotas based on company size, thereby maintaining competition between large and small firms.

- Tax Programs

Four of the resource areas studied (timber, rangelands, minerals, and migratory birds) use taxes or fees to generate revenue rather than to provide disincentives to produce. Using the opposite strategy, NMFS contemplated using an economic system to discourage the incidental catch of Atlantic billfish in a long-line tuna fishery. The "compensatory payment" concept assumed that incidental billfish catch by foreign fishermen represented a cost to the United States, but the proposal was rejected. Had the system been implemented and upheld by the courts, it would have been one of the most sophisticated responses to a problem of externalities by any government agency examined in this study.

- *Areal Rights*

Areal rights are common in stationary resources where the right to use, harvest, or extract is exclusive—timber, minerals, and rangeland. Fisheries provide few examples of areal rights. Exclusive rights to certain mollusc beds have been instituted at the state level, and lobstermen in Maine have informal territories radiating onto the continental shelf from their home ports. If an areal right were to provide exclusive, long-term use, the owner would have an incentive to conserve and to undertake stock-related research. Such a long-term areal right may approach private ownership. Unfortunately, sole ownership is not always sufficient incentive to conserve scarce or renewable resources, as the problem of soil conservation on private farms too well attests. Areal rights and fugitive resources, just as in timber and rangelands, could require extensive monitoring by a public agency to insure that all conditions associated with the right are fulfilled.

Initial Allocation of Rights

If the overall approach involves rights, agencies must allocate access rights to users based on some formula. One of the more common policies is "grandfathering" existing users, e.g., water, rangelands, and air pollution. Periodic auctions in timber, minerals, and park concessions allow new entrants. The "first come, first served" philosophy in the telecommunications spectrum and satellite orbits is another approach, but one that limits opportunities for future users. Some agencies use special boards to help distribute rights and reduce controversy while others rely on a simple lottery to distribute scarce rights.

In addition to the general allocation scheme, managers in most resource fields also make special considerations to meet local and cultural needs. Among existing programs are small business set-asides in timber and minerals, aesthetic set-asides in timber, minority ownership and local community service in telecommunications, treaty rights in water and fish, and programs banning migratory bird permit issuance to the same hunter in consecutive years.

In commercial and recreational fisheries, the first challenge will be to allocate the rights equitably. Experiences from other resource areas will be particularly valuable, especially dealing with issues such as preserving shares for future users, protecting the interests of small businesses, and dividing yields between sport, commercial, aesthetic, and foreign users. Among some of the specific experiences of other agencies which could apply to NMFS efforts to manage fish stocks are:

1. Survey work, like that which the U.S. Forest Service and the U.S. Geological Survey must conduct before timber and petroleum sales, may have to be expanded as NMFS tries to determine harvest yields, calculate fair market value, and lure industry to new fisheries;

2. "Preference rights," once used by the coal industry to entice prospectors into new claims, could be used to encourage exploratory fishing in new regions or on new stocks;

3. Overall principals such as "reasonableness" and "equitable apportionment," both used in water rights, could aid in recreational and commercial allocations;

4.   "Reciprocal water rights theory" could parallel management for transboundary stocks like striped bass or tuna;

5.   Stringent regulations can result in unintended access rights, as happened in air pollution where initial rights accrued by default to existing polluters; and

6.   A fisheries equivalent of "logical mining units" could be developed to divide resources equitably and to promote efficient harvest.

Of course, even with the wealth of government experience in allocating natural resources, NMFS should still anticipate problems because fish and the fishing industry are unique. Only rangeland management offers the problems of a short-lived renewable resource; only migratory birds, water rights, and air pollution offer the fugitive elements that require state, federal, and international cooperation. Other possible issues in fisheries management include "squatters rights" in long-established fisheries like Maine lobster or in places where fishermen have fished for generations. The fact that many vessels are small businesses with strong social, cultural, and community ties only exacerbates those issues. Allocation problems might be lessened if opportunities such as agricultural and habitat restoration or enhancement accommodate expanding fishing pressures; technological advances in telecommunications and timber growth have helped those fields meet growing demand for satellite orbits and stumpage, respectively.

Transferability of Rights

The issue of transferability (the authority to sell or trade rights) follows initial allocations. Rights can be fully transferable, transferable under conditions imposed by an agency, or non-transferable. Generally, timber, grazing, and mineral rights are fully transferable. Conditions are imposed on transfer of pollution rights but the trend has been toward relaxation. Spectrum and water rights are, in general, not transferable.

Transferability is a management option that is intended to allow the market to redistribute a resource to its most efficient user. That forecast assumes that rights owned by inefficient users will tend to be sold to more efficient users. Free and open trading is essential if economic efficiency is the ultimate goal. However, non-economic objectives may condition permit transfers. Oil lease sale restrictions lessen monopoly power in industry giants. Similar constraints in the fishing industry may affect small-scale fishermen or the vertically-integrated conglomerates that dominate certain fisheries.

Duration of the Rights

Rights in other resource areas vary in duration from one season or year to perpetuity. In general, park concessions, radio frequencies, rangelands, minerals, and timber are on a two to ten-year cycle, often renewed. Water and fishing rights tend to be perpetual, although some fishing rights may be seasonal.

The duration of the right has an important impact on other aspects of the management system. Short durations lead to little or no windfall profit to those who own the right and lessen the incentive to sell rights, but also reduce incentives to make capital investments or to conserve the resource. Still, short-term rights do offer administrative flexibility since poor systems can be improved or abolished. On the other hand, a permanent right is irreversible or reversible only at great cost and is inflexible in the face of inevitable change in resource availability or economics.

FINDINGS

These strategies are not mutually exclusive and deserve further discussion. Options to limit input factors should be considered on a case-by-case basis. Limits that might be acceptable to fishermen or are easiest to enforce may have proven to be inflexible or ineffective for managing other resources. Ultimately, the best combination of approaches for each fishery will depend on the objectives of management. The challenge in developing each system is to balance objectives such as national versus regional needs, market stability versus market dynamism, entrepreneurial freedom versus disruptive speculation, and others more specific to the fishing industry.

The mix of management measures selected will also have a major impact on the distribution of benefits. Either users or the public can benefit from the market right or access to a public resource. By design, auction systems as used in timber and minerals transfer benefits to the public; in the allocation systems of telecommunications and pollution, users can gain windfall profits; and fee systems such as those used in rangeland grazing try to balance public and users needs in establishing an equitable economic rent.

Under most existing fishery management systems, benefits are dissipated rather than focused on certain users. New management approaches could generate benefits and economic rent to the public and shift users, capital investments, and harvest levels toward some predetermined blend. Such redistributions are assumed by most proponents of change to be a net benefit to the society, even if some individuals suffer losses. The management system selected can also determine the distribution of benefits, access rights, and obligations within the fishing industry. Auctions and fee systems will eventually favor efficient fishermen with access to capital. Lotteries favor the lucky. Social criteria usually favor a specific sector. And experience indicates that any redistribution of benefits will generate controversy, beginning with discussions of innovative approaches to resource management. Fisheries are no different. Nonetheless, it is still educational to review the management approaches selected by government for different resources, as described in the following sections. Each capsule summary notes the aspect of the resource management program that was examined for application to fishery management. (Expanded discussions are in the full report.) Each area is described as noted below:

Focus—the particular management approach(es) examined;

Advantages—the management approaches that may have parallels to fisheries;

Disadvantages—features that weaken its application to fisheries; and

Relevance to fishery management—specific tools or lessons that may be most applicable to fisheries.

Fishing

Focus—state and foreign experiences with licensing schemes, allocation certificates, and other approaches

Advantages—effective management of specific fisheries by systems, etc. which convey ownership

Disadvantages—different cultural backgrounds and management authorities complicate applications to well-established U.S. fisheries

Relevance to federal fishery management—successes and failures are directly applicable to federal management problems, especially excess fishing power and declining economic returns

The National Marine Fisheries Service and Regional Fishery Management Councils have a wide range of available management techniques. A review of state and foreign programs reveals that many innovative approaches may be applied to our marine stocks. Those programs offer new ways to improve the economic efficiency of recreational and commercial fisheries. Many existing fishery management approaches, including some initiated by industry organizations, convey access rights to the industry. Table 1 in the complete report (see Note 1) summarizes the long record of innovative programs from which NMFS, the Regional Fishery Councils, and the fisheries industry may wish to consider new approaches.

Timber

Focus—U.S. Forest Service's role in public timber management, especially stumpage sale procedures, supporting programs, and set-asides for special interests

Advantages—timber management systems parallel those in some fisheries, offering tested approaches to dealing with small businesses, conservation interests, and controversy

Disadvantages—companies have alternatives in the private timber market or other federal agencies, e.g., Bureau of Land Management

Relevance to fisheries management—bidding systems and set-aside programs could apply to allocations and special procedures for recreation or small business interests

The Forest Service manages forests for multiple-use, including logging, recreation, and wilderness. The agency inventories its resources before each sale. Leases for harvesting timber stands (usually for a two- to ten-year term) are auctioned by sealed bids and determined to be acceptable either by appraising production costs and the value of finished products (residual appraisal) or by analyzing recent public and private sales in the region (transactions evidence). To promote social goals, small businesses compete for a special share of most auctions. Current policy issues center on the optimal tree size of logging, the appropriate mix of forest uses, and effects of changing markets on existing harvest contracts; each has application to the fishing industry.

Minerals

Focus—U.S. Department of Interior's leasing procedures for coal and petroleum

Advantages—lease sale and royalty systems generate economic rent; special programs protect small business interests; underground resources offer an interesting parallel to fish stocks in problems of resource assessment

Disadvantages—bidding systems require large support staffs for research and administration; resource is neither fugitive nor renewable

Relevance to fishery management—procedures for bidding, lease management, and royalties may apply, especially to sessile stocks

In the past, several types of coal leases have been used depending on whether bidders were original prospectors, interested in competitive sales, or bidding on special auctions for defaulted leases. Oversubscription eventually led to a ten-year moratorium on new leases. Today, lease lengths range from ten years for petroleum to 20 years for coal, with extensions available in most cases. Petroleum leases recently increased in frequency and acreage. Extended lease schedules, such as the five-year offshore plans, conveniently allow the industry to anticipate sale basins and dates but may not recoup full market value for the resource. All mining operations must satisfy economic criteria for "logical recovery units" and "diligence." Many royalty systems may be used. Like timber, regulations offer special set-aside programs for small or disadvantaged firms.

Water

Focus—state laws, legal decisions, and procedures governing use of surface water and underground aquifers in western states

Advantages—offers approaches to managing a mobile, transboundary resource affected by Native American treaties, conflicting claims, and multiple uses; also offers economic principles for allocation

Disadvantages—separate state-management regimes have created a disjointed body of law not comparable to an umbrella federal authority

Relevance to fisheries management—procedures for calculating equitable apportionment and economic benefit could help in developing fishery allocation systems; special procedures for transboundary and treaty consideration are relevant to migratory and anadromous stocks

Water rights are managed by the states, and are allocated according to the principles of prior use, beneficial use, and resource availability. Generally, users retain perpetual water rights (assuming beneficial use) unless rights exceed availability. When rights are not used by an owner, a series of policies determine how the water will next be used. Several policies on "reasonableness" determine pumping rates for various users and uses. Native Americans have "reserved" water rights, as they do with Pacific coast salmon via treaty; "nonreserved" rights are divided according to "equitable apportionment"— a doctrine which accounts for use patterns, resource availability, secondary benefits, and transboundary use and which could apply to transboundary fish stocks such as salmon and bluefish.

Rangeland

Focus—U.S. Department of the Interior's rangeland management systems, including the grazing permit process

Advantages—grasslands, as a renewable resource, are similar to fisheries; grazing rights have evolved from common property; the BLM permit system is a dynamic process that attempts to balance grazing effort and grassland health; and BLM determines annual grazing levels which are then implemented by local grazing boards

Disadvantages—some management approaches may not be applicable to underwater resources

Relevance to fishery management—the permit process, including leases, annual adjustments, grazing boards, and the evolution from common property to property rights, offers good insights for fishery managers

Because of past user abuses, grazing on public lands is federally controlled to prevent overuse. Regional advisory boards of ranchers now help to allocate grazing effort after total levels are set by federal office. Permits are issued for ten years and may be renewed and transferred, thereby enabling ranchers to make long-term plans for grazing land; rents are based on the amount of forage consumed each year. The government sets annual forage levels after field inspections for soil erosion, grass growth, and shifts caused, for example, by a change in rainfall. Forage levels also consider wildlife and other potential uses of the range. Though the government views grazing as a privilege, the ranchers see it as a *de facto* right accrued over decades of permitted use—the same argument that may be used by families who have fished the same waters for decades.

Telecommunications

Focus—the allocation system for satellite orbits and radio frequencies

Advantages—this field is currently undergoing a review of ownership rights, including a debate with less developed countries on future uses

Disadvantages—the resource is not similar to fisheries; unlike many fishing sectors, technological advances have kept pace with growing market demands

Relevance to fishery management—the debate on preserving access for future users could relate to recreational, small business, and habitat interests

The allocation policies governing space orbits and the electromagnetic spectrum may be evolving from open access to some form of controlled system, prompting debate on use. International arguments center on preserving a portion of the spectrum and orbits for future users, a source of heated debate between developed and developing nations. Domestically, a special advisor assists government agencies in allocation decisions. Radio and television licenses are reviewed regularly to insure compliance with permit conditions. One frequent problem is the proximity of one use to another; any interference can greatly reduce use and market value.

Park Concessions

Focus—methods of allocating permits to operate concessions in national parks

Advantages—concessionaires have "possessory rights" to their permits that entitle them to compensation if a contract is not renewed

Disadvantages—this topic offers few insights into possible fisheries allocations systems, largely because of the subject

Relevance to fisheries management—possessory rights could relate to
fishermen who lose a license or quota

The National Park Service authorizes private businesses to provide services and
facilities on park lands. The National Park Service issues initial contracts after
competitive bidding, and automatically offers options to renew concession permits. If
a contract is not renewed, concessionaires have "possessory rights" to compensation
from the government.

Migratory Birds

Focus—the process used to regulate migratory bird hunting

Advantages—Canadian, U.S. and state authorities manage this fugitive,
renewable resource; annual hunting quotas established for major
flyways offer a contrast to fishery-management procedures

Disadvantages—limiting hunting to recreational use avoids most
controversy and is unrealistic for most fisheries

Relevance to fishery management—regulatory process and annual
federal hunting licenses could apply; exclusive sport hunting license
could be useful to fishery managers as recreational interests gain
stature

The failure of state governments to fulfill their management responsibilities
prompted the development of federal authority over this resource. Now even though
licenses permit only recreational hunting, migratory bird management parallels
fishery management in several ways: in objectives and plans for each major flyway;
in annual changes in hunting levels; and in frequent problems with insufficient,
tardy data. One interesting difference from fisheries is a management approach
whereby federal agencies determine, and states implement, hunting limits. Since
1934, the duck stamp program has supported the acquisition of duck habitat and
helped to perpetuate stable populations of migratory birds.

Air Pollution

Focus—the regulation of air pollution

Advantages—air pollution is an industrial by-product which may relate
to incidental fish catch; evolving rights and their transferability offer
lessons, as does the failure to establish marketable rights in
chlorofluorocarbons (CFCs)

Disadvantages—except for the CFC experience, air pollution regulation is
not directly applicable to directed fishing

Relevance to fishery management—evolving property rights offer
timely insights to growing interest in fishing rights

States regulate most air polluters in order to control total emissions within a
specific area or "bubble." Industries may trade rights, but new rights are not created
once the emission level in a bubble reaches an established maximum. Enforcement is
predicated on precise measurements of key pollutants from each source and for the
entire bubble; violators face significant fines, though they are rarely put out of
business.

CONCLUSIONS

The fishing industry has many similarities with other industries. Most fish harvesting firms and many at the processing or marketing levels are small businesses thriving on the energies of hard-working individuals. To any industry, but especially one dominated by businesses with little corporate support, any disruption in the flow of normal operations draws immediate attention to the cultural, social, and economic implications of change. Still, the current plight of many fishing sectors invites change. One factor that is attracting broad scrutiny is the common property status of fish, the basis for commercial and recreational businesses with economic activity of over $30 billion annually.

While some government and industry leaders contemplate new management approaches, others argue that the fugitive, renewable, and cyclic nature of fish stocks render useless many alternative strategies. This paper summarizes a research project aimed at analyzing management strategies from other resource management programs for consideration by the fishing industry.

Based on the cumulative experience of management programs for fisheries and other resource fields, it seems plausible that other approaches may apply to fisheries. Fish and the fishing industry are not as different as has been claimed. Granted, changes will be slow. New programs are always slow to evolve, and new legislation may be needed if certain approaches are selected. But the biggest change, and one which this report hopes to enhance, is toward a new attitude of multi-disciplinary analysis. There are many common experiences in other resource fields that should help managers address fishing industry problems.

ACKNOWLEDGMENTS

This paper summarizes the report prepared by the National Oceanic and Atmospheric Administration's (NOAA) Office of Policy and Planning, with assistance from the National Marine Fisheries Service. The author thanks all contributors to that NOAA report, especially Clemens B. Bribitzer, Bruce Norman, Victoria Miller, Martha Umphrey, and Thomas J. Maginnis.

NOTES

[1] This paper is a condensed version of a full NOAA report entitled "Fishery Management—Lessons From Other Resource Management Fields." This paper and the report are background papers intended to spur dialog, not necessarily to set policy.

CHAPTER 4

Resource Management Strategies

APPROACHES UTILIZED TO MANAGE THE
FISHING INDUSTRY IN ATLANTIC CANADA

BEN FERGUSON
Chief
Resource Management Division
Department of Fisheries and Oceans
Resource Allocation Branch
Atlantic Fisheries Service
Ottawa, Ontario, Canada

INTRODUCTION

I am pleased to be here to talk about Canadian Fisheries Management approaches; more specifically on the advantages and disadvantages of management measures utilized in Canada. This presentation deals exclusively with management approaches followed in the *Atlantic* fisheries, with which I am most familiar. Some parallels can, however, be drawn as similar management techniques are used for certain Atlantic and Pacific fisheries.

Fisheries management in Atlantic fisheries will be addressed by first looking at the general objectives of Canadian fisheries management; secondly, by outlining briefly the resource management process generally followed; and finally, by looking at the pros and cons of various management measures utilized.

At the outset, I would like to put the Atlantic fishing industry in its proper economic context. The fishing industry in Atlantic Canada is comprised of 50,000 fishermen landing a variety of fish species with an annual worth of $620 million in landings. These fish resources are processed in over 700 fish plants distributed over the five Atlantic provinces. In most of the rural communities where fish plants are located, the fishing industry is the sole economic base for the population's livelihood.

The performance of the fishing industry in Atlantic Canada is characterized by boom and bust cycles—going through cyclical periods of good and bad economic times. To take advantage of periods of growth and profitability, the industry went through a period of expansion to the point that the capacity of vessels and plants now generally exceeds the resource available to sustain them. This overcapacity has threatened the viability of the fisheries and has shaken its structural base, particularly in the harvesting sector. Perhaps more than any other factor this excess capacity has influenced the manner in which the Government of Canada has managed the Atlantic fishery over the last ten years.

CANADIAN FISHERIES MANAGEMENT OBJECTIVES

First let's take a look at the objectives pursued in the management of the Atlantic fisheries.

1. The first objective could be described as the *maximization of the harvesting of the resource through proper conservation and protection of the resource.*

   This is the overriding consideration in fisheries management which determines at the outset the manner in which government manages particular fisheries and particular fish stocks. An important component of the Department's pursuit of this objective is fisheries research in order to argument our knowledge of fish stocks, to understand their dynamics and ways and means for their restoration and rejuvenation. We will see later how scientific advice in fisheries is important in the resource management process (i.e., the manner that determines the upper limits of resource exploitation of all important Atlantic fish stocks).

2. A second objective of fisheries management is to *strive towards economic viability and maximization of employment in the Atlantic fisheries.* There are, nevertheless, two general principles which guide allocation policies within the economic viability and maximization of employment context.

   - The first one is in *giving priority to those Canadian fishermen who traditionally have depended on particular fish stocks for fishing.*

     Because of the current state of the industry, this principle recognizes the dependence of fishermen in fishing particular geographic areas and in particular fisheries and is a paramount consideration in fisheries management. It means fishermen are guaranteed a share of the resource by virtue of having had an historical dependence on these resources.

   - A second one which should be indicated is *the principle of priority of access to fisheries resources to those closest or adjacent to these particular resources.*

     What this principle recognizes is the importance of the inshore sector in the economic fabric of the Atlantic fisheries and by allocating a significant portion of the resource to this sector the economic viability of fish plants which depends on inshore fishermen to supply them is thus maintained.

3. A third objective of fisheries management is *Canadianization of the fishing industry.*

Foreign investment is not extensive in the Atlantic fisheries and the intention is not to discourage such investment but there is a real need to foster utilization of Canadian fishery resources first and foremost for the benefits of Canadians through greater Canadian ownership of the means of production in fisheries.

THE RESOURCE MANAGEMENT PROCESS

To understand how fisheries management works in Canada, it is necessary to outline how the resource management process functions, how the maximum exploitable resource levels are determined, and how the various fisheries resources are allocated.

A cornerstone of the resource management process is the advisory and decision-making process for management of Atlantic fisheries resource. It is a complex process involving some 20 major scientific and management advisory committees and covering 25 different fish species.

Scientific Advisory Committees

There are several scientific committees which generate advice on fish stocks important to the Atlantic fishing industry. The most important is the *Canadian Atlantic Fisheries Scientific Advisory Committee* (CAFSAC) which provides scientific advice on all stocks managed by Canada. Each individual scientist's assessment of a particular fish stock has to be approved by CAFSAC before being submitted to fisheries managers for approval. Other scientific organizations are the North Atlantic Fisheries Organization Scientific Council, the International Council for the Exploration of the Seas, the International Whaling Commission, and the International Convention for the Conservation of Atlantic Tunas.

Management Advisory Committees

There are numerous management advisory committees in place in the Atlantic fisheries. There is, in fact, an advisory committee in place for all major Atlantic fisheries. Advisory committees can be on an Atlantic-wide scale (i.e., covering more than one province and/or they can be essentially local to a particular area or to a localized fishery). It depends on the particular fishery concerns and on the number and diversity of users involved. Membership on advisory committees, besides government representatives, are fishermen and fish producers who depend on the particular resource. They have an advisory role (i.e., they advise the Minister of Fisheries and Oceans on matters related to specific species including the condition of the stocks, allocation of the resource among fishermen, methods of harvesting, division of catch among processors, research needs and techniques, licensing policy, and economic analysis of fishing enterprises).

The Management Process

The management process from the generation of scientific advice to the drafting of regulations can be described as follows:

- The scientific advice on particular stocks proceeds from CAFSAC or other appropriate scientific councils to the

Atlantic Directors General Committee of the Department of Fisheries and Oceans for approval.

- Once approval is obtained on the scientific advice which determines the maximum total allowable catch (TAC) of particular fish stocks, this advice then is submitted to management advisory committees for consultations with industry representatives and for the development of a management plan. When the plan is finalized, it is reviewed by the Department and in some cases, referred to the Minister of Fisheries and Oceans for approval.

- Once management plans are approved, the need for fisheries regulations is determined and if required, new regulations or amendments to existing ones are requested.   While the approval of regulations is an important requirement it is not always feasible to promulgate passing of regulations on a timely basis. For management plans, regulations sometimes unfortunately lag behind the implementation of new management measures.

MANAGEMENT MEASURES

I would like now to turn my attention to the various management measures utilized in the Atlantic fisheries. These measures are the means by which the government controls fishing activities for the benefit of its users: fishermen and fish producers. The management measures can be generally categorized in two categories: input and output measures.

Input Management Measures

Input measures are intended to include those which control the number of fishermen and fishing effort utilized in fishing. One of the most important measures included in this category is licensing. *Licensing* is utilized to control the number of fishermen permitted to fish commercially. Licensing policies can vary considerably geographically and by fisheries but generally it is intended to control fishing activity and restrict it to those fishermen dependant on the resource for their livelihood. This is achieved through limited entry licensing schemes and through categorization of fishermen. Licensing is not only used to restrict who fishes but also to govern the type of vessel and fishing gear utilized by the fishermen.

Zoning and *seasons* are other input management measures extensively utilized in the Atlantic fisheries. The Atlantic area is divided into homogeneous fishing areas for which management measures most appropriate to the fishermen in the individual areas can be implemented. Most major Atlantic fisheries are divided into zones and have fishing seasons established. One of the impacts of zones is in restricting access to a particular geographic area to a privileged number of fishermen. Zones and seasons have been utilized extensively in the management of the Atlantic lobster fishery for over 20 years. Zones are also used in certain fisheries to restrict offshore fishermen from encroaching into traditional fishing areas of inshore fishermen.

Another input control utilized is *gear* controls. Such gear controls are, for example, the number of traps that can be utilized by a lobster fisherman or the size opening of mesh utilized in gillnetting etc. They generally aim at preventing the capture of small size, immature fish and shellfish species which could be harvested at a later date by fishermen at greater size and greater value.

The use of input controls has been the traditional way of managing the Atlantic fisheries. These forms of controls have evolved over time as the government's response to fisheries problems and to the needs expressed by Atlantic fishermen. The general approach was to deal with the problem of overcapacity through controlling fishing effort and capacity utilized in these particular fisheries. It can be effective if a balance can be achieved between fishing capacity on the one hand, and the size of the available resources on the other hand. It means though that a reduction of fishing effort has to be achieved and this, however, can only take place through attrition.

Output Management Measures

Along with input management measures, output measures were also found necessary in order to control the maximum quantity of harvest and insure the conservation of the resource for future utilization. Output controls were necessary in the context of significant harvesting overcapacity and as a means of restricting catches to scientifically recommended levels.

Falling into this broad category are TACs and apportioning these into *quotas*. Quotas are established for most Atlantic fish stocks. They are divided amongst a number and variety of often conflicting users. Determining an equitable, fair distribution of quotas is a most difficult task which the Department is constantly faced with. The unfortunate result of limited resource availability and quota apportioning in an overcapitalized fishery has brought an uncontrollable race for the resource among fishermen. In some fisheries, it has shortened the harvesting period, and compounded overcapitalization in the fishery.

One means of overcoming some of the shortcomings of quota management has been through further apportioning quotas amongst various participants or users. This provides each enterprise with a specific share of the resource which can be harvested when it is most appropriate or when it is to the advantage for the fishermen to harvest it. Guidelines and rules are established to govern these enterprise allocations but flexibility is given to the user on the manner in which he wishes to use his share of the TAC.

While relatively new, this concept has been implemented on a trial basis in numerous Atlantic fisheries notably the offshore groundfish fishery, the offshore lobster, certain inshore crab fisheries and inshore groundfisheries and in the herring purse seine fishery. The intention is to extend this approach to all major Atlantic fisheries where practical. The obvious advantages of individual quotas or enterprise allocations are the lessening of necessary regulations governing a particular fishery; allowing more flexibility to particular fishermen in using the technology better suited for achieving optimum enterprise efficiency; allowing companies to make investment decisions based on their own needs and fishing strategy; permit greater integration of harvesting, processing and marketing operations and lastly, provide a mean through transferability mechanism by which harvesting capacity can be in line with resource availability over the long term.

Drawbacks to the implementation of enterprise allocations are the difficulty to strictly enforce without deploying significant departmental resources thus the serious danger or temptation by users to misreport catch levels and the potential threat to conservation of the fish resource. Another potential drawback is in the possible distortion of traditional landing patterns thereby threatening the traditional economic base of coastal communities. This last point is a specific concern of inshore fishermen. However, experience gained from the implementation of enterprise allocation in the offshore groundfishery since 1982, has shown that traditional landing patterns have not been affected as was initially feared.

CONCLUSIONS

I hope the above has been helpful in elaborating, in capsule form, management approaches followed for the Atlantic fishing industry in Canada. While the enclosed has attempted to be complete, it may be appropriate to indicate future trends which may shape the future of the industry. The first consideration is continuing to manage the Atlantic fisheries resources through sound conservation and protection principles.

The second consideration is a trend towards lessening regulations in the industry with the objective to contribute to greater efficiency and profitability of fishing enterprises. Consistent with this management approach is to continue the implementation of enterprise allocations in as many sectors and fisheries of the Atlantic industry while at the same time removing restrictions which may adversely affect the mobility of the vessels in those fisheries.

The opinions expressed here are those of the author and not necessarily those of the Department of Fisheries and Oceans or the Government of Canada.

FISHERIES MANAGEMENT IN JAPAN

HIROYUKI TAKAGI
Designated Representative
Japan Fisheries Association
Washington, D.C.

BACKGROUND

Japan is located in an area where cold and warm currents meet. This blend of currents produces a great amount of marine life and provides the Japanese people a rich fishing ground. The diet of Japanese people depends highly on sea foods, 45.3 percent of all protein intake comes from seafood in comparison to a mere 3.2 percent for Americans. The land of Japan where almost 120 million people live is small—about the size of the State of Montana. In order to utilize the aquatic resources to the maximum extent, fishery management became important to the Japanese government at both national and local levels. The Japanese fishing industry consists of roughly four groups of different levels of development, ranging from numerous small-scale fisheries in the inland and coastal waters to a small number of large-scale fisheries which operate offshore and in distant water.

The total production of fisheries was 12.8 million metric tons in 1984, with inland fisheries accounting for 2 percent, coastal 26 percent, offshore 54 percent and distant water 18 percent, respectively. However, 95 percent of the catch of the fishery management units, or 76 percent of fishery operators and their employees are engaged in the inland and coastal fisheries with small vessels of less than 10 gross tons or in fish culture activities. The total supply of fishery products in 1985 was 14.4 million metric tons (own catch 11.8 million metric tons, aquaculture 1.2 million metric tons and import 1.4 million metric tons) which is eight times higher than the level of 40 years ago.

MANAGEMENT SYSTEM

The Fisheries Law and other relevant laws and regulations govern every phase of fishing activities. The Fisheries Law was enacted in 1949 to establish a fundamental system relative to fishery production and to insure overall utilization of the waters by means of fishery adjustment mechanisms (constituents of which are fishery operators and their employees) and at the same time to enforce democratization of the fishery. Under the law, the entry system controls admission of new people into the fishing industry. The law provides regulations mainly in the following three fields: fishing rights; fishing licenses; and fishing adjustments.

Fishing Rights

The fishing right is the right with which one can operate certain fishery activities exclusively in a given water. The fishing right is a property right with certain restrictions and is granted by the Governors of the Metropolis, Hokkaido or Prefectures. In accordance with the type of fishery, the fishing right is classified as follows:

- *Fixed net fishing right*

    Fixed net fishing right means the right under which fixed net fisheries are operated. The fishing gear is fixed at specified sites. There were 1, 763 management units holding the right as of 1979.

- *Demarcated fishing right*

    Demarcated fishing right means the right to operate a demarcated fishery. Demarcated fishery is aquaculture where the operational area is limited to a certain demarcated area. This type of fishery includes oyster, pearl, seaweed, and certain fish such as yellowtail, sea bream, and carp cultures. The total units which held the right were 12,176 as of 1979.

- *Joint fishing right*

    Joint fishery means the fishery which is conducted by fishermen in a community by using commonly adjacent specified waters. Because of the nature of this type of fishery, the fishing right is granted to local fishery cooperative associations for their management. The majority of the coastal fishermen belong to one of these types of fisheries which include: 1) collecting seaweeds, shellfishes or aquatic animals; 2) submerging stationary net gears other than those of fixed net fishery. This is a rather small-scale set-net or fixed gillnet fishery; and 3) beach seine fishery, hand-operated trawl fishery by boat and angling by aid of baiting. There were 5,315 units granted this (3) type of fishing right in 1979.

The total production as of 1982:

1)	category	337,000 metric tons
2)	category	940,000 metric tons
3)	category	564,000 metric tons
	Total	1,841,000 metric tons

All these small- to medium-scale fisheries are operated in inland and coastal waters.

FISHING LICENSES

A fishing license is required to operate a certain type of fishery. The license is issued by the Minister of Agriculture, Forestry, and Fishery. The fishing license differs from the fishing right. Issuing the license by the Minister (or by Governors) is to lift the prohibition. Such general prohibition is needed to protect the aquatic resources and to adjust fishery activities. The license is issued to a vessel and most licensed fisheries represent important fisheries.

- *"Designated Fishery" (license issued by the Minister)*

  This includes: distant water trawl fishery, North Pacific longline fishery, mothership trawl fishery, large and medium purse seine fishery, distant skipjack, tuna fishery, mothership salmon fishery, etc. There were 4,435 vessels permitted in 1985.

- *"Approved Fishery" (license issued by the Minister)*

  This includes: squid jigging, saury fishery, herring gillnetting, Japan Sea tanner crab fishery, etc.

- *"Governor License Fishery"*

  This is the fishery licensed by a Governor and includes: small scale purse seine fishery, boat seine fishery, off-shore boat seine fishery, etc. The vessels used in this category of fishing are between 5 and 40 gross tons.

FISHING ADJUSTMENT

To achieve democratization of the fishery and utilize the waters in a comprehensive and coordinated manner, two commissions were formed:

- *Area Fishery Adjustment Commission*

  This commission is under the jurisdiction of the Minister and there are currently 66—one in each area. Each commission consists of 15 members, 9 are residents elected by the industry, 4 are knowledgeable and experienced experts appointed by a Governor. The following are the functions of the commission which are close to those of Regional Councils in the U.S.

- *Advisory Functions*

  Preparation of fishing grounds plans and granting fishing rights. All other matters that the Fishery Agency handles in regard to the fishing right must be carried out after consulting with the commission.

- *Decision Functions*

  The commission has the power to make decisions concerning the arbitration, instruction, and authorization, such as deciding on the establishment, change, and abolishment of common piscary rights, etc.

- *Area Joint Fishery Adjustment Commission*

  A Governor may establish, when deemed necessary, the joint fishery adjustment commission for a region which consists of two or more sea areas. This commission handles the issue which cannot be handled by an area fishery adjustment commission alone.

FISHERIES MANAGEMENT IN THE EEC

RICHARD R. BANKS
Fishery Economics Research Unit
Sea Fish Industry Authority
Edinburgh, United Kingdom

INTRODUCTION

In any discussion of fisheries management, there are three common elements which have to be identified: the meaning of fisheries management; its objectives; and its implementation. The European Economic Community (EEC) has provided a frame to work from but as with the Articles from the Treaty of Rome, the meanings and objectives are often vague and confusing.

....to promote harmonious and balanced development of the fishing industry within the general economy and to encourage national use of the biological resources of the sea....(European Commission Regulation 101/76).

....to determine conditions for fishing with a view to insuring protection of fishing grounds and conservation of the biological resources of the sea....(Article 102 of the Accession Treaty).

The fact that these statements tend to be vague is not a criticism of the EEC policy since the above articles refer to an admission and an identification of the problems of fisheries management. These, therefore, provide the impetus and, more importantly, the background for legislation to implement a formulated management policy with objectives of achieving a desired fishing mortality rate (F max) or a desired size of the spawning stock. These are biological objectives, and it is usually biological criteria which are used to estimate the level of catch that should be taken. However, increasing importance is being attached to the economic, social, and political objectives, such as the need to maintain an economic and efficient fishing fleet, the need to maintain employment, and the need to insure stability.

The impetus for the EEC's management policy was created by the extension of the member states fisheries limits to 200 miles (or the appropriate median line) in January, 1977. The failure of the Northeast Atlantic Fisheries Commission (NEAFC)[1] to influence the activities of its member nations (which included both EEC and non European Commission (EC) members), and the creation of the "community pond" made it necessary for the EEC to establish and implement a policy on behalf of the nine-member states. The EEC was empowered to manage the community's fish stocks and to determine the fishing rights of its members, and to negotiate mutual fishing rights with third countries (which prior to 1983 included the Eastern Bloc states as well as Norway, Sweden, the Faroes, Spain and Portugal). The area of specific concern was the Northeast Atlantic and, thus, Mediterranean waters were not subject to the same degree of scrutiny with the result that Italy and Greece do not feature significantly. The subject area, therefore, is concentrated between the International Council for the Exploration of the Seas (ICES) Area IIa in the North and ICES Area IX in the South. Table 1 shows the distribution of the catch by member states prior to 1975, and in 1980 and 1983.

The establishment by 1983 of a Common Fisheries Policy identified the concise framework for management as well as structural and marketing policies (although since 1977 piecemeal management measures had been implemented). In effect, the

Table 1

Northeast Atlantic Catch by EC Fishing Nations
(000' tons liveweight)

	1971-75 (av./annum)	1980	1983
Belgium	54	46	49
Denmark	1,567	2,010	1,836
France	647	670	538
Germany	362	259	238
Ireland	86	149	203
Netherlands	335	338	269
Spain	663	468	512
Portugal	280	228	245
United Kingdom	1,172	903	849
Total	5,166	5,071	4,739

Source: Eurostat.

policy held true to the concept of Article 39 of the Treaty of Rome guaranteeing free access for all community vessels to all community grounds subject to a number of negotiated restrictions on exclusive rights:

- Access by member states to between three and six miles of the national coastal zones were restricted to historic rights. For example, French rights to fish herring off the northeast coast of England. In some areas including Scotland, N. Ireland, the Irish Republic and parts of southwest England, the coastal limit was extended to 12 miles;

- Access within three miles may also be restricted to member states. This rule is not EEC-wide and often applies to areas which require protection. An exception exists between the Irish Republic and the UK (N. Ireland) where vessels from each nation are entitled to fish in each other's coastal waters.

Other carefully-defined exceptions to the access arrangements established special protection to fishermen in the Shetland and Orkney Islands, more commonly known as the Shetland Box, where the number of boats from the distant water fleets of member states was restricted. In addition, the Norway pout box was established in recognition of the need to conserve haddock and whiting stocks. More recently, as a result of Spain and Portugal's entries into the EEC, the "Irish Box" has been created effectively restricting access to the Irish Sea and Irish west coast to historic participants only, thereby excluding vessels from Spain and Portugal.

The 1983 Common Fisheries Policy was in effect a compromise between the continental and island member states over access and quotas, thereby recognizing the need for cooperation between member states prior to the entry of Spain and Portugal. The policy was intended to be relatively stable over a 20-year period. The ten wished to present a settled policy to the new entrants which could be tuned in as much as possible to suit the established members.

MANAGEMENT MEASURES

The management measures adopted by the Community as a whole consist of:

1.   The control of the catch more commonly interpreted in EC terms as the total allowable catch (TAC);

2.   Conservation control measures such as restrictions on fishing gear and type of trawls; and

3.   Direct control of fishing effort such as limiting the number of vessels as well as certain technical and physical features of those vessels, or more indirect limitations on effort such as production quotas.

The EC's main management tool is that of the TAC, complemented by conservation measures directed at fishing activity. The catch quotas are divided into national quotas, whereby each member country controls its exploitation rate where necessary through direct controls on fishing effort.

THE TOTAL ALLOWABLE CATCH

The TACs are a control technique directed at the level of exploitation of the stocks. Levels of TAC are determined by the desired fishing mortality rate (F max) and the desired spawning stock biomass based on ICES[2] advice. The EEC formulates levels of TAC from the advice given. Prior to reaching TAC decisions, however, the advice is subjected to the EEC decision making process i.e. the two principal administrative organs: The Council of Ministers (consisting of the Ministers of fishing from 12 nations) and the European Commission (EC). Other bodies may also play a role—one of which is the Scientific and Technical Committee (STC) which provides advice on both biological and socio-economic issues and reports directly to European Commission.

Where joint stocks are involved the EC is responsible for negotions. Examples include the Baltic Sea (International Baltic Sea Fisheries Commission) and Norway. Occasionally conflict arises with joint stocks as has been the case from time to time with Norway in the North Sea over definitions of allocations, i.e. joint or autonomous stocks. Since management objectives are predominantly similar, negotiations usually resolve the situation. Exchange takes place by means of cod equivalents where tonnage weights are expressed in terms of market values.

ALLOCATION BETWEEN MEMBER STATES

After negotiations have been finalised on the total TAC allowed for each species, within individual or groups of ICES areas, catch possibilities (TAC) are formulated. The country allocations are determined on the basis of historic access and do not differ significantly from overall allocations agreed to in 1983 i.e., the UK 36 percent, Belgium 2 percent, Denmark 24 percent, France 13 percent, West Germany 13 percent, the Netherlands 7 percent and Ireland 4 percent. Both Spain's and Portugal's EC entitlements remain undecided and current access is based on a policy of restricted licenses for the first ten years.

The reasons for national allocations are for: 1) effective management by member states in order to prevent a global scramble for quota take ups; and 2) to allow member states to coordinate quota entitlement with fleet development and marketing. The guidelines for interpretation (EC Regulation 158), although not weighted in order of importance, encompass support of traditional fishing rights, special regional needs and the need to minimize the cost of lost access to fishing grounds in third countries.

One set of problems relating to TAC formulation can be linked to the criterion used to establish the level of production. Criticism of these criterion include:

- The advice on most stock levels is received a year prior to implementation;

- The assessment of mortality levels and stock biomass may be far from ideal (assessments based on young stocks rather than old);

- Many questions related to stock interdependences;

- Difficulty in assessing the discard level;

- The inability to take account of by-catch effects; and

- The role of abiotic factors (density, temperature and salinity) is seldom understood.

The second set of problems relates to the relationship between production restrictions and fishing effort itself:

- The TAC does nothing to limit over-investment and, therefore, a dissipation of profit;

- The late fixing of TACs often hampers fishing plans;

- The uncertainty of closing dates;

- The internal consistency of the Common Fisheries Policy is based on coordination of three of its components: resources; structures; and markets. Specifically, the multi-annual investment programs are normally implemented with a precise objective:

  ....in respect of the fishing sector, a satisfactory balance between the fishing capacity to be deployed by the production facilities covered by the programs and the stocks which are expected to be available during the period of validity of the programs....(EC Regulation 2908/83).

  Where the TAC system is implemented, the follow-up of changes in catch capacities and fishing effort has often been neglected. The result has been that it is not possible to assess adjustment between catch capacities and stocks. Action taken to reorganize and modernize fleets and action relating to stock management are, therefore, liable to get out of phase; and

- Incompatibility between the TACs on the one hand and fleet catch capacity and profitability on the other, often leads to false catch declarations, thus leading to increased monitoring difficulties.

The final criticism is that despite the overriding need for fisheries management, political expediency relating to quota entitlement is often included in the decision-making process. These include situations where:

- Quotas are fixed well above recommended levels (e.g., 1985 western mackerel stock); and

- Trade-offs have been made in relation to access rights for other species or preferential treatment relating to other policy issues; an example of the former being the Norway pout box, and the latter, the establishment of an Irish Box and restrictive license agreement prohibiting Spain's access into EEC water traded off partly against their overall enthusiasm for EEC entry, and for an extremely generous restructuring program.

OTHER EEC IMPLEMENTED CONTROLS

The EEC, has introduced conservation orientated control measures which are adopted irrespective of national boundaries. The main objective of these regulations is to influence the sustainable yield in the long-term. Other objectives are to protect juvenile fish from capture and insure that sufficient fish survived to maturity. The most common technique used by the EC is one of minimum mesh regulation, examples for haddock, cod and whiting, are 65mm, 70mm and 80mm for the Bay of Biscay, Irish Sea, and North Sea respectively. In the case of nephrops, the required minimum mesh in UK waters is 60mm, a by-catch of 60 percent of the total weight is permitted. If using a 70mm net mesh, no by-catch limitations are imposed, thereby creating an incentive for fishermen to change.

In addition, the EC imposes minimum landing sizes per species i.e. cod, 35cm; whiting, 30cm; and haddock, 27cm. These may be increased to protect spawning stocks in certain areas. Other examples of restrictions relate to the lengths and circumference of lifting bags, the common interpretation being that the mesh size of a lifting bag must be at least twice that of the cod end. The EC at times encourages passive fishing methods as a means of conservation. An example of this can be found in the Mourne herring fishery (North Irish Sea) in which the specified method of capture is drift net only.

CRITICISMS OF CONSERVATION MEASURES

The short or medium term measures are again subject to criticism. The problems associated with operational restrictions relate to:

- The inability to measure the direct effects of a restriction;

- The difficulty in persuading the industry to accept regulatory measures when different sectors of the industry are likely to be affected to different degrees—for example, the conflict between industrial fishing mesh sizes and larger mesh sizes required when fishing for human consumption; and

- The different regulatory measures applied in different EEC regions. An example is the minimum mesh sizes for nephrops in the Irish Sea (60mm) compared with that of the Bay of Biscay (50mm).

ACTION TAKEN BY MEMBER STATES

Interpretation of quota allocations to the fisheries sector differs, although not markedly, between member states. The common interpretations include a management regime usually administered by the representative government departments with occasionally some form of sectoral participation. Examples of sectoral involvement include the Comite interprofessionals (France) which are empowered to: 1) fix open and closing dates of fisheries subject to seasonal controls; 2) determine the number of vessels allowed to participate; and 3) determine the number of fishing trips for which vessels may operate. In addition, in some countries the Producer Organizations (POs) also play a more active role. In France, POs play an active role in marketing, often controlling fishing effort and daily landing schedules. This example is one of the only situations in which marketing regulations are specifically adhered to in fisheries management. The idea of sectoral quotas has also been encouraged, although perhaps in name only, within the UK: Scottish POs are empowered to monitor and, if necessary, control quota uptake, although no effective control has been implemented. In Denmark, vessels remain in port once their catches have exceeded specific amounts and are financed through a government inducement/compensation scheme.

Control of the fisheries tend to consist of two basic concepts: the first, "permission" to fish either by restrictive licensing, either determined according to available stocks or by some historic rights access; or second, a virtual open access fishery often applied to those species which are not covered under the TAC regime, or in areas not presently involved in current fishing effort.

In most countries some form of restriction occurs. The UK interprets from the EC definition, a pressure stock licensing scheme when the UK's quota is considered to be insufficient to allow unrestricted fishing. Some well-known examples include herring, mackerel, haddock, plaice and sole. Pressure stock licenses are only issued to vessels over ten meters and to those who have exhibited historic access to the stock. The licenses may be transferred to new owners or to replacement vessels irrespective of size. While no monetary value is attached, the license does attach a form of inducement to increase the value of the vessel to be sold. An example of the system in operation can be demonstrated by the Southwest England Beam trawl fishery[3] where authorization via the license entitles the vessel to fish for certain whitefish stocks designated as pressure stocks and non-pressure stocks. The problems of this fishery are well documented since closures are frequently imposed following the fulfillment of the quota entitlement leaving a virtually redundant fleet for much of the year.

Although the pressure stock licensing system is restrictive, it is often subject to widespread abuse since vessel licenses may be transferred irrespective of size or horsepower. However, the Danish licensing system incorporates gross registered tonnage restrictions which limits license transfers thereby restricting construction of large vessels. Effort restriction with management regimes is common among most European countries. The most documented of these is that of the western mackerel stock where the UK effort by purse seiners and pelagic trawlers are limited with respect to vessel length and fortnightly quotas where the fortnights run in sequence until the national quota has been reached. This scheme was recently exacerbated by an extension to include freezer trawlers. The freezer trawler extension was a problem since this fishery already demonstrated sufficient effort to meet the quota allocations.

The western mackerel stock poses problems for two other participating countries: notably the Irish Republic which imposes individual vessel quotas, and the Netherlands in which the number of vessels allocated to the distant water fleet are restricted. Transfer of the license is, as in the case of the UK, restricted by historic quota entitlement of the original vessel. In the case of the Netherlands, the scheme has proved to be extremely controversial since its overall quota entitlement is well below the historic catch levels of the 1970s.

Other examples of effort limitations in management of EEC fisheries can also be found in Belgium where licenses for plaice and sole are restricted to an overall horsepower limitation of 65,000 hp. No vessel is allowed to exceed 500 hp, and if fishing within 12 miles, 70-300 hp. Restrictions of 300 hp for beam trawlers fishing within 12 miles are accepted throughout the EEC. The Netherlands has a similarly restrictive system based on horsepower with predefined vessel quotas.

Examples of restrictive licensing relating to vessel numbers include: the St. Brieuc Scallop fishery (N. Brittany); the Charente narrows trawl fishery (France); and the Manx herring fishery (Irish Sea). The Manx herring fishery is one area in which restrictive licensing has been subject to abuse in relation to its interpretation and implementation by the Isle of Man Board of Agriculture (IOMBA). The IOMBA placed an eligibility criterion of participation in the herring fishery during the two previous seasons, before granting a license to fish in 1977. The result was to allow 100 British vessels, 24 Irish vessels, and the Manx fleet to take the 8,000-ton TAC. While this seemed to work well during the first season, partly as a result of rising herring prices, the authorities gave way to pressure from producer groups to relax the entry conditions in subsequent seasons.

The concept of open and closed seasons are used widely in the EEC. The western mackerel stock again is restricted largely to a winter fishery. Similar restrictions apply to herring in the North Sea, the Clyde and the Irish Sea; to the Dutch cutter fisheries; and in the Danish Kattegat, Baltic and North Sea Fisheries.

The Dutch mussel bed fishery reflects a unique licensing scheme among EEC countries and parallels in some sense the agricultural rent type system. The number of vessels operating are restricted by nontransferable licenses. Although sales are not permitted, mergers are encouraged thus enhancing the degree of self-regulatory effort.

It would appear that from the forementioned examples management regimes are highly restrictive in the community sense and open access is severely limited. However, even within the UK which has probably been subject to more rigorous levels of restraint than its contemporaries (even before EC entry) allowance is made for non-pressure stocks which are those species not perceived to be in any danger of exceeding or meeting F max. Licenses for non-pressure stocks are freely available, as is the case in the Irish Republic. Most of the other nationals have no reason to impose any form of licensing, the French for example, have confidence in their Comites who themselves loosely distinguish between artisanal and industrial fisheries.

A POSSIBLE SOLUTION TO THE DIFFICULTIES

Some of the problems associated with TAC formulation and to a lesser extent short-term conservation measures will never be resolved. However, the aim of relating production to fishing effort should be attainable, if precise objectives are adhered to and the level of political expediency is overcome. One way for this to be achieved is to harmonize the global EEC Policy which would mean the EC needs to increase its influence over the Member States.

Current management policy on fisheries regulation fails, in most cases to deal with the fundamental problem of free access to a common property. By eliminating the common property elements and establishing property rights, the fishing industry could respond to changes in resource utilization in a similar manner to other renewable resource sectors.

Efficient stock management should lead to resulting economic and social changes. From this, it is essential to introduce some method of restricting fishing effort through: 1) limiting vessel numbers; 2) aiming at fleet efficiency; and 3) insuring the long-term livelihood for those currently engaged in fisheries. A combination of methods is often the soft option, the adopted policy should, therefore, center around one concise policy which conforms to the above objectives and the TACs: notably, private quota ownership or individual transferable vessel quotas.

Private quota ownership is a policy unexplored in the EEC, although the concept has been tried in various regional fisheries and applied to individual fish species (for example, the southern bluefin tuna fishery in Australia). The allocation scheme could be applied as easily on an EEC-wide basis or alternatively by country or region, although the former could promote EEC harmonization between stock availability and capacity.

The means or suggested conditions for private quota ownership are as follows:

- Initial allocation should be based on historical performance for individual species within individual ICES areas;

- Subsequent exchange could take the form of saleable quotas by sealed bids or an open auction market on an annual, monthly or quarterly basis;

- Renewal of quota entitlement should relate to the overall TAC allocated and to previous historical performance;

- Vessels unable to fish their quotas due to physical disabilities which restrict their fishing activity should be able to sell their quotas to a clearinghouse with the provision that first access is guaranteed in repurchase; and

This type of scheme has a number of benefits:

- Since the total catch which could be taken would correspond with the EC quota, there would be no reason for the management agency to interfere with the choice of gear, fishing area and time of capture;

- The incentive to improve efficiency will still be there or the option to market at a time more favorable to themselves;

- Increases in efficiency resulting from technological change would be reflected in vessel numbers without the need for government interference;

- It would be easy to introduce given the herring/mackerel experience with the added benefit of being able to trade the quota; and

- Licenses would gravitate to the most efficient/skillful fishermen.

However, this type of scheme has a number of difficulties:

- It inhibits efficiency if restricted to vessel size criteria;

- The number of vessels makes the scheme difficult to implement;

- This scheme has enforcement problems similar to the current system;

- The formulation of TACs requires a considerable amount of secrecy;

- There is a danger of excessive discard rates and selection;

- Success may be limited only to a single species fishery, the policy may require a wide combination accommodating by-catches and catching methods;

- The current objections to quota administration can still be applied to transferable vessel quotas;

- Without any institutional control, social and equity problems may arise; and

- This policy could accelerate declines in regions currently facing difficulties—this could be argued on social grounds only.

CONCLUSION

Experience with the errors shown in EEC management and national schemes are useful in improving the current system and expanding on it in the full EEC tradition. The EEC needs to play a more definitive role in the decision-making process in order to overcome some of the previous outlying difficulties once associated with the Northeast Atlantic Fisheries Commission. That concern should not only relate to predefined objectives but also to techniques of regulation, the basic contention that economic oriented methods need be given serious consideration alongside biologically oriented ones. Though there may be problems associated with such a radical scheme as quota ownership there is no reason why a staged development on a regional scale could not be considered before a general application throughout the EEC. Certainly, a move towards individual transferrable vessel quotas would remove the inherent problems associated with overcapacity in the community context.

NOTES

1 Prior to 1977 NEAFC was an essential body as the majority of fisheries limits did not extend beyond 12-mile limits making control outside the national barriers exceedingly difficult.

2 International Council for the Exploration of the Seas comprises members of nations within the N.E. Atlantic region ICES is an independent organization financed by contribution. Estimates of resource availability are made by the Advisory Council on Fisheries Management (ACFM) of ICES.

3 Beam Trawl ICES Sub Area VII and VIII Whitefish Pressure Stock License.

REFERENCES

Holden, M.J.   The procedures followed and the problems met by the European Economic Community in implementing the scientific recommendations of the International Council for the Exploration of the Sea on total allowable catches; Expert Consultation on the Regulation of Fishing Effort (Fishing Mortality), 1983.

Meuriot, E. and Maucoups, A.   Alternative Management Strategies: Potential and Limits of Licensing systems. Working Paper submitted to the STCF, September 1985.

Whitmarsh, D. and Young, J. Management of UK mackerel fisheries, Marine Policy July 1985.

Western Mackerel License for Freezer Trawlers, 1985.

NATURAL RESOURCE TARGETING:
OPPORTUNITIES FOR FISHERIES AND FORESTRY

RICHARD P. GALE
Professor
Department of Sociology
University of Oregon
Eugene, Oregon

INTRODUCTION

This paper examines renewable natural resources from a sociological perspective. Renewable natural resources, specifically forests and fisheries managed in sustainable flows, will receive more attention than nonrenewable resources, such as oil, gas, and minerals, in which developmental impacts occur in large "lumps" during exploration and early extraction. The orienting framework for this analysis is the natural resource management system (NRMS) (Gale and Miller 1985). Each NRMS is composed of four elements. Three are social: profit seeking industries; organized and unorganized publics; and management bureaucracies. The fourth is the natural resource itself.

This paper gives special attention to forest and marine fisheries NRMS which are federally managed, particularly the National Forest System of the U.S. Forest Service. Examples will also be drawn from forest and fisheries NRMS under other jurisdictions.

Many conceptual parallels exist in the management of forest and fishery resources. Although not the central focus of this paper, they help to set the stage. Concepts exhibiting cross-resource comparability include quasi-common property, rotation, sustained yield, optimum yield, maximum sustained yield, and allowable harvest. Table 1 provides some cross-resource examples. These concepts form the core of federal management of forests and marine fisheries in our society (Gale, 1985a). This comparability serves as a base to explore opportunities for what I will call resource targeting.

A number of circumstances suggest that forest and fisheries (especially marine fisheries) systems can learn from each other. First, much of this nation's forest land, and most of its marine fisheries resources, are under federal management, by agencies such as the U.S. Forest Service, National Marine Fisheries Service, and Bureau of Land Management. Second, both forests and marine fisheries, as well as other marine resources, occupy complex ecological settings, in which they are only one of many resources harvested or present within the same ecological base. Third, forest and marine fisheries exist in systems involving both large, multi-layered federal bureaucracies, and small, often geographically isolated, resource dependent communities. Fourth, exploitation of each resource often involves a mix of small-scale harvesters (and sometimes processors), and large, vertically integrated regional and national corporations.

Table 1

Basic Forestry and Fishery Management Concepts

Concept	Forestry Example	Fishery Example
Quasi-Common Property	-public timber sales	-sale of net set sites
Rotation	-old growth, market impacts on "Quaker puffed trees"	-trophy fish, impact of effort on size & age class
Sustained Yield	-likely decline & application of "even flow" management	-appropriate lower level to sustain stock under varying conditions
Maximum Sustained Yield	-Maximize biological potential	-upper limit with worry about decline & collapse
Optimum Yield	-accelerate old growth harvest market responsive harvest levels	-increase harvest to save boats
Allowable	-annual allowable cut	-allowable harvest, TALFF

NATURAL RESOURCE TARGETING

Of the issues facing renewable natural resource systems, one of the most compelling is expressed by resource-dependent communities worried about maintaining access to resources, and controlling resource exploitation to assure the economic survival of these communities.   This new locality-based resource populism has emerged in spite of, or perhaps because of, a national political administration which advocates deregulation and corporatism.

Recent economic changes have hit many of these communities hard.   Traditional patterns of resource exploitation have been altered, and local, small-scale economic benefits of such exploitation reduced.   Although one could argue that these changes should accelerate, that is not the view taken here.   Instead, communities are seen as important elements in this nation's social and economic fabric.   Thus, programs which increase the likelihood of sustaining local economies are defensible, even though not always maximizing economic efficiency (Alperovitz and Faux 1984).

"Resource targeting" is the term used here for such programs.[1]   Examples of targeting are found throughout the economy.   The long history of federal forest management has meant that the forest system, specifically the U.S. Forest Service, has evolved policies which target resources toward local communities.[2]   Similarly, there are examples of resource targeting for marine resources.   Given the parallels between management of these two renewable resources, it seems wise to explore the cross-resource applicability in detail.[3]

The basic goal of this paper is to expand resource targeting options by looking in detail at the segments of the natural resource process to which management programs might be applied, and the range of social units which might be affected by resource managers. The matrix in Table 2 arrays process components and target social units. The columns represent eight natural resource process components, and the rows show seven different social units to which resource management programs might be targeted. Each cell represents a possible resource management program which is oriented toward a specific process component and targeted to a particular social group or unit.

NATURAL RESOURCE PROCESS COMPONENTS

This section outlines eight components associated with the exploitation of natural resources. Management schemes are typically organized in terms of these eight components. While the components discussed here do not exhaust the universe of possibilities, they appear to be those most typically associated with forests and fisheries. The eight components can be grouped into four categories. The first includes components oriented to the resource ecosystem: (1) ecosystem rehabilitation; and (2) stock raising or growing. The second cluster includes harvest activities: (3) commercial harvesting; and (4) noncommercial harvesting. The third differentiates two processing activities: (5) processing of dominant products; and (6) processing of secondary products. The fourth group includes two activities which link the resource product with a larger society: (7) marketing; and (8) new products.

The process components are not new. However, focusing on each in terms of resource targeting may suggest new program or management opportunities. As will be seen, forest and fishery management have emphasized primarily only two components: commercial harvest (Column 3); and processing of dominant products (Column 4).

(1)   *Ecosystem rehabilitation*—Natural resource programs focus on providing the ecosystem needed to support the stock. Reforestation, clearing debris from streams, building spawning beds, road closure, water pollution abatement programs, and minimum water flow programs for fish are examples.

(2)   *Stock raising or growing*—The primary concern is on the production of the resource product, such as Douglas fir, alder, salmon, or groundfish. Component activities focus on stock condition, age and size class distribution, resource maturation and rotation, and protection of stock from premature harvesting. This component also includes activities to preserve over-rotation stock, old growth timber and trophy-size fish.

(3)   *Commercial harvest*—Component activities are oriented toward harvest of the stock for sale. "Sale" could include barter and exchange among recreational harvesters. For many resources, regulation of this component is a major agency focus. Harvester access and limits, provision of the sale of harvest rights, privatization through commercial harvest of common property resources, and the seasonal timing of harvest are all component activities regulated by natural resource agencies.

(4)   *Noncommercial harvest*—Although generally under the umbrella of recreational harvest, activities also include subsistence harvesting, and provision for ceremonial harvests, such as Indian fishing and family Christmas trees. Resource

Table 2

Natural Resource Process Components and Targeted Social Units

Targeted Social Unit	Natural Resource Process Component							
	(1) Ecosystem Rehab.	(2) Stock Raising	(3) Commercial Harvest	(4) Non-Commercial Harvest	(5) Process (Dominant)	(6) Process (Secondary)	(7) Marketing	(8) New Product
(A) Household/ Subsistence			(X)	X				
(B) Household/ Nonmarket (Recreation)	X							
(C) Community Targeted	(X)		X		X			
(D) Enterprise Ownership	(X)	(X)			(X)			
(E) Enterprise Size	(X)		X	(X)				
(F) Enterprise Technology			X				X	
(G) Public Enterprise								

Forest Example   Fishery Example

Explicit Targeting - X
Implicit Targeting - (X)

conflicts are often framed in terms of competition between these two components for scarce resources. Issues sometimes emerge concerning the sharpness of the distinction between commerical and noncommercial harvest. Sale of firewood from federal lands and qualifications for holding commercial fishing permits are examples.

(5) *Processing of dominant products*—In most ecosystems, the direct economic (market) value of one or two products outpaces all others. Salmon in west coast and Alaskan marine fisheries systems, Douglas fir in the Pacific Northwest forest systems, and lobsters and oysters on the east coast are examples of natural resources which command high (relatively) economic value. High economic value means powerful economic constituencies and attention by natural resource agencies. Targeting politics thus often focuses on access to these dominant products. While this access competition typically occurs for harvesting, it also focuses on processing.

(6) *Processing of secondary products*—There are few ecosystems which produce only one economically valuable product, even though the dominant product may be far ahead of the next most valued product. Programs focusing on secondary products, however, expand the economic productivity of ecosystems as well as product diversity.[4] Other fish species and hardwoods in predominantly coniferous forests are examples of secondary products from ecosystems.

(7) *Marketing*—Obviously, the marketing of natural resource products is central to the pattern of their economic viability. Programs to develop new markets for these products, and to increase the competitiveness of products within existing markets are examples undertaken by natural resource agencies.

(8) *New products*—Activities in this category include developing new products from an increasing range of ecosystem outputs. Research and market testing are critical. New seafood products, the ability of U.S. sawmills to manufacture lumber in dimensions suitable for Asian markets, and research to develop new seafood products are examples.

TARGETED SOCIAL UNITS

Few, if any, resources are simply available for the taking. Harvest of most forest and fishery products is heavily regulated, and even an apparently unlimited commodity, such as beach sand, is regulated if taken commercially, or in large volumes for personal use. Thus, harvest regulations always constrain access to the resource, and, in doing so, target resources to specific social or economic groups.

However, targeting varies both in degree and in the extent to which resource allocation programs consciously target particular social groups. In other words, regulatory options exist. A distinction between explicit and implicit resource targeting programs may elucidate program options.

Explicit targeting involves the usual regulations—rules are promulgated, reviewed, and implemented. The focus is on explicit, written regulations. Both forest and fisheries systems are full of examples of explicit management. Implicit targeting refers to other management actions that, in effect (although not explicitly), target resources to specific social groups. Forest Service personnel know that low elevation, roadside timber sales scheduled in the winter will be most attractive to smaller, local loggers, even though these sales are not explicitly targeted. Regulation of charterboats to assure predictable seasons with no sudden weekend closures has an important impact on the extent to which sport fishermen travel long distances to fish. Extending fishing seasons into winter months may disadvantage smaller boats and increase safety risks. Harvesters themselves may engage in implicit targeting, by agreeing to informal "territories," as in the "lobster fiefs" (Acheson 1975). What is notable about implicit management, and what angers publics, is that implicit targeting has direct social and economic impacts but is hard to get at because the practices do not derive from explicit policy. This paper will include examples of both explicit and implicit targeting, even though policy discussions typically focus on the former.

What are the different social units to which natural resources have been targeted? Natural resource management programs in the United States have typically encompassed six target groups, although obviously they do not use the labels to be discussed presently. These six social units fall into four categories. The first category includes two methods of categorizing households: (a) household subsistence; and (b) nonmarket recreational household use. The second category includes only: (c) resource-dependent communities. The third category encompasses different characteristics of private enterprises involved in natural resources: (d) enterprise ownership; (e) enterprise size; and (f) enterprise technology. The fourth category refers to the role of the state: (g) public enterprise.

(A)   *Household subsistence*—Household subsistence refers to the ability of natural resources to provide part of the basic livelihood of households located in resource-abundant areas. This category involves products which are not marketed, but which are harvested and processed by the household. Portions of programs to provide fishing opportunities for Indians in the Pacific Northwest and Eskimos in Alaska, as well as others in small Alaskan villages fall in this category. Fundamental to these activities is the fact that products are used at the individual household level.

(B)   *Nonmarket recreational household use*—Natural resource activities or products which result from outdoor recreation fit this category. Hunting, fishing, foraging for wild mushrooms, and cutting Christmas trees are examples. These activities are nonmarket, in the sense that they are not engaged in to generate household income (although they may have market value in a family or household exchange system). Other household-based activities fall into both categories—cutting firewood for household use is both subsistence and nonmarket recreation.

(C)   *Resource dependent communities*—A major force motivating concern with natural resource policy is the survival of small, often geographically isolated, resource-dependent communities. Fishing communities, company towns, communities whose livelihood is based on one or two sawmills, and even oil and mineral based communities reflect a pattern of economic dependence on natural resources. Improvements in transportation systems, larger economic units with higher levels of capital, and technical improvements have often reduced the viability of these communities. Although it is difficult to determine any single level of community viability or stability that would be deemed most desired, many of these communities face bleak economic futures.

(D)   *Enterprise ownership*—This concept refers to characteristics of the person who owns the enterprise. Such characteristics can include minority group membership, sex, residence, public versus private ownership, and enterprise structure (cooperatives). Programs can be focused on the total enterprise (corporations, company), or on specific locations or establishments which may or may not be part of a larger enterprise.

(E)   *Enterprise size*—The existence of the Small Business Administration and provisions in some agencies for special programs to target resources toward small businesses are examples of the focus on enterprise size. The extent of horizontal and vertical integration is a corollary of the focus on size. Concern expressed about small enterprise survival is countered with arguments that economic efficiency and the ability to compete internationally require increasingly larger enterprise units. A related issue is the correlation of enterprise size with ability to generate new capital. Finally, enterprise size may relate to the mix of natural resource and other economic units under the same organizational umbrella. In the Pacific Northwest, for example, forest products companies used their profits to diversify into other activities, such as real estate and auto parts retailing. Targeting timber programs for these companies may, instead, have the perverse effect of contributing to other nontimber corporate or company activities.

(F)   *Enterprise technology*—As with enterprise size, the focus may be equally on opposite ends of the spectrum. Some programs are designed to encourage improvements in technology, such as mechanization and computerization. Others would encourage retaining more traditional, labor-intensive practices. Obviously, programs focusing on enterprise technology are not independent of those which consider enterprise size.

(G)   *Public Enterprise*—Public enterprise refers to programs which place responsibilities for particular resource activities on different agencies, or instances in which public enterprises become directly involved in resource process components. This can include dividing management responsibilities, as well as assigning responsibility to agencies which have special connections with other targeted units. Agency targeting can also occur in cases where both public and private organizations coexist and potentially compete with each other for opportunities to participate in natural resource processes (harvesting, processing, etc.). Commingling of private aquaculture and public hatchery salmon in the Pacific Northwest is an example.

RESOURCE TARGETING IN FORESTRY AND FISHERIES

The matrix in Table 2 suggests a number of potential options for resource targeting. Each cell represents a possible program. (The Xs in Table 2 indicate examples in the following discussion.) The components will be discussed in four clusters–harvesting (3,4), processing (5,6), ecosystem and stock raising (1,2), and marketing and new products (7,8). (In this discussion a number-letter designation refers to cells in Table 2. For example, 3A refers to commercial harvests which are community targeted.)

Resource Harvesting

In general, most examples of targeting occur in two components–(3) Commercial Harvesting and (4) Noncommercial Harvesting. Explicit and implicit targeting of commercial timber harvests on National Forests benefits many social units. National Forests in Alaska are studying household subsistence dependence (3A), and, in Oregon, seasonally unemployed woodsworkers seek out favored old cedars for shake bolts during winter months (3A). Community targeting of timber harvests (3C) was legislatively established in 1944 by the Federal Sustained Forest Management Act but implemented only in a few areas, such as Lakeview, Oregon, and Shelton, Washington (Hoover 1978). The Forest Service Small Business Set-Aside program reserves some timber sales for smaller companies (3E). Technology targeting (3F) occurs at both ends of the spectrum, and includes horse logging in fragile ecosystems and helicopter yarding on steeps slope and other fragile areas.

Noncommercial harvesting of forest products includes many activities, some of which parallel commercial harvesting and/or contribute to household subsistence. Fishing and hunting (typically state-regulated), gathering of mushrooms and firewood, and harvest of Christmas trees are examples. Allocation of many of these resource products occurs in a partial market setting. The Forest Service charges for firewood and Christmas trees, and state governments have elaborate fee schedules for fishing and hunting licenses.

Commercial fishing also includes examples of targeting, although to a lesser extent than federal forestry programs (see Gale 1985b). Many, if not most, occur on the sub-federal level. For example, Massachusetts imposed a 90-foot boat limit (3F) for fishing in state waters, a move designed to protect local fishermen from competition with large freezer-trawlers (National Fisherman 1986). Chatham, Massachusetts, issues commercial shellfish licenses only to town residents, and the licenses are valid only in that town (Schwind 1986). In Wellfleet, Massachusetts, 80 acres of public flats are managed by 25 leaseholders (Schwind 1986), presumably local operators.

A judge provided one of the most comprehensive explicit targeting programs for marine fisheries. The targeting in the Washington Indian fishing rights dispute includes nearly all social units, as well as several process components (primarily 3 and 4). Currently, tribes are working with the state to expand their activities into other components, especially 1 and 2. Processing and marketing are still in the hands of non-Indian groups. (I'm not sure how many Seattle sports fishermen would choose Lummi-caught salmon at their local supermarket.)

Explicit and implicit targeting are also central issues in discussions of limited entry. The extent to which commercial fishing licenses should be restricted to state residents (3C), or full-time fishermen (3D), or tied to boat ownership (3E), or size (3E/F) all, to a large degree, fundamentally concern resource targeting.

Noncommercial harvest is clearly a major activity in marine and freshwater fisheries. Licensing often includes both implicit and explicit targeting. In states, such as Idaho, which are dependent on resource-based tourism, local sportsmen find themselves in direct competition with programs targeting resource access to non-local tourists.

Resource Processing

Resource targeting for processing activities occurs for both dominant and secondary products. In federal timber management, targeting has focused more on harvesting than on processing since the Forest Service has direct control over harvest activities on its lands. However, the community sustained yield program mentioned in the previous section also targets on community mills. Significantly, however, small business programs directly affect only harvesting—a small logging company can sell its logs to a large, distant mill for processing. The lack of an effective mechanism for community targeting of processing of federal timber (4C) led one Oregon politician to propose giving preference to companies agreeing to process Forest Service timber in designated resource-dependent communities (see Detzel 1986). Implicit targeting to enterprise ownership (5D) is currently operative in the Pacific Northwest, where workers, often with the assistance of local government credit, have purchased sawmills to save their jobs. Targeting is implicit in that these mills typically have few competitors for federal timber. (However, no explicit targeting programs exist for worker-owned mills.)

With respect to fisheries processing, battles over boatside retail sales (5D) and port landing requirements (5C) are targeting examples. Community participation in the construction of processing facilities (5C) is another example.

Ecosystem Rehabilitation and Stock Raising

These two process components reflect a broader environmental concern. Management is extended beyond harvesting and process. Obviously, these concerns are not new to resource management agencies. What is new is agency cooperation with the private sector, some of which includes program targeting.

In the federal forest system, ecosystem rehabilitation has included clearing and reforesting lands covered with brush because of earlier inadequate reforestation, cleaning logging debris from forest streams, and rebuilding spawning areas. Implicit targeting has included extensive use of expense-paid volunteers (which approximates 1B), and other projects which have typically been contracted to small, locally-based cooperatives (1D and 1E).

Although one could argue that "stock raising" is the basic business of federal forest agencies, emphasis on reforestation and stock management has accelerated. There are at least two examples of implicitly targeted stock raising. One is the Bureau of Land Management's "stewardship" program, in which a three-year contract is negotiated for the reforestation of logged land, with the payment withheld until a given level of reforestation success is achieved (Smurthwaite 1983). Although not enterprise ownership targeted, the program was requested by tree planting cooperatives seeking contracts providing multiple-year job stability. The first stewardship contract was let to one of these firms. Extending the concept for a longer period has occurred on National Forest lands in southern Oregon, in which contracts are let for repeated interval, precommercial thinning (logging) of reforested stands.

In the fishery system, the geographic range of many fish species complicates parallel activities. However, in the Pacific Northwest, the sport-fishery-oriented Salmon and Trout Enhancement Program (STEP), which supports stream rehabilitation and placement of "hatchery boxes" for raising fish has been undertaken as a (nonpaid) community activity (1C). The Oregon Fishing Industry project has suggested paying unemployed commercial fishermen to rehabilitate coastal streams and watersheds (St. Claire 1985). In Maryland, the governor's Commercial Fishermen's Compensation Program supported hiring of displaced bass fishermen by the state Department of Natural Resources. Their work included maintaining state fish hatcheries (Valliant 1986:9).

Marketing and New Products

Although responsibilities of agencies in both forest and fishery systems include these activities, these process components typically receive less attention. Some would argue that these activities are inappropriate for the public sector, while others would criticize agencies such as the Forest Service and National Marine Fisheries Service for their lack of aggressiveness in these areas. Consequently, few examples of resource targeting exist for these activities. However, ongoing debates deal with whether such activities should be targeted.

Example of such targeting for wood products are scarce. However, one way of attracting local interest in tax-supported construction projects in Oregon communities has been to promise the use of local workers, and when possible, locally-produced materials. In an innovative fish marketing program, Oregon trollers can voluntarily "tag" each salmon caught with their name and delivery date (Granahan 1986). Fresh groundfish are marketed with a less personal, but technology linked "Oregon Trawler Caught" label.

CONCLUSIONS

There are many empty cells in Table 2. One could certainly find examples to fill some of the empty cells. Although those endorsing deregulations might object, the perspective in this paper is that the health and local economic contributions of both forestry and fishery systems will improve as the cells are filled. It is obvious that this perspective might provoke disagreement from economists who would argue an inverse relationship between cells filled and economic efficiency. Those pushing privatization of natural resources would also object to many of the cells—the most effective privatization might be that directly tied to targeting programs.

A portion of this paper was written on the Oregon coast. Several salmon trollers were within sight—some small boats under 30 feet, and one 50-foot vessel rigged for multiple fisheries, with its troller poles contrasting with the deck drum and towed skiff. How would this fishery be with more targeted management?

All boats would have participated in some sort of license auction, which was also tied to individual boat (or company) allocations. (No "tax loss" or two-day-a-year "commercial fishermen" would be out there.) Some of the small boats would have received a portion of a Small Business Administration targeted allocation. A larger boat would have only a limited landing allocation from this area—most of its catch would have to come from a coastal belt several miles out (and therefore its activities might be under federal management).

Some of the boats would choose to be eligible for a "homeport credit" for fish landed at their homeport (most likely Florence, Newport, or Winchester Bay). The credit could either be against the current license fee (a percentage of the auctioned license cost) or against next year's license (as an incentive to encourage multiple-year, "career" fishermen). Also available would be a "direct consumer allocation" which, perhaps in conjunction with the "homeport credit," would be available to fishermen delivering fresh fish to private-, port-, or fisherman-owned consumer outlets in Florence, Newport, or Reedsport.

Issuing licenses based on "landed allocation" would be especially desirable for small boats (under 45 feet) which may choose to remain in port during the strong summer northerlies. They would have an established period during which to harvest their allocated share.

A portion of the salmon landed in Oregon ports would, as mentioned above, be available as a "direct consumer allocation." Another portion would be divided between noncoastal in-state, and out-of-state, consumers. Processing (a portion of which is currently located in northern California) might shift to port-backed processing facilities, some of which would encourage new products (excellent pickled salmon is available in Seattle but not on the Oregon coast). Some salmon would be targeted to food processing facilities in the Willamette Valley, 60 miles east. Some of these plants operate only seasonally to freeze and can fruits and vegetables—fish processing might increase employment stability.

The small fishing boat dock in Florence would include a well-refrigerated "fresh by-catch" box providing free fish to local residents. (Natural resource scavenging is familar to many local residents.)

Both charter and private sportsfishermen would encounter a complex regulatory environment. Perhaps participating in a bid/total catch size allocation system, they might enjoy a season which had better distributed sports openings. The four-day Memorial Day weekend claimed four Oregon fishermen, whose boat was swamped by large jetty waves associated with very low tides. Sports fishermen from other states would have paid a premium for an Oregon coastal permit. In exchange, charterboat operators would be granted more flexibility in scheduling fishing trips for those with these special permits.

These are but a few examples of a more targeted management system. Obviously, there are enforcement problems and management costs not addressed here. There are no easy answers. Thinking in a comparative resource framework might, however, broaden the experience base, and yield creative solutions. I have a personal interest here—the lumberyard in Florence, Oregon ten miles south will sell me lots of locally produced Douglas fir two-by-fours. For troll-caught salmon, however, the odds are better at a fancy restaurant than my local supermarket.

NOTES

[1] It should be noted that resource-targeting and other community preservation or protection programs have sometimes not survived Constitutional and other legal challenges. Thus, such programs might not pass legality tests. However, many do exist in other areas of the economy. Further, some programs persist without legal challenge, such as an Oregon law prohibiting exports of logs from state forests. The legal problems should, thus, stand as a general reminder of the complexities of implementation of such programs (see Koch 1985), but should not dissuade us from exploring innovative programs.

[2] It is not the purpose of this paper to argue that such forest management practices have been glowing successes. Indeed, some of these practices have received only minimal application while others seem to have done little to slow the pace of more general economic change, to the detriment of many resource-based communities.

[3] Other recent analyses have taken a similar cross-resource approach. One of the most comprehensive surveys of resource allocation and management strategies was completed by NOAA's Office of Policy and Planning (NOAA 1985).

⁴   Some would argue that increasing the diversity of products can limit the ability of the ecosystem to produce the dominant product efficiently. Managing lower elevation forests for anything except Douglas fir has the potential to reduce productivity of that species on a given unit of land.

REFERENCES

Acheson, J. 1975. "The lobster fiefs: economic and ecological effects of territoriality." Human Ecology 3:183-207.

Alperowitz, Gar and Jeff Faux. 1984. *Rebuilding America.* New York: Pantheon Books.

Detzel, Tom. 1986. "DeFazio outlines timber set-aside." Eugene (Oregon) Register-Guard.

Gale, Richard P. 1985a. "Federal management of forests and marine fisheries: a comparative analysis of renewable resource management." Natural Resources Journal 25:275-315.

Gale, Richard P. 1985b. "Fisherman, would you rather be a logger? federal resource regulation in the Pacific Northwest." Fisheries 10(4):6-8.

Gale, Richard P. and Marc L. Miller, 1985. "Professional and public natural resource management arenas: forests and marine fisheries." Environment and Behavior 17:651-78.

Granahan, Andrea. 1986. " 'Signed' troll caught salmon proposal." The Fishermen's News 42(3):3.

Hoover, R. 1978. "Public Law 273 comes to Shelton: Implementing the Sustained Yield Forest Management Act of 1944." Journal of Forestry History 22:86-101.

Koch, Christopher L. 1985. "Legal tools and restrictions affecting fisheries management." Pp. 149-69 in T. Frady (Editor), *Proceedings of the Conference on Fisheries Management: Issues and Options.* Fairbanks, Alaska, Alaska Sea Grant College Program, University of Alaska.

National Fisherman. 1986. "90' Boat Limit." 66(13):27-8.

National Oceanographic and Atmospheric Administration. 1985. Fishery Management - Lessons from Other Resource Management Areas. NOAA Technical Memorandum, Office of Policy and Planning, July, 1985.

Smurthwaite, Don. 1983. "Stewardship: a new way of completing an old task." Your Public Lands 33(2):6-9,22.

St. Claire, Judith. 1985. Economic Adjustment Strategy for the Oregon Fishing Industry - Draft Summary and Recommendations. Newport, Oregon: Oregon Coastal Zone Management Association, Inc., Oregon Fishing Industry Project.

Valliant, Joe. 1986. "Tightened fisheries thinned out ranks of Chesapeake watermen." National Fisherman 66(13):9,92.

MANAGEMENT OF THE OIL AND GAS RESOURCES OF THE OUTER CONTINENTAL SHELF

GERALD D. RHODES
Chief
Branch of Development & Production
Minerals Management Service
Reston, Virginia

INTRODUCTION

The Minerals Management Service (MMS) manages and regulates many of the activities associated with the leasing, discovery, development, and production of oil and gas from the Outer Continental Shelf (OCS). These functions are part of the practices and procedures used in the multiple-use management of all the resources (renewable and nonrenewable) of the OCS. The Offshore Minerals Management program is intended to assist in achieving national economic and energy policy goals, to insure national security, to reduce our dependency on foreign energy sources, and to maintain a favorable balance of payments in world trade. These activities are conducted under a number of laws but primarily under the authorities delegated to the Secretary of the Interior under the provisions of the OCS Lands Act of August 7, 1953, and the September 18, 1978, amendments to that act.

During the 1984 calendar year, bonuses, rents, and royalties paid to the federal government in connection with OCS oil and gas leases exceeded $8 billion. During the same period of time, bonuses, rents, and royalties paid in connection with onshore federal and Indian oil and gas leases amounted to another $1.3 billion. Since its inception in May 1954 through December 1985, the OCS oil and gas leasing program has paid more than $81 billion in bonuses, rents, and royalties into the U.S. Treasury. The OCS oil and gas leases currently provide about 1/8 of the nation's domestic crude oil production and 1/4 of the natural gas produced in the United States.

Background

The federal claim to jurisdiction over offshore minerals was spelled out in President Truman's 1945 proclamation that "the Government of the United States regards the natural resources of the subsoil and seabed of the continental shelf beneath the high seas but contiguous to the coasts of the United States as appertaining to the United States, subject to its jurisdiction and control."

In 1953, the enactment of the Submerged Lands Act and the OCS Lands Act divided the jurisdiction over the resources of the continental shelf between the portion managed by the adjoining coastal states (in most instances from the coastline to 3 miles seaward of the coastline) and the "Outer Continental Shelf" portion managed by the federal government. Thus, the term "Outer Continental Shelf" is a legal term created by a federal statute which established the division of responsibilities for the exercise of federal jurisdiction over the outer portion of the submerged lands of the continental shelf.

Continental Shelf

Under the 1958 Geneva Convention on the Continental Shelf, the shelf is defined as those submerged offshore areas lying seaward of the territorial sea to a depth of 200 meters (656 feet) and beyond that area to a depth which admits of exploitation of natural resources.

The configuration and extent of the continental shelf varies from one coastal area of the United States to another. It is relatively narrow along the Pacific coast, wide along much of the Atlantic coast and in the Gulf of Alaska, and widest in the Gulf of Mexico and around western and northwestern Alaska.

History of Offshore Oil and Gas Development

Offshore oil and gas resources were first developed off Summerland, California, in 1896, 38 years after the first oil well was drilled at Titusville, Pennsylvania, and 42 years before the first development of oil and gas in the Gulf of Mexico. Oil and gas were produced off Summerland, California, from wells drilled from piers, the longest of which stretched 1,230 feet from the coast. Approximately 400 wells were drilled in this manner off California. The 1938 discovery of the Creole field, 1 1/2 miles off the Louisiana coast in the Gulf of Mexico, marked the first successful venture into open waters. The discovery well was drilled in 14 feet of water from a drilling platform constructed on a foundation of timber piles. In November 1947, a well was drilled almost out of site of land. That well was drilled in 16 feet of water, approximately 12 miles south of Terrebonne Parish, Louisiana. This well was the first to be drilled in open waters from a fixed platform/drilling tender combination—a major technical breakthrough in offshore drilling-unit design.

Today, there are 3,400 production platforms on the OCS and another 1,000 in state waters. Bottom-founded steel-jacketed production platforms have been installed and are producing oil and gas in water depths of 850 feet off the California coast and 1,025 feet off the Louisiana coast.

In 1983, a compliant guyed-tower production platform was installed in 1,000 feet of water, 110 miles southeast of New Orleans, Louisiana. Plans are currently being implemented which involve the development of production facilities in water depths in excess of 1,500 feet. In 1984, the drillship, Discoverer Seven Seas, successfully drilled an exploratory well in 6,952 feet of water off the New Jersey coast. Drilling structures designed for use in the ice-infested waters of the Arctic include artificial islands constructed of dredged sand and gravel, specially designed caisson-retained islands, and ice-resistant mobile drilling units.

EVOLUTION OF OCS OIL AND GAS MANAGEMENT: PRACTICES AND PROCEDURES

Shared Responsibilities

The OCS Lands Act and the amendments to that act give the Department of the Interior (DOI) and a number of other federal agencies specific responsibilities for administering those provisions of the act which govern mineral development and production activities on the OCS. Examples of other federal agencies having specified responsibilities under the OCS Lands Act are the U.S. Coast Guard (USCG), the Federal Energy Regulatory Commission, and the U.S. Army Corps of Engineers (Corps).

Many of DOI's responsibilities for the management of minerals on offshore and onshore federal lands were assigned to MMS in January 1982 when MMS was created by Secretarial Order 3071. In May 1982, the Secretary amended that order to consolidate within MMS all of DOI's offshore minerals management functions. While MMS is only four years old, the minerals management functions it performs have evolved as the result of experiences gained through the federal government's management of public lands and minerals during the past 200 years with special attention to the past 100 years.

During the last part of the 1800s and the first part of this century, the federal government abolished its previous practice of privatizing public lands and minerals by allowing the ownership of public lands which were valuable for certain minerals, such as oil and gas, to be transferred to individuals through a process of staking a claim and "proving up" the lands as provided under the various early homestead and mining laws.

The acquisition of the title to lands containing certain minerals is still subject to the mining laws of the late 1800s. For oil, gas, coal, and other "leaseable" minerals, practices and procedures were established under which the government retains ownership in the land and minerals but authorizes a lessee/operator to discover, develop, and extract specific minerals in accordance with provisions (terms and conditions) of the governing lease agreement.

Federal Management of OCS Oil and Gas Resources

Regulations implementing the OCS Lands Act of August 7, 1953, became effective in May 1954. Under the law and implementing regulations, provision was made for the validation of mineral leases previously issued for OCS lands by a coastal state and for the issuance of new oil and gas leases for previously unleased OCS lands using a competitive leasing process which called for a fixed royalty rate of not less than 12 1/2 percent with a cash bonus bid or a fixed cash bonus with the royalty rate as the bid variable. Between May 1954 and January 1986, 41 million acres (less than 1/10) of the OCS lands offered for lease (420 million acres) were actually leased. These leases have produced 7.1 billion barrels of oil and 70.7 trillion cubic feet of natural gas.

Scheduling of OCS Oil and Gas Lease Sales

Initially, the Secretary of the Interior exercised relatively unrestrained discretion in the scheduling of OCS oil and gas lease sales. In the early 1970's, the Secretary issued the first 5-year planning schedule for OCS oil and gas lease sales. The issuance of a 5-year planning schedule was designed to provide qualified bidders and other interests with a more predictable schedule of when OCS oil and gas lease sales would be held and in what areas. The idea was to provide a useful planning tool for potential bidders, adjacent State and local government officials, and the general public.

Preparation of an oil and gas leasing program is no longer discretionary. Section 18 of the OCS Lands Act, as amended, requires the Secretary of the Interior to prepare and maintain an OCS oil and gas leasing program covering the 5-year period following the approval or reapproval of the program. The oil and gas leasing program which the Secretary adopts must reflect a proper balance between the potential for environmental damage, the potential for the discovery of oil and gas, and the potential for adverse effects on the coastal zone. The Secretary is also required to design the program in a way to assure the receipt of fair market value for the lands leased and rights conveyed.

The approved schedule indicates the timing and locating of sales and their maximum potential size. The schedule is reviewed on a continuing basis, and insignificant revisions may be made as necessary without having to undergo the same steps required for its initial adoption.

Development of a new oil and gas leasing program progresses through a number of stages, each one building on comments and new information received during previous stages. During the preparation of a new leasing schedule, the Secretary solicits the views of interested federal agencies, the Governors of affected states, the executives of any affected local governments (local governments' comments are submitted through the Governor of the state), and members of the public.

Comments are requested before the publication of the draft proposed program, before the publication of the proposed program, and before the adoption of the final program. The proposed program is also submitted to the Attorney General for review. Sixty days prior to final approval, the oil and gas leasing program for a new 5-year period is submitted to the President and Congress. In addition to the steps required by section 18 of the OCS Lands Act, a programmatic environmental impact statement (EIS) is also prepared to assess the impacts of the new program. A new OCS oil and gas leasing program for 1987 to 1992 is now under preparation and review. It should be issued in early 1987.

IMPLEMENTATION OF GOVERNING LAWS

Regulations

The MMS administers the provisions of the OCS Lands Act through regulations promulgated by the Secretary of the Interior and codified in Title 30 of the Code of Federal Regulations, Chapter II. All elements of the leasing and operations programs are covered in these regulations which implement the mandates of the OCS Lands Act, as amended. They provide the framework for participation in the minerals management process including the review by and coordination with state governments, consideration of the approved coastal zone management (CZM) programs of coastal states, and the solicitation of information from state and local governments and the public regarding proposed actions.

In addition, the regulations expand upon the statutory requirements governing rental and royalty payments, environmental studies, and consultation with appropriate federal and state agencies. The regulations spell out the procedures to be followed by a lessee when it submits its exploration plans and development and production plans to MMS for approval.

OCS Orders and Notices to Lessees and Operators

- OCS Orders

Each MMS OCS Region issues OCS Orders which elaborate upon the provisions of the regulations to cover most of the day-to-day drilling and production operations required to maintain a lease. The OCS Orders are numbered directives which establish specific requirements for performing different types of oil and gas lease operations. These include drilling, completion and abandonment of wells, transportation of oil and gas to shore, and other important offshore oil and gas activities.

Although separate OCS Orders have been issued for each OCS Region, similarly numbered Orders usually specify similar requirements. The requirements, however, are modified or expanded as necessary to recognize unique local concerns. The Alaska OCS Region, for example, must consider the effects of permafrost, ice cover, and severe oceanographic conditions upon the conduct of oil and gas operations.

The MMS is currently studying its regulatory program and is proposing to incorporate all the requirements in the OCS operating regulations and OCS Orders into a single set of regulations. A Notice of Proposed Rulemaking was published in the *Federal Register* on March 18, 1986, that would accomplish that merger.

- Notice to Lessees and Operators

Notices to Lessees and Operators (NTL) are used to notify lessees and operators of specific MMS administrative practices or of new or revised procedures for complying with rules and regulations. The NTL's themselves do not impose requirements on lessees that are not already established by the law and implementing regulations.

Special Lease Stipulations

Through the years, special stipulations have been included in OCS oil and gas leases as a means of responding to concerns of affected coastal states, commercial and sports fishermen's associations, federal agencies, and others. These stipulations forewarn a lessee of these special concerns. For example, a lessee may be required to provide biological surveys of sensitive seafloor habitats, special training for its operating personnel, special waste discharge procedures, archaeological resource surveys to determine the potential for harming historic or prehistoric sites, special operating and platform evacuation procedures near military bases or their zones of activity, or to accept other special restictions which will apply to activities under an OCS oil and gas lease issued for a specific tract.

Conditions of Approval

In order to facilitate approval actions and to avoid unnecessary recordkeeping and reporting requirements, it is normal to find specific conditions placed upon the approval of a lessee-submitted proposal such as an Application for Permit to Drill, Deepen, or Plug Back (APD). Conditions of approval cover a broad range of subjects. They may specify such things as the frequency that a certain report (e.g., drilling report) must be submitted, the materials (chemicals) that may or may not be added to the drilling mud system, or the manner of disposal for drilling mud and cuttings.

Coordination and Consultation

The DOI and MMS are working to reach a consensus with affected states and others through greater coordination of activities and consultation with state and local governments. The coordination and consultation process permeates the entire minerals management program.

Figure 1 is a graphic presentation of the interactions between the Secretary of the Interior, MMS, other federal agencies, state and local governments, industry, and the public during the prelease process.

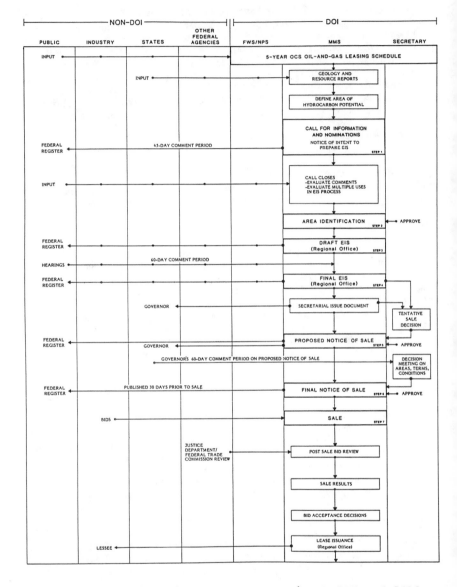

Figure 1.   OCS leasing process—prelease phase.   (MMS, Office of Offshore Information Services, 1985.)

PRACTICES AND PROCEDURES FOR GRANTING RIGHTS TO DRILL FOR AND PRODUCE OCS OIL AND GAS

Preliminary Activities

In frontier areas and areas where there has been little or no previous leasing, potential bidders for OCS oil and gas leases may drill Continental Offshore Stratigraphic Test (COST) wells (also referred to as Deep Stratigraphic Test wells) on unleased lands to assess the potential of the area for the accumulation of fluid hydrocarbons (oil or gas or both) and to identify, to the degree that they can, special problems that may exist in the area. The permits under which COST wells are drilled include specific requirements for the release of geological and geophysical data including analyzed and interpreted information. Those conditions include release of the information 60 days after the issuance of the first federal oil and gas lease within 50 miles of the drill site or ten years after the well is completed, whichever is earlier.

The MMS prepares an initial geologic report which covers the planning area. That report includes the locations of hydrocarbon potential in the planning area and a description of the geology of the area including a characterization of regional geologic hazards. The analysis and refinement of the estimates of hydrocarbon potential continue throughout the leasing process. As data and information are updated, hydrocarbon potential and resource estimates are assessed and refined.

Call for Information and Nominations/Notice of Intent to Prepare an EIS

These Notices signal the formal initiation of the process which eventually leads to the issuance of OCS oil and gas leases.

A Call for Information and Nominations is an invitation to potential bidders, the governors of affected states, and other interested parties to indicate the portions of the planning area which are of special interest or concern to them. Potential bidders are asked to identify specific areas that they would be interested in considering for bidding purposes. Affected states and other interested parties are asked to provide comments on any portions of the area which should not be offered for lease based upon the potential for adverse environmental impacts or the potential for unacceptable levels of conflict with other uses of the area. Concerns regarding compatibility with a state's approved CZM plan should also be raised at this time.

The Notice of Intent to prepare an EIS which is usually published simultaneously with the Call for Information and Nominations invites all interested parties to participate in the EIS preparation process. That participation is part of the open process for determining the scope of issues, alternatives, and potential effects on the environment to be addressed in the EIS prepared in accordance with the requirements of the National Environmental Policy Act (NEPA) and the regulations of the Council on Environmental Quality. Informal consultations to clarify and address concerns of affected states are held between the staffs of MMS's Regional Directors' offices and the Governors of affected states throughout the prelease process. Those discussions include potential resources and conflicts with other uses of the area together with appropriate mitigating measures to be considered during the decision-making process. The informal consultation process includes discussions with representatives of federal, state, and local government agencies who can help to identify the significant issues associated with the proposed lease sale.

Area Identification

This step involves the identification of the blocks which should (or should not) be considered for offering, i.e, the area to be evaluated in the EIS. Generally, blocks which appear to have hydrocarbon potential and are of interest to potential lessees are included in the area identified for continued consideration. Blocks which fail to meet an initial test, which balances their potential value as a source of oil and gas against their potential for harm to the environment or for creating an unacceptable level of conflict with other uses of the area, are eliminated from further consideration at this time.

Draft Environmental Impact Statement

The draft EIS is usually published approximately one year after the publication of the Notice of Intent to Prepare an EIS. The draft EIS describes the existing marine, coastal, and human environment, the action proposed and alternatives to the proposed action, estimates of resources in the area, and probable risks to the environment. Mitigating measures (such as provisions to be incorporated into the leases as special stipulations), unavoidable adverse impacts, cumulative effects, and irreversible and irretrievable commitments of resources are analyzed. Other issues of concern raised during the scoping of the environmental analysis are also discussed in the draft EIS.

Public Hearings

The notice announcing the availability of a draft EIS specifies a period of time (usually 60 days) during which comments and recommendations may be submitted to MMS. That announcement also announces the locations, dates, and times that public hearings have been scheduled to enable MMS to receive oral comments and recommendations.

Final Environmental Impact Statement

The MMS staff assesses the oral and written comments received as a result of the publication of the draft EIS and prepares a final EIS which incorporates substantive comments and responses to those comments together with any new findings and new information developed or acquired during the review period.

Notice of Proposed Sale

Copies of a Notice of Proposed Sale are sent to the Governors of affected states at the time the notice is forwarded to the *Federal Register* for publication. Publication of the notice informs the public, including potential bidders, of the terms and conditions which will govern the proposed offering of OCS lands for lease. A Secretarial Issue Document (SID) is prepared to assist the decisionmaker in deciding whether or how to proceed with the proposed lease sale. The SID presents and analyzes options and issues including total or partial sale delay or cancellation, special mitigating measures, and proposed bidding systems. Once a decision is made to proceed with a sale, copies of the SID are sent to the Governors of affected states and made available to others for their review and comment. This action allows the Governors of affected states and others to review the Secretary's decisions which attempt to address or resolve outstanding issues and concerns.

The Notice of Proposed Sale includes (1) either a listing of the blocks being considered for leasing or a listing of the blocks in the planning area which will not be available for leasing and (2) information relative to the procedures to be followed and the methods of bidding to be used in conducting the proposed sale. The Notice of Proposed Sale also includes the text of proposed lease stipulations and other measures which may be used to mitigate the potential for adverse effects of oil and gas activities on the blocks offered for lease. Governors of affected states are allowed 60 days within which to submit recommendations to the Secretary regarding the size, timing, or location of a proposed lease sale. After review and evaluation of the Governor's comments, the Secretary makes a written reply to each Governor which discusses the Secretary's reasons for accepting or rejecting recommendations made by that Governor.

Notice of Sale

If the Secretary decides to proceed with a lease offering, a notice is published in the *Federal Register* at least 30 days before the scheduled sale date. That notice includes the date, time, and place the sale is to be held; identification of the blocks which will be offered for bid; the text of any special lease stipulations or any other mitigating measures; the bidding systems to be used; and the term(s) (five, eight, or ten years) of leases for which bids are accepted together with other information considered pertinent.

Lease Sale (Bid Opening)

Each qualified bidder submits a separate sealed bid for each of the blocks or bidding units that he wishes to lease. Each bid submitted for a lease must contain a payment of 1/5 the amount of money bid. The "lease sale" is conducted as a public meeting during which all the bids that have been received are opened, recorded, and announced. Bids are neither accepted nor rejected during the bid opening and announcing process. The bid evaluation and acceptance or rejection process is carried out on a block-by-block basis during the 90 days which follow the "lease sale." During this period, information is forwarded to the Department of Justice and the Federal Trade Commission. A Department of Justice clearance is obtained before the final decision is made to accept or reject the highest qualified bid on a block.

Lease Issuance

Once a bid has been accepted, the bidder has 30 days within which to submit the remaining 4/5 of the monies bid and to submit a signed lease agreement which incorporates the special lease provisions stipulated in the lease sale notice.

RIGHTS GRANTED A LESSEE UNDER AN OCS OIL AND GAS LEASE

Rights Granted to Lessee

Under an OCS oil and gas lease, the lessee is granted the exclusive right to drill for and produce oil and gas from the tract of submerged land covered by the lease for a specified period of time (i.e., five, eight, or ten years). If a discovery is made and actual production of oil or gas commences before the end of the fixed term, the lease continues in effect for as long as oil or gas is produced in paying quantities or approved drilling operations are conducted to restore production.

A lessee must reduce the oil and gas located within the leased area to his possession and control before any proprietary right attaches. If the lessee fails to develop and extract the oil and gas from the leasehold or if oil and gas from deposits on the leasehold are drained through wells located off the leasehold, the lessee loses its opportunity to translate the rights granted by the lease contract into proprietary rights in oil and gas. A lessee can be held liable for damages suffered by the lessor due to drainage of oil and gas to adjacent lands as a result of a lack of diligence on the part of the lessee.

Rights Reserved to the United States

Under the OCS oil and gas lease, the federal government, as lessor, retains the rights to helium and reserves the right to grant leases for minerals other than oil and gas, to issue permits for geological and geophysical exploration, to approve pipeline and other rights-of-way, to take its royalty share in value or amount of production (i.e. production in kind), to extract its helium from produced gas, to direct or approve the suspension of lease operations including production, and to cancel the lease. The lease spells out requirements for surety bonds, royalty payments, rental payments, and the assignment or transfer of the lease or any interest therein. Every OCS oil and gas lease issued since September 18, 1978, includes a requirement that the lessee offer 20 percent of the crude oil, condensate, and natural gas liquids produced from the lease to small or independent refiners. The crude oil, condensate, and natural gas liquids must be offered to small or independent refiners at the market value and point of delivery applicable to federal royalty oil. During December 1985, a total of 3,195,880 barrels of crude oil and condensate were produced from Gulf of Mexico OCS oil and gas leases which obligate the lessee to offer produced liquids to small or independent refiners.

The lease also requires that the lessee comply with existing rules and regulations and any additional rules and regulations that may be issued after the lease is awarded in order to provide for the prevention of waste and the conservation of the natural resources of the OCS.

Provisions of OCS Oil and Gas Lease

Typically, OCS oil and gas leases have been issued with a fixed royalty of not less than 12 1/2 percent of the value or amount of oil and gas produced, saved, and sold with a cash bonus as the variable (bid) factor. However, beginning in 1974 and from time to time since then, DOI has exercised its authority to test other bidding systems. In addition to cash-bonus bidding with a fixed royalty rate, the following systems have been used: cash-bonus bidding with fixed net profit share, cash-bonus bidding with a fixed sliding-scale royalty rate of 16 2/3 to 65 percent, and a royalty bid of 33 1/3 percent or more with a fixed cash bonus. The MMS is currently using a cash-bonus bidding system with fixed royalty rates of 12 1/2 percent or 16 2/3 percent.

The OCS oil and gas leases usually become effective the first day of the month following the date they are signed by the authorized MMS official. In a few instances, leases have become effective the first of the month in which the lease was signed. The earlier effective date allowed the lessee to commence drilling operations prior to the end of the month of issuance. Leases are usually granted for an initial term of five years, but they may be granted for a term of up to ten years when it is determined that longer terms are necessary to encourage exploration due to unusually deep water or other unusually adverse conditions.

Typically, an OCS oil and gas lease covers a tract of land described as a block three miles by three miles on a protraction diagram (leasing map).

Figure 2 is a graphic presentation of the interactions among DOI, MMS, and others after OCS oil and gas leases are issued.

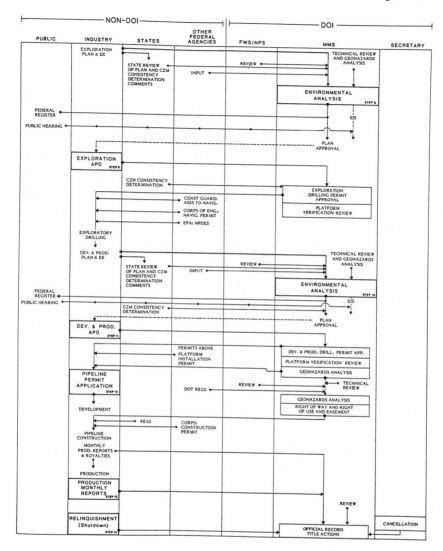

Figure 2. OCS leasing process—postlease phase. (MMS, Office of Offshore Information Services, 1985.)

PRACTICES AND PROCEDURES USED TO MONITOR AND CONTROL
ACTIVITIES OF OCS LESSEES TO DISCOVER, DEVELOP, AND PRODUCE
OCS OIL AND GAS

Preliminary Activities

With the exception of preliminary activities, no exploration activities may be
commenced or conducted on any lease except in accordance with an approved
exploration plan. "Preliminary activities" are defined as geological, geophysical, and
such other surveys as may be needed to develop sufficient information to prepare an
exploration plan. Preliminary activities are limited to activities which do not result
in any physical penetration of the seabed greater than 300 feet of unconsolidated
formations or 50 feet of consolidated formations and which do not result in any
significant adverse effects on the natural resources of the OCS. Exploration activities
mean "any activities which are part of the process of searching for minerals including
the drilling of wells which discover oil or natural gas in paying quantities and the
drilling of any additional well which is needed to delineate any reservoir and to
enable the lessee to determine whether to proceed with development and production."

For leases issued with an initial term of five years, lessees must submit an
exploration plan prior to the end of the fourth year unless the Director authorizes the
submission of an exploration plan at a later date but before expiration of the lease.
For leases issued for an initial term greater than five years, lessees must submit an
exploration plan before the end of the period of time specified in the notice
announcing the lease offering.

Figure 3 is a graphic presentation of the review process for an exploration plan
and the accompanying environmental report.

Exploration Plan and Environmental Report

An exploration plan may apply to one or more leases held by an individual lessee
or may be submitted by an operator for a group of leases which are subject to an
approved unit agreement. An exploration plan includes the following:

1. The proposed type and sequence of exploration activities to be
    undertaken together with a tentative timetable for their
    performance from commencement to completion;

2. A description of any drilling vessel, platform, or other
    installation or device to be permanently or temporarily
    attached to the seabed indicating the important features
    thereof with special attention to safety features and
    pollution-prevention and control features including oil spill
    containment and cleanup plans;

3. The types of geophysical equipment to be used;

4. The general location of each proposed exploratory well
    including surface and projected bottomhole locations;

5. Current structure maps and, as appropriate, schematic cross
    sections showing expected depths of marker formations; and

6. Such other relevant information as the Director may require.

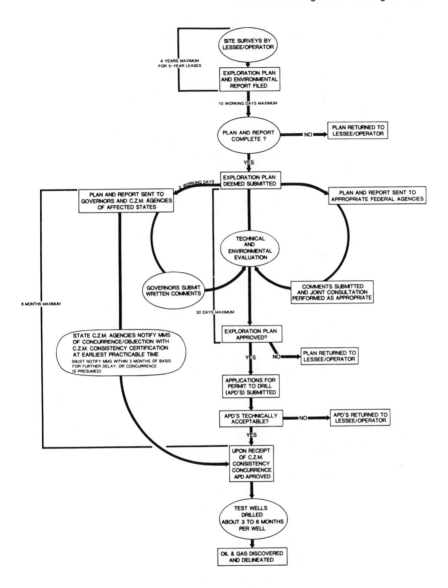

Figure 3. Exploration plan review.

Exploration plans are accompanied by environmental reports which include a brief description of the following:

1. The procedures, personnel, and equipment that are to be used to prevent, report, and clean up spills of oil or waste materials which may occur during the exploration activities including information on responsetime capability, capacity and location of equipment, and sites and methods of disposal;

2. The location, description, and size of any offshore and onshore requirements (including rights-of-way and easements) for support and storage facilities and, where possible, a timetable regarding the acquisition of lands and the construction or expansion of facilities;

3. The estimated number of persons expected to be employed in support of offshore, onshore, and transportation activities and, where possible, the approximate number of new employees and families likely to move into the affected area;

4. The most likely travel routes for boat and aircraft traffic between offshore and onshore facilities, the probable location of onshore terminals, and the estimated frequency such routes will be traveled;

5. The quantity and composition of solid and liquid waste and other pollutants likely to be generated by offshore, onshore, and transport operations;

6. Major supplies, services, energy, water, or other resources within affected States necessary for carrying out the exploration plan;

7. Environmentally sensitive or potentially hazardous areas including the following:
   a. Site-specific geology, e.g., bathymetry, seismicity, extent and type of bottom sediments and geologic features which pose a potential hazard to the activities proposed;
   b. Historic patterns and other meteorological conditions including storm frequency and magnitude, wind direction and velocity of offshore areas and listing, where possible, the means and extremes of each;
   c. Physical oceanography including onsite direction and velocity of currents;
   d. Onsite flora and fauna including bottom communities, where present, transitory birds and mammals that may be in the area when proposed activities are being conducted, identification of endangered species and their habitats that could be affected by proposed activities, and typical fishing seasons of the area;
   e. Environmentally sensitive areas (onshore as well as offshore), e.g., refuges, preserves, sanctuaries, rookeries, calving grounds, and areas of particular concern identified by an affected state pursuant to the CZM Act which may be affected by the activities proposed;

f. Onsite uses of the area, e.g., shipping lanes, military exercises, recreation, boating, and commercial fishing;

g. Archaeological and cultural resources located within the area that may be disturbed by the activities proposed; and

h. Existing and planned monitoring systems that are measuring or will measure environmental conditions and provide information and data on the impacts of activities in the area.

The environmental report accompanying an exploration plan also includes an assessment of the direct effects implementation of the exploration plan may be expected to have on the offshore and onshore environment with special emphasis upon issues related to air quality and identification and evaluation of unavoidable and irreversible impacts.

The MMS has 30 days in which to approve or disapprove an exploration plan. Copies of the exploration plan with the accompanying environmental report, oil spill contingency plan, and coastal zone consistency certification are forwarded for review to other federal agencies including the Fish and Wildlife Service, the National Marine Fisheries Service, U.S. Army Corps of Engineers, Environmental Protection Agency (EPA), USCG, and the Office of Ocean and Coastal Resource Management (formerly Office of Coastal Zone Management). Copies are also sent to the Governor(s) of affected states, other interested state agencies, and to the office responsible for the CZM review of each affected state that has an approved CZM program. The MMS regional office also makes copies of exploration plans available to the public (except for those portions of the exploration plan that have been determined to be exempt from disclosure under the Freedom of Information Act).

Engineers and other MMS personnel conduct a technical review and assessment of the exploration plan and accompanying environmental report. The proposed type and sequence of exploration activities along with the tentative timetable for accomplishment are analyzed for reasonableness and possible conflict with other activities in the vicinity of the lease. Descriptions of the geophysical equipment, the drilling vessel, and pollution-control devices are reviewed for compliance with rules, regulations, provisions of the lease, etc. The oil spill contingency plan is evaluated (by MMS and USCG under a cooperative agreement) to ensure that proper equipment, materials, and personnel will be available if, and as, needed.

The MMS regional environmental staff conducts an analysis of all activities proposed in the exploration plan. In completing this analysis, the staff utilizes information contained in the environmental report. The environmental report is often documented in an environmental assessment which is prepared when MMS determines that no significant environmental impacts would result from implementing the exploration plan. In those instances, a finding of no significant impacts is made. In the event that approval of an exploration plan were found to constitute a major federal action significantly affecting the quality of the human environment, a full-blown EIS would be prepared. To date, the preparation of an EIS for an exploration plan has not been considered necessary.

Following completion of its review and prior to the expiration of the 30-day deadline prescribed by law, the MMS regional office notifies the lessee of the approval or disapproval of the proposed exploration plan. An exploration plan will be disapproved should the proposed activities threaten serious harm or damage to life, property, any mineral (in areas leased or unleased), the national security or defense, or to the marine coastal or human environment.

The MMS cannot issue permits authorizing a lessee to implement exploratory drilling activities described in an approved exploration plan until the lessee has obtained state concurrence with the coastal zone consistency certificate filed with the exploration plan unless the Secretary of Commerce makes a finding for the lessee on appeal.

Application for Permit to Drill, Deepen, or Plug Back (APD)

Before any drilling operations are commenced on an OCS lease, the lessee must obtain MMS approval for an APD. An APD must be filed and approval obtained each time a lessee proposes to drill, deepen, or plug back a well. The APD includes detailed information of the lessee's drilling program including the blowout prevention system and the well casing, cementing, and drilling-mud programs.

During MMS's review of an APD, structure maps and cross sections are analyzed for accuracy in interpretation and mapping. Well logs are examined for pressure abnormalities that may be important to the well-control program. Proposed casing, cementing, and drilling-mud programs are reviewed to ensure that they are sufficient to maintain well control. Formation pressures are checked against mud weights, casing setting depths against formation fracture gradients, and blowout-prevention systems against maximum possible surface pressures. Other features checked are well-control equipment and procedures, operational safety and pollution-prevention systems, and the rig inventory for drilling mud and mud additives. In the Arctic where permafrost or occasional hydrate zones may be encountered, the casing, cementing, and drilling-mud programs are reviewed for proper design to address these special problems.

Conditions may be placed upon the approval of the APD. These conditions usually amplify or explain requirements for specific procedures that are to be complied with at the well site.

Other federal permits required before drilling begins include permits for aids to navigation and certification of mobile offshore drilling units from USCG, navigation permits from the Corps, and National Pollutant Discharge Elimination System permits from EPA.

Figure 4 is a graphic presentation of the review process applied to development and production plans.

Development and Production Plans and Environmental Report

All development and production operations on an OCS oil and gas lease must be conducted in accordance with an approved development and production plan. (For leases in the western Gulf of Mexico, i.e., leases not within that part of the Gulf of Mexico that is adjacent to Florida, a development operations coordination document may be submitted instead of a development and production plan.) Development is defined as "those activities which take place following discovery of minerals in paying quantities, including geophysical activity, drilling, platform construction, and operation of all onshore support facilities, and which are for the purpose of ultimately producing the minerals discovered." Production means "those activities which take place after the successful completion of any means for the removal of minerals including such removal, field operations, transfer of minerals to shore, operation monitoring, maintenance, and workover drilling."

A development and production plan may apply to one or more leases held by an individual lessee, or it may be submitted by an operator for a group of two or more leases that are subject to an approved unit agreement. A plan is supposed to provide for the effective and efficient development and production of all known

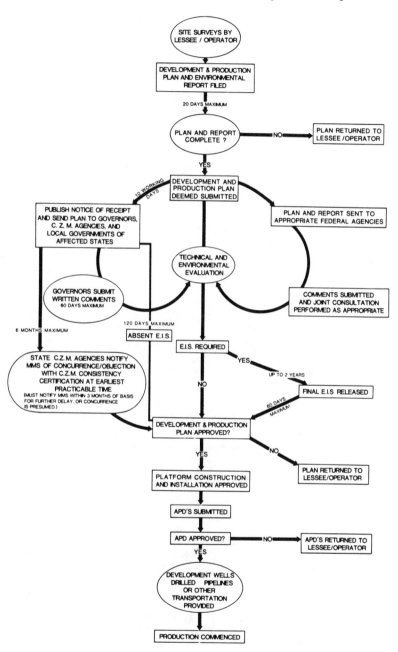

Figure 4. Development and production plan review.

accumulations of hydrocarbons found on the leasehold that are capable of producing in paying quantities.

A development and production plan is to include the following:

1. A description of the specific work to be performed including all the development and production activities that the lessee proposes to undertake during the time period covered by the plan and all activities to be undertaken up to and including the commencement of sustained production;

2. A description of any drilling vessels, platforms, pipelines, or other facilities and operations located on the OCS which are proposed or known by the lessee (whether or not they are owned or operated by the lessee) to be directly related to the proposed development including the location, size, design and important features of the facilities and operations (with special attention to safety and pollution-prevention and control features including oil spill containment and cleanup plans) and the labor, material, and energy requirements associated with the facilities and operations;

3. The location of each well including the surface and projected bottomhole locations;

4. Current interpretations of all available relevant geological and geophysical data including structure maps and schematic cross sections of productive formations;

5. A description of the environmental safeguards to be implemented in the course of development and production under the plan together with a discussion of how such safeguards are to be implemented;

6. All safety standards that are to be met and the safety features to be utilized in order to meet those standards;

7. The expected rate of development and production and a time schedule for the performance of activities from commencement to completion of both; and

8. Such other relevant information and data as may be required.

The development and production plan, like the exploration plan, is accompanied by an environmental report. The environmental report for a development and production plan must be as detailed and comprehensive as necessary to enable identification and evaluation of the environmental consequences of the proposed activities. In order to eliminate the repetition of information and data discussed in the associated development and production plan, the presale EIS done on the planning area, other environmental reports, environmental analyses, or EIS's prepared for the geographic area, the lessee summarizes the data, information, and issues addressed in those documents and concentrates on the issues which are specific to the site(s) of development and production activities covered by the proposed development and production plan.

The level of detail required for data, information, and issues discussed in the environmental report is dictated to a large degree by the scope, nature, and content of the proposed development and production plan. The environmental report describes the extent and timing of proposed offshore and land-based operations; requirements for land, labor, material, and energy; means proposed for transportation of oil and gas to shore; disposal of solid and liquid wastes; cultural and historical concerns; oceanographic, meteorological, and geological conditions; and the significance of any impacts on aquatic biota due to the use of a proposed site for development and production facilities. The lessee must also submit a copy of a certificate which asserts that the proposed development and production activities comply with and will be conducted in a manner which is consistent with any CZM plans approved for affected States.

The MMS's review and analysis of a proposed development and production plan is very similar to its practices and procedures for review and analysis of exploration plans. There are, however, certain differences in the timetable for processing and the approval/disapproval actions mandated by the law. Where MMS has only 30 days within which to approve or disapprove an exploration plan, it must allow the Governors of affected states and the executives of affected local governments 60 days within which to comment upon a development and production plan. The MMS can take up to 60 days following the release of the final EIS prepared pursuant to NEPA to approve, disapprove, or require modification of a proposed development and production plan. When an EIS is not prepared, MMS may take up to 60 days after the close of the 60-day period during which Governors of affected states and executives of affected local governments are invited to submit comments and recommendations.

Development and Production Plan Disapproved or Modification Required

A development and production plan must be disapproved—

1. If the lessee fails to demonstrate that it can comply with the requirements of the OCS Lands Act or other applicable federal law;

2. If any of the activities described in the plan for which a federal license or permit is required that affects any land or water use in the coastal zone of a state with an approved CZM program and fails to receive that states' concurrence with respect to the consistency certification accompanying the plan and the Secretary of Commerce does not make a finding for the lessee on appeal;

3. If operations threaten national security or national defense; or

4. If it is determined that because of exceptional geological conditions in the lease areas, exceptional resource values in the marine or coastal environment or other exceptional circumstances that (a) implementation of the plan would probably cause serious harm or damage to life, property, mineral deposits, the national security or defense, or marine, coastal, or human environment, (b) the threat of harm or damage will not disappear or decrease to an acceptable extent within a reasonable period of time, and (c) the advantages of disapproving the plan outweigh the advantages of development and production of the resource covered by the plan.

Modification of a development and production plan will be required when it is determined that the lessee has failed to make adequate provision for safe operations on the lease area or for protection of the marine, coastal, or human environment.

EIS Preparation for Development and Production Plan

If it is determined that approval of a proposed development and production plan would constitute a major federal action significantly affecting the quality of the human environment, MMS initiates the procedures for developing a full-blown EIS. The OCS Lands Act, as amended, requires that the Secretary declare, at least once in any Region or area of the OCS other than the Gulf of Mexico, the approval of a development and production plan to be a major Federal action.

The State of California's Environmental Quality Act places requirements on the state's agency permitting activities which are similar to the requirements that the NEPA places upon federal agencies. Since development and production plans for OCS oil and gas leases off California have also involved near-shore and onshore facilities subject to state and local government permitting authorities, elements of those plans have been subject to the NEPA and the California Environmental Quality Act. These requirements have been addressed through coordinated environmental analyses which were incorporated in a document called an "Environmental Impact Statement/ Environmental Impact Report."

Unitization of Lease Operations

Exploration plans and development and production plans may be applicable to one or more leases held by an individual or to two or more leases which are subject to an approved unit agreement. Unitized operations permit exploration, development, and production operations to be conducted on two or more leases as though these operations were being conducted on a single lease. Under unitized operations, protection of lease lines within the unitized area is no longer a driving force in the design and execution of development and production activities. Royalties and other benefits are allocated on the basis of constructive production from each lease rather than actual production as would be the case in the absence of unitization.

Unitized operations may be approved or required by MMS when the action is necessary to prevent waste, conserve natural resources, and to protect correlative rights. Agreement upon what constitutes equity between the owners of competing interests can be difficult to obtain. In the absence of unitization, equity in the amount of oil and gas produced from a reservoir is determined by the diligence of each lessee's drilling and production activities. The OCS Order No. 11 spells out the procedures followed when involuntary unitization of lease operations is directed.

The criteria considered during review and approval of the voluntary unitization of operations on two more leases include the following:

1.　　To allow the optimal number of artificial islands (or other devices) necessary for efficient exploration, development, and production of a reservoir or potential hydrocarbon deposit(s);

2.　　To embrace a single reservoir or structure where potential hydrocarbon accumulations are anticipated;

3.　　To delineate a reservoir or determine the existence of a potential hydrocarbon accumulation; and

4.   To embrace the minimum area necessary to accomplish the above purposes.

Drilling, producing, and well reworking activities to continue the unit agreement and the leases subject to the unit agreement must meet the standards applied to drilling, producing, and well reworking activities that can continue a lease in effect beyond the initial phase of the lease term. Proposed exploration units which involve one or more leases that are due to expire soon must include drilling commitments which are designed to continue leases for the time required for hydrocarbon accumulations to be delineated and to develop a plan for development and production. In the absence of actual drilling or reworking operations, the unit and leases are in danger of terminating.

Suspension of Operations/Suspension of Production

The OCS oil and gas leases are issued for a specified period of time (five, eight, or ten years), and so long thereafter as oil or gas, or both, is produced from the leasehold in paying quantities. Thus, in the absence of actual production, a lease is susceptible to expiring even when it contains a well which is recognized as having discovered oil or gas, or both, in paying quantities. The OCS Lands Act, as amended in 1978, specifically requires the Secretary of the Interior to promulgate regulations which include provisions as follows:

(1)   For the suspension or temporary prohibition of any operation or activity, including production, pursuant to any lease or permit

(A) at the request of a lessee, in the national interest, to facilitate proper development of a lease or to allow for the construction or negotiation for use of transportation facilities, or

(B) if there is a threat of serious, irreparable, or immediate harm or damage to life..., to property, to any mineral deposits..., or to the marine, coastal, or human environment, and for the extension of any permit or lease affected by suspension or prohibition...by a period equivalent to the period of such suspension or prohibition...,

(7)   for the prompt and efficient exploration and development of a lease area;...

The present policy under which suspensions of production (SOP) are granted has evolved through years of surplus production capacity and nationwide shortages of oil and gas. The four basic elements of DOI's policy on suspensions are as follows:

1.   The DOI expects that under normal conditions, lessees will explore and commence development of production from a lease within the primary (fixed) term specified in the lease.

2.   Suspension of operations (SOO) or production which have the effect of extending a lease beyond its primary (fixed) term are granted when that action is in the national interest.

3.   Leases which are about to exceed their primary term and which are not actually producing oil or gas will be considered for an SOP if sufficient exploration to delineate areas capable of production have been completed and development commenced. The commencement of production must be evidenced by a discovery of minerals in paying quantities and by submission of a schedule of work designed to lead to the commencement of production within a reasonably short period of time.

4.   Develoment plans must provide for the development of all known significant accumulations of fluid hydrocarbons on the lease. The MMS determination of national interest includes consideration of difficult or unforeseen environmental, safety, development, transportation, and construction issues. It also includes consideration of whether the lessee has experienced inordinate delays in the issuance of needed governmental permits and other relevant circumstances.

The MMS determination of whether a schedule of work is designed to lead promptly to the commencement of production includes the time required to design, fabricate, and install needed facilities.

Suspensions are normally approved for a specified period of time with provision for earlier termination under conditions specified in the instrument of approval. Directed SOOs have been issued for a number of reasons. Following the 1969 blowout in the Santa Barbara Channel off California, SOOs were issued for leases with approved drilling permits. This action was taken to allow time for a case-by-case reevaluation and reapproval of the previously approved exploratory drilling activities described in the lessees' applications for permission to drill. In 1984, SOOs were issued for OCS oil and gas leases in the eastern Gulf of Mexico to implement a special lease stipulation which precluded exploratory drilling until after the completion of an environmental study. Those suspensions were extended through February 18, 1987, to allow time to evaluate the results of the environmental study.

Compliance Inspections

The OCS Lands Act Amendments of 1978 required the promulgation of regulations to provide the following:

1.   Scheduled onsite inspection, at least once a year, of each facility on the OCS which is subject to any environmental or safety regulation promulgated pursuant to that act. Said inspection is to include all safety equipment designed to prevent or ameliorate blowouts, fires, spillages, or other major accidents; and

2.   Periodic onsite inspections, without advance notice, to the operator of a facility on the OCS which is subject to environmental or safety regulations promulgated under the act to assure compliance with those regulations.

Thus, MMS performs both scheduled and unannounced inspections to assure compliance with governing requirements. To assure consistency and uniformity of action by its inspection force, MMS has reduced the requirements that are to be checked to a listing of Potential Incidents of Noncompliance, referred to as the PINCs list. Each PINC is presented as a question that can be answered yes or no. A "no" answer means that an incident of noncompliance or INC has been found, and corrective actions must be initiated. Enforcement actions to ensure that corrective measures are taken range from the issuance of a warning notice that correction must be accomplished within a specified timeframe to an order requiring immediate shutdown of the facility. In those instances where a well or facility is ordered shut in, those operations must remain shut in until the required corrections have occurred. In those instances where a lessee fails to initiate corrective measures within the time allowed, the lessee may be found liable for a civil penalty of up to $10,000 per day. Royalty income to the United States from OCS leases during 1984 was approximately $11 million per day. That income is directly related to the volumes of oil and gas produced. Thus, it is important to assure that accurate measurements are made with respect to the volumes of oil and gas produced. The MMS must approve the methods of measurement to be used as well as the location of equipment used to measure oil and gas from OCS leases.

The MMS Offshore Minerals Management personnel witness the monthly calibration of sales meters whenever possible. If an inspector detects apparent irregularities in the measurement of oil or gas, Royalty Management personnel are immediately notified, and appropriate action is initiated. Similarly, if Royalty Management personnel should detect discrepancies in the volumes of oil or gas reported or royalties paid, Offshore Minerals Management personnel are requested to investigate or inspect the facilities in question.

Training

All individuals who are employed on the OCS on an artificial island, installation, or other device and who operate or supervise the operation of pollution-prevention equipment must be trained to operate or to supervise the operation of the pollution-prevention equipment. Lessee and drilling contractor personnel are required to be trained and qualified in accordance with MMS Standard MMSS-OCS-T 1, "Training and Qualifications of Personnel in Well-Control Equipment and Techniques for Drilling on Offshore Locations." This standard includes guidelines for training course curricula and the qualification procedures for personnel employed as rotary helpers, derrickmen, drillers, toolpushers, and operators' representatives. All personnel employed on the OCS in one of these five occupations must be able to show evidence that they have been properly trained and qualified.

The MMS also requires that all persons involved in installing, inspecting, testing, and maintaining safety devices on production facilities be qualified in these areas. To qualify, these persons must attend a training program recommended by the "American Petroleum Institute [API] Recommended Practice for Qualification Programs for Offshore Production Personnel Who Work With Anti-Pollution Safety Devices (API RP T-2)."

Outer Continental Shelf Oil and Gas Information Program

Section 26 of the OCS Lands Act, as amended, requires the Secretary of the Interior to carry out an OCS Oil and Gas Information Program. Section 26 specifically requires the Secretary to prepare summary reports and indexes which are designed to assist states and local governments affected by OCS activities in their planning for the onshore impacts of possible oil and gas development and production. Since enactment of section 26, regional indexes have been prepared which list relevant, actual and proposed programs, plans, reports, EIS's, and other lease sale information.

Presidential Proclamation of the Exclusive Economic Zone

On March 10, 1983, a Presidential Proclamation established an Exclusive Economic Zone (EEZ) around the United States. The EEZ extends seaward 200 nautical miles from the "baseline" (the legal coastline) of the territorial sea of the United States, the Commonwealths of Puerto Rico and northern Mariana Islands, and other U.S. overseas territories and possessions. The EEZ extends over 3 billion acres which are subject to U.S. jurisdiction and control. Within the EEZ, the United States exercises sovereign rights, to the extent permitted by international law, to manage the natural resources, both living and nonliving, of the seabed and subsoil. The Secretary of the Interior is authorized by the OCS Lands Act and the Statehood Acts of Alaska and Hawaii to manage the leasing of oil and gas and other mineral resources within the EEZ contiguous to the 50 states.

OTHER LAWS APPLICABLE TO OCS ACTIVITIES

The leasing of OCS lands and the conduct of operations to discover, develop, and produce oil and gas and other minerals from the OCS are also subject to many other federal laws, the more important of which are as follows:

National Environmental Policy Act establishes procedural requirements for preparing environmental assessments and environmental impact statements for major federal actions that could significantly affect the quality of the human environment.

Endangered Species Act requires federal agencies to ensure that their actions are not likely to jeopardize the continued existence of any threatened or endangered species.

Coastal Zone Management Act, as amended, provides for state review of exploration plans, development and production plans, and other permitted activities not covered by an approved plan which might affect the land and water use of the coastal zone.

Federal Water Pollution Control Act (commonly known as the Clean Water Act) requires that in-water discharges of pollutants generated by OCS operations comply with the limitations and restrictions that are included in an applicable National Pollution Discharge Elimination System (NPDES) permit.

Ports and Waterways Safety Act authorizes certain actions by USCG to develop means of improving the safety of navigation.

Marine Mammal Protection Act charges the National Marine Fisheries Service with enforcement of rules to protect marine mammals.

PART THREE

Alternative Strategies and Arrangements

One of the obvious possibilities in any rethinking of fisheries management policy is to increase the role of individual states in managing their offshore living resources. At the outset, it is important to remember that coastal states have been in the "fisheries business" far longer than the federal government. Their role was overshadowed when U.S. jurisdiction was extended to 200 miles, but they continue to control some of our nation's most valuable fisheries. The issue is what can be learned from that experience and utilized in a refined version of our federal/state management system.

Although management at the state level can be less cumbersome than the complex regional council process, problems certainly do exist. Adequate research funding is always an issue but is more acute at the state level. Interstate management of shared stocks inevitably creates problems with each jurisdiction protecting its "share" of the resource.

The papers in this chapter will examine the federal/state balance in an effort to promote the "rethinking" of fisheries management currently underway. The three states represented, Massachusetts, Texas, and Alaska, are excellent examples of different styles of management. Collectively, they demonstrate the extraordinarily diverse nature of the U.S. fishing industry and the administrative structures designed to regulate it.

DENNIS W. NIXON
Assistant Professor
Graduate Program in Marine Affairs
University of Rhode Island
Kingston, Rhode Island

CHAPTER 5

Increasing the Role of State and Local Governments

In Fisheries Management

THE FEDERAL GOVERNMENT PERSPECTIVE

RICHARD H. SCHAEFER
Acting Regional Director
Northeast Region
National Marine Fisheries Service
National Oceanic and Atmospheric Administration
Gloucester, Massachusetts

Instead of "Increasing the Role of State and Local Governments in Fisheries Management," perhaps the title of this session should be the reciprocal, "Decreasing the Federal Role...." The issue of *federalism*, which has vacillated between federal and state supremacy since the founding of our nation, is again leaning strongly toward increased state responsibility. As sure as history repeats itself, in the not very distant future, I suspect a conference may be convened having the title "Increasing the Federal Role in Fisheries Management."

The current administration's "new federalism" policy is designed to reduce federal and to increase state and local government responsibilities. This political philosophy is a pragmatic one and the fiscal approach means there will be less federal dollars and man-hours available for the conservation and management of fisheries resources. This will leave a void that must be filled one way or another. I hope that the way chosen will be well thought out and effectively implemented. Otherwise, many of the positive things we have accomplished in fisheries management in the last decade will be lost.

BACKGROUND

From a historical perspective, state authority was initially limited to "internal waters." Liberally interpreted, internal waters were anything shoreward of islands, or even rocks awash at low tide. In the 1940s, interstate marine fisheries commissions were established by Congress to discuss common fisheries issues and coordinate research programs, between and among coastal states, but there was no management or enforcement authority conveyed to these commissions. The Submerged Lands Act of 1953 granted authority to the states to manage marine fisheries out to three miles beyond the internal waters baseline. The incompatibility and incongruity of managing widely distributed, frequently migratory fish stocks with authority confined to restrictive political boundaries was, and still is, a serious problem.

The evolution of state involvement in marine fisheries management continued in the late sixties and through the seventies. The Stratton Commission Report provided the impetus for formulation of the National Marine Fisheries Service (NMFS) state/federal fisheries management program in the early seventies. The report pointed out that the rehabilitation of domestic fisheries depended upon elimination of overlapping, and often conflicting, laws and regulations that existed in neighboring states.

The state/federal program started with the management of American lobster in 1972, and cooperative management of a substantial number of other important species has been addressed since that time. Through the cooperative efforts of state and federal fisheries managers and the marine fisheries commissions, significant funding (primarily federal) and advisory assistance from concerned industries, plans to manage these species throughout their range have been prepared. This has been the success of the program; the failure has been in the attempts to implement effective management measures. Too often intrastate imperatives have overridden interstate needs, and compatible regulations in each of the concerned states have not been forthcoming.

The passage of the Magnuson Fishery Conservation and Management Act of 1976 (MFCMA) raised great hopes in the minds of both the fishing industry and the fishery managers. Each state was to be represented on a regional fishery management council by state officials having the primary responsibility for marine fisheries management. Other members would be well qualified industry representatives and funds would be made available for a professional staff capable of translating the wishes of the council into comprehensive management plans. Plans would be implemented by federal regulations promulgated by the Secretary of Commerce and the states would adopt complementary regulations or face the possibility of federal preemption. In practice, the federal preemptive authority has been limited by the requirement that a fishery occur predominantly in the Fisheries Conservation Zone (FCZ) and by political constraints. Despite numerous examples of conflicts, preemptive authority has only been invoked twice against the wishes of any state. Classic examples of conflicts in the Northeast region, where preemption was considered seriously but ultimately rejected, include regulatory loopholes in early groundfish regulations in some state waters that allowed fishermen to ignore quotas; and differences in Atlantic herring regulations that made effective management impossible. There is no question that the MFCMA has greatly strengthened interjurisdictional cooperation in fisheries management, but there are also some glaring examples of failure. I believe the states have the expertise to manage effectively the marine fisheries resources, but all too often interstate concerns have been overridden by intrastate political realities.

Another limitation of the MFCMA has been the large number of very important species that do not meet the "predominantly FCZ" requirement and, therefore, are not subject to management under the act. Striped bass, bluefish, menhaden, anadromous herring, sea herring (since the collapse of the Georges Bank stock), summer flounder, sciaenids and many shellfish and crustaceans are found predominantly in state waters off the east coast. These species can be managed only through interstate cooperative agreement.

AN INCREASED STATE ROLE: A POSITIVE PERSPECTIVE

There are several sound reasons why the states should assume a greater role in managing marine species. It is recognized that the majority of commercial landings still come from state waters, and this is true to even a greater degree in the case of recreational fisheries landings. Since it has been well established that the states are very reluctant to give up control of marine fisheries management authority in territorial waters, the implication is that there is a willingness to assume the responsibility of establishing appropriate and complementary management measures. It appears that now is the time to do just that. In addition, the current emphasis on the restoration of anadromous fish stocks, and the growing recognition of the importance of marine recreational fishing issues provide the states with even greater direct involvement. Add to these the responsibility for marine/estuarine habitat problems and it is obvious that the states' role in fisheries management is critically important.

POTENTIAL MECHANISMS—INSTITUTIONAL

Under these circumstances it is necessary to establish the means by which the states can address adequately their common problems. Perhaps we would do well to examine a mechanism paralleling the structure and authority of the Connecticut River Atlantic Salmon Commission in the Connecticut River. This body was established through interstate agreement (compact) for Atlantic salmon restoration. The commission is comprised of governmental and private representatives from each of the four participating states, as well as officials of the U.S. Fish and Wildlife Service and the National Marine Fisheries Service. The compact was adopted by the legislative system of each of the four states. It was then submitted as legislation to the U.S. Congress, where it was passed and signed into law by the President in October, 1983. The compact provides direct regulatory authority to the Commission to regulate fishing in the mainstem of the Connecticut River. There is no reason why groups of states with interests in specific fisheries could not form compacts to provide overall regulatory authority to manage them.

Another possible approach would be to pursue direct authority for the existing Interstate Marine Fisheries Commissions. This would require some years to accomplish since each of the compact states would have to adopt identical state legislation and then submit it for congressional action at the federal level. It would appear more realistic to attempt to establish separate compacts for individual fisheries or groups of closely-related species. The necessary unanimous agreement of all the concerned states is more likely and the passage of individual state legislation would be less time-consuming.

The Studds Bill for the management of striped bass has shown us that a serious threat of federal preemption of state management authority is useful in strengthening the will of cooperating states to adopt complementary management measures. This has shown that congressional intent need not always be subtle!

More important than the measures by which it is accomplished is the need for all concerned, particularly the individual States, to recognize and accept the fact that *regional* authority is absolutely necessary in order to manage *regional* stocks. When and if this happens, it will be a short step to an agreement on the way this can be best accomplished.

POTENTIAL MECHANISMS—FUNDING

The very next question, of course, is where do the funds come from to do these things? It is clear that the usual sources of federal funds are unlikely to be available. An exception will be the Wallop/Breaux money which comes from a special fund administered by the U.S. Fish and Wildlife Service. It is earmarked for recreational fisheries purposes but is certainly appropriate for funding a wide range of stock enhancement measures. The licensing of marine fishermen, both commercial and recreational, is a viable consideration. There is always some constituent opposition to "new taxes" as license fees are sure to be called, but there is strong precedent for user fees of this type. User fees for specific marine activities such as whale watching are also possible sources of income.

LIKELY CONSEQUENCES

If the present circumstances of federal funding and program emphasis continue for an extended period of time, I believe we will find that most finfish resources in state waters will be allocated to recreational interests. Recreational interests have the votes and the organizations to make this happen. The U.S. Fish and Wildlife Service, through the administration of Wallop/Breaux funds, will play a much greater role in marine fisheries management in the near future. The National Marine Fisheries Service will continue to be directly involved in recreational fisheries matters in the Exclusive Economic Zone (EEZ) with responsibility for billfish, swordfish, sharks, and tunas, but it will be significantly diminished from the present level in state waters.

National Marine Fisheries Service concerns will be necessarily limited mostly to the commercial fisheries predominantly present in the EEZ. In the Northeast region, these will include groundfish, squid, mackerel, butterfish, surf clams, ocean guahogs, and scallops. Work with the regional fishery management councils on these and similar species will continue at some reduced level of activity but, again, state input will be a major factor in the management scenario until, at least, the end of the century.

PROSPECTS AND POTENTIAL PROBLEMS OF A
GREATER ROLE FOR THE STATE OF ALASKA

GUY THORNBURGH
Deputy Director
Commercial Fisheries Division
Alaska Department of Fish and Game
Juneau, Alaska

INTRODUCTION

I am enthused to be at this conference because it is important to clarify federal and state roles, particularly in this period of fiscal constraint. It is also important when one considers the size of the Bering Sea And Gulf of Alaska fisheries. National Marine Fisheries Service (NMFS) records for 1984 show that 40 percent of the poundage landed by U.S. fishermen (including joint venture participants) came from waters in and off of Alaska. Except for oil, fishing is the number one industry in Alaska.

CONCLUSIONS

Let me start this discussion with my two conclusions so that you will get a feel for where I am coming from.

First, since I look at fisheries management from the inside out, it is not surprising for me to conclude that intensive management and regulation, although they appear expensive, are necessary. There is little hope of ever changing the established techniques, programs, and processes that industry and government have become accustomed to.

Second, I conclude that in the Alaska region, the immediate avenue to optimizing benefits from limited state and federal fiscal resources is to change the type of cooperation we presently share between our two levels of governments. By cooperation I do *not* mean that the NMFS "coos" and the State of Alaska does all of the operations as currently exists; by cooperation I do *not* mean duplication of state and federal regulations which leads to frustration and wasted dollars; and by cooperation I do *not* mean that the state will expand its role in federal management. I *do mean* that cooperation is the role of the state alone in managing selected U.S. fisheries while the federal government manages the remaining U.S. fisheries. In other words, I mean that cooperation is to use state and federal dollars, and our people, to divide and conquer. Those are the two conclusions I wish to explain.

WE MUST MANAGE—BUT HOW MUCH REGULATION?

All of us who deal in actual day-to-day fishery activities have learned that we must control the use of our natural resources—either through the rare instances of private property rights which take less control, or through the much more typical form of managing the resources as common property. These concerns for control in

Alaska peaked several decades ago as one of the major reasons for statehood. Of course, similar concerns with foreign and interstate fisheries motivated the Magnuson Fishery Conservation and Management Act of 1976 (MFCMA). There is no doubt in my mind that we must manage, and it must include regulation. The question is, how much regulation?

Recent dramatic declines in oil revenues for Alaska have forced us to review our own system. Our regulation books for commercial and subsistence fisheries have hundreds and hundreds of pages filled with detailed regulations. We find though that this extensive regulatory system is institutionalized. It has become a way of life, where industry and communities demand it and help direct it. Our elaborate regulatory system of size, sex, time, area and gear limitations, including a limited access system, is necessary to keep pace with the incredible intensity of fishing effort and to fine-tune the allocation between user groups. We have 30,000 resident and nonresident permit holders and 10,000 subsistence families in Alaska and every one of them wants his fair share and each wants to continue his "inherent" right to a life-style related to fish. Even though the economic schooling that you and I have had may rationalize that long-term social benefits are optimized under some alternative approach, I conclude that the majority of the users will not tolerate any major change. The challenge is making the current system work.

In 1980 it was projected that by 1986 Alaska oil would be selling for $50/barrel instead of the current $13/barrel. This revenue status has also convinced myself and several colleagues to begin investigations of the financial returns that are realized from monies invested in the conduct of our research and management programs. Next fall we plan to publish a quantitative analysis of the Bristol Bay salmon fishery which will demonstrate that dollars spent on the program, both research and in-season management, have had positive financial returns to industry. For example, we will show that in the Bristol Bay salmon fishery, for every $50,000 increment of management and research we have realized a $2,000,000 return in the fishery. Also, after 30 years of research, a recent decision to completely restructure our escapement goals will net a $20,000,000 annual increase during the next decade. I am convinced that when we put money into the management program we get positive value out. The response from government should not be to throw away the system when monies get tight. I have experienced more than a 20-percent budget cut in two years. Two things had to be done. First, we had to tighten our belts, even though it meant eliminating long-standing programs and occupied facilities, and laying off staff. Second, we reprogrammed remaining monies into projects with positive payoff. Day-to-day fisheries management and applied research were top priority. Back home, in Alaska, I have argued that as oil revenues decline, we must keep money in our fisheries program because fisheries is our largest industry. At the national level, I suggest that the National Oceanic and Atmospheric Administration (NOAA) should not dramatically reprogram away from NMFS into some other NOAA program, but should instead help NMFS tighten its belt and then reprogram into those fisheries management and research programs with positive returns.

So, looking at it from the inside out and without being too pessimistic, I conclude we have inherited a system we must work with. The regulatory aspect appears costly to agencies and industry, but it is a fixture in society. Politics will not let it change. Management and research aspects have proven over time, in Alaska at least, to increase financial returns to industry, and we plan to continue this investment.

SHOULD ALASKA'S ROLE IN FISHERIES MANAGEMENT BE EXPANDED?

Given this system, should we expand Alaska's role in offshore fisheries management? I will speak first to totally domestic fisheries, those without foreign or joint venture participants. In Alaska I am referring to salmon, herring, and crab. There is no room for expansion of the actual management in these fisheries because Alaska already does most of it.

Prior to the MFCMA we did it all—daily intensive management with an annual regulatory process, all the way out to 200 miles It worked well! It withstood court tests; it offered adequate protection to the resource; and it helped to maintain and build some of the strongest and most valuable fisheries in the nation. We have a substantial investment in facilities, communications and information systems, vessels and other equipment, coupled with a cadre of experienced personnel capable of carrying out the management, research and enforcement programs. Each day we operate an intensive program for Kotzebue at the Arctic Circle, to Kodiak at the heart of the eastern Bering Sea and western Gulf of Alaska, to Ketchikan which is the farthest north suburb of Seattle. It was our desire to continue to participate and to contribute to the management of offshore domestic fisheries. Our interest in doing so was to provide a management regime that would continue to foster the development and maintenance of a stable fishing industry.

When the MFCMA came along in 1976, we jumped in with both feet to help the North Pacific Fishery Management Council (NPFMC) and NMFS prepare and implement several fishery management plans (FMPs) for domestic fisheries. Cooperative agreements have continued our lead role in daily management, research, and enforcement activities, but the regulatory duplication has become far too excessive.

Even though there is no room for expansion in these totally domestic fisheries, there is a need for change. Alaska, the operator, has been burdened by accommodating the "Federal Management" process. We believe Alaska should no longer be expected to use state dollars to discharge federal responsibilities while at the same time being "rewarded" with the burdens of the federal system. Remember, the federal government asserted exclusive jurisdiction and supposedly assumed responsibility out to 200 miles. Yet I do not see where they budgeted much money to execute the actual daily obligations they established for themselves. There is no need to continue this approach in Alaska. Neither the state, the federal government nor industry can continue to afford the duplication. Fortunately, the pressure valve is finally releasing and some changes are occurring.

The salmon FMP is nearly a shelf item because of the role of the newly formed Pacific Salmon Commission. The tanner crab FMP and its regulations are so far outdated and so inoperable that NMFS has been requested by the NPFMC to rescind the regulations and the NPFMC will soon consider either an entirely different form of FMP or hopefully no FMP at all because of the state's role. Most importantly, a change Alaska is initiating is that in all likelihood before the end of June 1986, the state will decline the Secretary's offer of delegation of regulatory authority to the state under the federal management plan. We have made this decision for two reasons. First, we no longer have the same economic climate to cooperate in the costly federal system, and second, the delegation has far less discretion than the state originally bargained for. We are now very concerned that Washington, D.C. (the central office of NMFS and the Office of Management and Budget) will stay too involved in policy issues. They are too slow and they will probably overrule us with their own interests.

COOPERATION V. SPLIT RESPONSIBILITIES

As a program administrator, I have had to learn to delegate responsibility to program elements. Yet, we continue to witness how Washington overrules even their own council and their own regional office on far too many policy issues. We are unwilling to use our resources and to subject our open, public rule-making process to such oversight.

The only acceptable solution, and one we have stressed for six years now, is to split up the responsibility. We are willing to do it. We are able to do it. It is the only way in Alaska that this nation can make the process work and the only way to afford the attention this valuable industry needs. I by no means suggest that NMFS and NPFMC have no role in Alaska. On the contrary, there is a very large, important, time-consuming role for them.

The final question to address is, should Alaska expand its role in the management of the huge U.S. groundfisheries? These are the Bering Sea and Gulf of Alaska fisheries that are rapidly converting from a history of foreign dominance to domestic fisheries.

Last year the Alaska Department of Fish and Game (ADF&G) spent one-half million dollars to help manage the totally domestic aspect of these fisheries. However, we eliminated it from our FY 1987 program because we believe it is a federal responsibility. This is where the MFCMA is needed most! Let's not, as a nation, run away from it now. The management is critical. As the foreigners leave, so does the data base. These fisheries need observer programs, landing data, logbooks, etc.

Where is the plan to take care of the resource? In the 40-percent budget reduction NOAA proposes for NMFS? No. We want the federal government to concentrate its resources in Alaska groundfish, before it's too late. We will help in the short run, but not at the expense of our salmon, herring and crab. The federal government needs to accept its responsibility to americanize and effectively manage groundfisheries off Alaska. It must make the system work.

THE STATE OF MASSACHUSETTS
AND INCREASED
FISHERIES MANAGEMENT RESPONSIBILITIES

PHILIP COATES
Director
Division of Marine Fisheries
Department of Fisheries, Wildlife,
*   and Environmental Law Enforcement*
Boston, Massachusetts

It is a pleasure to participate in any discussion concerning fisheries management. This year in particular, marking the tenth year of national fisheries management under the Magnuson Fishery Conservation and Management Act of 1976 (MFCMA), it is appropriate to examine where we are and where we are going as we attempt to conserve and allocate our renewable marine resources.

MASSACHUSETTS MANAGEMENT HISTORY: A CASE IN POINT

My colleagues and I on this panel have been requested to discuss the potential of the states to increase their fisheries management roles. As the east coast representative of this august group, may I say at the outset that what Massachusetts lacks in area is more than made up by our catch. Thanks to our proximity to extremely productive fishing grounds and a historic fishery out of several large ports and many smaller harbors, Massachusetts continues to dominate east coast commercial fishing in value, ranking fourth nationwide in value in 1985, and New Bedford continued its national ranking as the number one port in value for the third consecutive year.

Our recreational fishery is also significant; and, although we suffer from the states' common problem of possessing an inadequate recreational fisheries data base, the National Marine Fisheries Service estimated 970,000 recreational fishermen caught 12,216,000 fish in 1984.

The development of our extensive fishery is paralleled by a long history of attempts to manage and allocate the fishery resources between the various user groups. It is no surprise that our colonial forefathers issued numerous local ordinances to control salt cod production and even protect anadromous fish. These initial attempts at management were followed by three centuries of literally thousands of largely local ordinances, special and general legislative acts, and county regulations aimed at fisheries. Even as recently as the mid-sixties, there were still several hundred special fisheries acts on the books, mostly giving some level of management authority to various components of municipal or county government.

It is fairly safe to say that 1960 signalled the dawn of contemporary fisheries management in Massachusetts. The Marine Fisheries Advisory Commission was established *then* by Gubernatorial Executive Order. Their charge was to examine and report on fisheries problems within the Commonwealth with particular focus on the territorial waters. Following this report, the commission gained authority to promulgate regulations as a result of legislation passed in 1962. Unfortunately, several years passed before the commission began to exercise its regulatory authority due to uncertainty over the commissions's authority to deal with the myriad special acts that were still technically on the books. Several recodifications of the marine fisheries laws had taken place over the years resulting in the elimination of many of these local bylaws and ordinances.

It was not until 1969, however, that the Attorney General issued a legal opinion concerning the commission's authority. Essentially, Attorney General Quinn determined that the commission was created to provide a modern focus on fisheries management and that, indeed, regulations approved by that body could override and preempt so-called special acts which usually dealt with local issues. Obviously, the commissions's authority to preempt did not extend to the general fisheries laws of the Commonwealth.

Although most regulations promulgated by the commission focused on the territorial waters or so-called three mile limit, the Skiriotis Doctrine[1] gave impetus to the commission to explore management beyond the territorial waters through the imposition of so-called landing limits. An early effort to establish a possession size limit for yellowtail flounder failed because of intense lobbying by the fish processors. In 1972, however, due to strong support by the harvesting sector in New Bedford, a per/man poundage landing limit for yellowtail flounder was established by regulation. This was clearly an effort by the commission to address high seas fishing beyond territorial waters since the bulk of yellowtail flounder are landed from beyond Massachusetts waters.

The promulgation of regulations controlling possession and landing was not the only means the Commonwealth developed to extend its jurisdiction over fisheries. In order to focus on the severe foreign overfishing and the need for extended U.S. jurisdiction over fishing, the Commonwealth enacted the first 200-mile limit through passage of emergency legislation in 1971. It should be noted that this act was primarily intended as a publicity device and was never utilized by the Commonwealth to exercise control over fisheries beyond the three-mile limit, even though legal opinions indicated this statute could be used over Massachusetts citizens.

The development of general licensing of fishermen in 1970 marked another milestone in the evolution of fisheries management control in the Commonwealth. For the first time, regardless of where they had caught their fish, harvestors were required to obtain a commercial fishing permit in order to land their fish in Massachusetts. The implementation of general licensing obviously gave greater authority and flexibility to the Marine Fisheries Advisory Commission (MFAC). Since licensing sanctions could be tied to regulatory as well as statutory violations.

As mentioned, most of the myriad special fisheries acts passed over the centuries had a strictly local flavor. The general fisheries laws also implied territorial water control only, even when establishing size limits and methods of taking certain species. Certain laws relating to lobsters were exceptions to this limited jurisdictional control, however, since both the short and egg-bearing lobster prohibition statutes were enacted as possession and landing limits.

Ironically, although the early legislative and regulatory history of fisheries management in Massachusetts could be characterized as conservative as far as extending authority beyond three miles, a review of the special acts reveals that the Commonwealth was quick to deal with fishermen from out of state. Several special acts were passed barring all out-of-state fishermen from access to Vineyard Sound. These special acts were ruled unconstitutional by the landmark *Douglas v. Sea Coast Products* Supreme Court case which also included the more locally significant *Westcott v. Massachusetts* case.

It should be noted that the physical dimensions of the Commonwealth's jurisdiction, as well as those of the other coastal states, were extended in 1971 as a result of application of the international convention that embodied the principle of headland to headland jurisdiction.

Lastly, to round out this brief historic perspective on fisheries management in Massachusetts, a few words about northern shrimp are pertinent since this effort, as cooperatively practiced by Maine, New Hampshire, and Massachusetts, has had success at relatively modest expenditures of time and funding. The three states agreed to cooperatively manage the northern shrimp resource in 1972 and, through applying both the Skiriotis doctrine plus the somewhat tentative authority of the Atlantic States Marine Fisheries Commission (ASMFC) compact, have implemented a series of management measures controlling mesh size and seasonal closures. Although the seasonal closures readily lend themselves to dockside enforcement and possession prohibitions, the mesh size has been enforced at sea beyond the states' jurisdictional limits through cooperative enforcement cruises involving the three states. This relatively unique management program still continues despite the MFCMA.

It is evident through this brief review that, until the creation of the MFAC and legal definition of their regulatory authority, few previous management initiatives had extended beyond the immediate jurisdiction of the Commonwealth. Recognizing that regulatory authority, few previous management initiatives had extended beyond the immediate jurisdiction of the Commonwealth. Recognizing that regulatory management through the commission and Division of Marine Fisheries brought with it greater overall fisheries expertise than statutory control by the legislature, it is only logical that more innovative management would ensue including actions that utilized then existing principles of law such as the Skiriotis doctrine and the authority of the Atlantic States Marine Fisheries Commission. It is also understandable that, despite implementation of the MFCMA with its provisions for state preemptions, Massachusetts has continued to develop innovative ways to extend its management authority beyond the territorial sea as well as develop regulations designed to complement council fisheries management plans (FMP) regulations.

MANAGEMENT ALTERNATIVES

Since the primary purpose of this conference is to examine possible management alternatives as well as the existing management framework involving the MFCMA, an examination of the present and future role of an active state such as Massachusetts appears appropriate. In any discussion of possible alternatives, one should bear in mind our strongly-held belief that the future success of fisheries management depends upon a strong, cooperative, positive relationship between all the management entities be they states, councils, commissions, or whatever else evolves in the future.

INCREASING THE STATE ROLE: CLEARLY IDENTIFIED OBJECTIVES

A major question that one must ask is, "Why would Massachusetts want to further expand its management role beyond what it currently exercises through participation on the council?" Obviously, such action would be triggered in response to the identification of some kind of fisheries resource or allocation problem such as overfishing, excessive fishing effort, conflicts between user groups, lack of protection of spawning fish, a nursery ground, or some other ecologically-significant area. Based on our previous experience, it is important that the problem the state is attempting to address be clearly defined or confusion as to why the state is acting in such a manner will exist within the harvesting sector being regulated, as well as with the general public.

The somewhat diffuse management objective of reducing fishing effort in Nantucket Sound was a case in point. Lack of species specific objectives and adequate documentation of the problem in the sound generated much contention and confusion among the various harvesters over the proposed effort reduction initiatives.

On the other hand, the idea of protecting spawning winter flounder, although equally if not more contentious that the Nantucket Sound effort, was generally a more acceptable and understandable management objective. The winter flounder decline in Massachusetts waters as well documented through several years of division data and verified by harvesters. For a number of reasons, similar documentation was not available for the migratory scup, sea bass, and squid seasonally present in the Nantucket Sound Area.

UNILATERAL MANAGEMENT—SOME PROS AND CONS

I would like to address some of the possible advantages and disadvantages of a state, such as Massachusetts, unilaterally undertaking management actions.

Advantages:

1.   A public perception that Massachusetts is a "Good Guy:" a conservation leader concerned about fisheries management and

the need to maintain renewable marine resources at optimal levels;

2. The notion that some management is better than none at all in the absence of a federal FMP or interstate plan—This would be particularly applicable for a state that may be adjacent to a major fishing ground or a biologically-significant area such as a nursery ground or spawning area;

3. Unilateral action by a so-called progressive state may trigger other, less aggressive states to respond to a resource or management problem. The strategy of setting an example for others to follow has been employed by Massachusetts on several occasions, particularly with regard to adoption of striped bass management measures and size limits for various species;

4. The state (or states) may be able to react to a problem in a more timely fashion. Even though the timeframe has been shortened, the federal FMP and amendment development process is still slow compared to a Massachusetts management system that can promulgate a regulation within 45 days of the problem being identified. The Director of Marine Fisheries also has broad emergency authority subject only to approval of the commissioner (although this director likes to run an emergency by the MFAC for obvious reasons);

5. It may be less costly for a state to develop and implement unilateral management action than the councils. This is particularly important with the current relative economic viability of states such as Massachusetts as compared to the federal government; and

6. Under certain conditions, law enforcement will be more effective. The strength-in-numbers doctrine applies here: there are more state enforcement agents along the Massachusetts coast-line than there are federal agents in the Northeast region.

Disadvantages:

1. Lack of equity resulting in discrimination against that state's fishermen—particularly if the state lacks effective control over other state's fishermen either inside or outside its territorial waters. Such discrimination may cause significant negative economic impact on local fishermen and/or processors;

2. Ineffective or negligible conservation benefits—As an example, it has been argued that recent actions by Massachusetts to limit fishing effort in Nantucket Sound on key migratory species such as sea bass, scup, and squid will have little positive benefit, since the species may be harvested without constraint elsewhere by other states' fishermen;

3. Ineffective enforcement—past lessons learned from the lack of federal enforcement in fisheries conservation zone fisheries,

are particularly applicable to the states, especially if they unilaterally promulgate regulations with little prospect of enforcement such as offshore mesh sizes or area closures. Even for regulations that impact states' territorial waters, the application of landing limits with only dockside checking may totally miss the migratory harvesters who land their catch elsewhere;

4. Limited effect on harvesters—Although the state can exercise control over harvesting by residents or non-residents within its waters, it has only limited control beyond its waters on other states' fishermen;

5. Fragmented Management—If the various states on an uncoordinated basis all attempt to do their thing unilaterally, it will frustrate harvesters, confuse the public, and may likely be ineffective. A possible example of this was Amendment II of the Interstate Striped Bass FMP which authorized each state to develop its own methodology to reduce fishing effort by one-half over the most recent previous year;

6. Cost of management may increase—More time spent by state managers developing, implementing, interpreting and enforcing regulations, not to mention the additional costs of compliance on the harvesters;

7. Internal political problems—Nothing infuriates a legislator more than to find out his constituents are being subjected to more management (paperwork, regulation, restriction) than fishermen in the adjacent political subdivision; and

8. Displacement—Frustration with a state's unilateral management controls may drive local fishermen elsewhere or deter other fishermen from landing at local ports, depriving the state of potential revenue. Several New Bedford fishermen threatened to land in Rhode Island when Massachusetts implemented the previously mentioned yellowtail flounder per/man trip limit.

MECHANISMS TO ALLOW A GREATER STATE ROLE

Having weighed the advantages and disadvantages of strong or unilateral state action, let's take a look at some of the mechanisms available for Massachusetts as an individual state to achieve a greater role in future fisheries management. In my opinion, this examination reveals a surprisingly short list. The options are limited because the MFCMA and the federal supremacy doctrine severely limit what authority a state can exercise beyond its jurisdiction.

Although the Skiriotis Doctrine is not technically dead, it has been largely emasculated. Previously a state could manage its citizens wherever they fished. Now, Massachusetts can only control vessels (and citizen owners thereof) registered under the laws of the state who are not participants in a federal FMP. In the presence of a federal FMP, the state is limited to acting more restrictively. This means that we can establish any size limits we want for sea bass and scup and enforce them either inside or outside the territorial waters, or dockside, since there is no FMP. For yellowtail flounder, however, we can only enact size limits larger than the present 11 inches. Massachusetts has recently acted more restrictively by implementing a 12-inch yellowtail possession size limit. In this instance we jumped the gun, fully expecting that the New England multispecies plan was going to get federal approval and would be implemented.

Our other option is to consider implementing our 200-mile limit. Again, as in Skiriotis, its application is severely limited affecting only Massachusetts citizens in boats registered under the laws of the state. Our legal experts tell us: while a Massachussetts fisherman's permit probably suffices as a registration standard, an out-of-state fisherman possessing a Massachusetts permit is not subject to control by Massachusetts within the claimed 200-mile limit.

It is evident after examining the limited options available to expand its authority that, under the current constraints imposed by federal management and constitutional considerations, the best opportunity for any state to expand its management may be through the existing system. It appears that we are likely to continue with some level of federal management control in the immediate future despite the upcoming reauthorization of the FCMA.

SUGGESTED CHANGES TO THE PRESENT SYSTEM

We are left, then, with working within the existing system and perhaps attempting to make some changes that will make this system more effective and responsible. By the system, I am referring to MFCMA/FCZ management and interstate management under the ASMFC. Although the individual states are unlikely to have significantly expanded future roles in management, the states collectively working through plans established under the commission certainly have the potential to be more effective managers. In fact, it is arguable that the state's efforts concerning northern shrimp and striped bass have provided far more effective and less costly stewardship over resources than federal management would have provided. I am not advocating one management entity over another, and it's evident that federal management is here to stay.

CONCLUSION

I want to leave you with three simple suggestions, doubtless suggested before, to make the current system better and to provide for a greater future management role for an active manager such as Massachusetts.

First of all, Massachusetts should strive to change council at-large membership to make its representation proportional to the values of the member states' recreational and commercial fisheries landings. Using 1985 New England commercial landings value, this would change the council representation from the present: Maine (4); New Hampshire (2); Massachusetts (4); Rhode Island (3); Connecticut (3); To: Maine (4); New Hampshire (2); Massachusetts (5); Rhode Island (3); and Connecticut (2). Recognizing that council members' intrastate differences are sometimes stronger than the interstate members' differences, it will be incumbent upon the governor to appoint a congenial, compatible and competent delegation from each state.

Secondly, within the interstate management system, federal legislation should be passed to give the ASMFC regulatory teeth, or a broadened generic version of the federal preemption authority in the Atlantic Striped Bass Conservation Act which should be enacted to give the commission some clout.

Thirdly, legislation tying in the ASMFC planning process and the relevant councils' process should be enacted, and this legislation should lean toward simple methodology for for reciprocally adopting each other's plans in the respective jurisdictions.

In quick summary, it appears that the greatest potential for the states to exercise a greater role in future fisheries management exists through cooperative interstate management and asserting a stronger role in the MFCMA. Short of a major overhaul of the existing system, the states just don't have the legal authority to dominate fisheries management. Our modest efforts to assert a greater role in conserving our fisheries resources has taught us some valuable lessons and these efforts have their pros and cons. Certainly, non-migratory species that inhabit state's waters may be amenable to unilateral management, but migratory species are probably most appropriately managed through cooperative interstate management or through a federal FMP.

NOTES

[1] The Skiriotis case clarified the extraterritorial authority of a state to regulate its citizens beyond its three-mile territorial waters by holding that Florida may control the conduct of its citizens on the high sea with respect to matters in which the state has a legitimate interest and where there is no complaints with acts of Congress.

INCREASING THE ROLE OF TEXAS IN U.S. FISHERIES MANAGEMENT

GARY C. MATLOCK
Acting Director
Fisheries Division
Texas Parks and Wildlife Department
Coastal Fisheries Branch
Austin, Texas

Texas has historically possessed the right to manage its natural resources and their harvest within its territorial sea (Bubier and Rieser 1984). However, once these resources migrate beyond Texas' jurisdictional limit, management has generally been nonexistent. For example, the brown shrimp (*Penaeus aztecus*) fishery has had a closed season (45 to 60 days in June and July) imposed annually in the Gulf of Mexico off Texas since the 1950s (Anonymous 1981). The objective of this closure is to increase the ex-vessel value of the shrimp recruited to the gulf each year by delaying harvest until shrimp are larger and more valuable. However, enforcing this closure at Texas' nine-nautical-mile limit was extremely difficult because there was no closure beyond that limit. Indeed, there were no harvest restrictions for shrimp beyond the state's limit.

This situation changed dramatically with the passage of the Magnuson Fishery Conservation and Management Act of 1976 (FCMA). The federal government established the Fishery Conservation Zone (FCZ) and assumed specific management authority therein (out to 200 miles). One of the first fishery management plans

(FMP) implemented was the shrimp plan. Its primary component was a complementary brown shrimp fishing closure of the FCZ off Texas (known as the "Texas Closure"). The dates of the FCZ closure are identical each year to those of the closure for Texas waters. Indeed, the FCZ closure dates are determined by the Texas Parks and Wildlife Department (TPWD). This cooperative state/federal management approach has resulted in increased economic benefits to Texas and the U.S. (Jones et al. 1982). However, the benefits may be further increased in 1986 because of a modification to the Texas Closure to reduce its geographic limit from 200 to 15 nautical miles offshore. This will provide for continued fishing all year without compromising the objectives of the federal plan. This modification was made at the request of TPWD and reflects the present involvement of Texas in U.S. fisheries management.

The state is little more than an advisor to the federal government on management beyond its territorial sea. If an FMP is implemented by the U.S. Secretary of Commerce, the state has no legal authority to manage the fishery in the FCZ. Indeed, the state's authority to manage fisheries within its territorial sea can be usurped once a plan is implemented. Even in the absence of a plan, the state has only limited authority in the FCZ. It can regulate only its own state-registered vessels.

The current advisory role should be changed for Texas. Fisheries management in the FCZ off Texas for those fisheries occurring predominantly within state waters should be the responsibility of Texas. The following reasons support this position:

1. Texas has been managing fisheries much longer than the federal government;

2. Most fisheries off Texas rely on species that spend all or part of their lives in state waters;

3. The federal government is inadequately equipped to manage most FCZ fisheries;

4. Management would be more responsive to fishermen, more efficient, less costly, and more timely in responding to emergency situations;

5. Resource conservation would be given a higher priority than maintaining commercial fishing; and

6. State/federal conflicts would be reduced.

These same reasons were the basis for the Gulf Council's opposing proposed federal legislation to extend the Secretary's authority to preempt state management in its internal waters (Matlock 1986). Perhaps the best example of the need for this change is the red drum (*Sciaenops ocellatus*) fishery. This species has historically been harvested in estuaries and the adjacent territorial sea (Perret et al. 1980). Each gulf state, including Texas, has regulated this harvest through minimum and maximum size limits, bag and possession limits, and gear restrictions. Commercial quotas have also been used in some states, and two states (Texas and Alabama) currently prohibit the sale of red drum caught in their waters. Florida and Mississippi are considering a similar prohibition. All states prohibit using purse seines to take this fish in state waters. But, a purse seine fishery has developed in the FCZ off Alabama, Mississippi, and Louisiana, and the harvest is increasing at an alarming rate. These states' territorial seas extend only three miles offshore; Texas and Florida territorial sea limits are nine miles. The National Marine Fisheries Service (NMFS) response to this developing fishery has been to allow its development without any attempt to assess its impact on traditional state fisheries. Instead of simply prohibiting the use of purse seines in the FCZ, the Secretary of Commerce will implement a secretarial plan that will allow purse seines in the FCZ throughout the gulf. This plan will adversely impact Texas' current management of red drum by removing the authority to regulate its state-registered vessels in the FCZ. Present maximum size limits, purse seine regulations, and sale restrictions could be in jeopardy. If the federal government must be involved in this fishery, it should limit its involvement to the FCZ off Alabama, Mississippi, and Louisiana. Texas has the necessary expertise, authority, jurisdictional limit, and data necessary to manage this fishery off Texas without the federal government.

The federal government should eliminate duplicating Texas' efforts in fisheries management. Some steps have been taken recently toward this end. The National Marine Fisheries Service (NMFS) no longer duplicates TPWD's effort to estimate sport landings in Texas. However, this was accomplished only after the Gulf States Marine Fisheries Commission and the Gulf of Mexico and South Atlantic Fishery Management Councils notified NMFS that their duplication of state efforts was inefficient, unnecessary, and should be discontinued. The NMFS and TPWD have formulated a commercial landings data collection program in which each agency collects data from different segments of the commercial fishery and then combines these data into one total estimate. However, NMFS has unnecessarily duplicated TPWD reporting requirements for fishermen and dealers. The NMFS requirements should be repealed. Additional action that could be taken include the following:

1. Amend the FCMA to allow Texas to regulate all fishing vessels in the FCZ;

2. Restrict the Council's management authority off Texas to only those species that occur completely within the FCZ;

3. Allow Texas the opportunity to veto any federal fishery management plan affecting fishing off Texas if it adversely impacts Texas' efforts to manage a fishery occurring predominantly in its waters;

4. Remove NMFS as a voting member on the Gulf Council; and

5. Amend the national standards of FCMA to allow gear prohibitions and complete allocation among user groups, if these actions are not already permitted.

These changes should improve fisheries management in the FCZ off Texas.

REFERENCES

Anonymous. 1981. The Texas shrimp fishery. A report to the Governor and the 67th Legislature. Tex. Pks. Wildl. Dep., PWD Book 3000-104. 13 p.

Bubier, J., and A. Rieser. 1984. Preemption or supersession of state regulation in the territorial sea. Territorial Sea, Legal Developments in the Management of Interjurisdictional Resources. Mar. Law Inst., Portland, Maine. IV(1):1-9.

Jones, A.C., E.F. Klima, and J.R. Poffenberger. 1982. Effects of the 1981 closure on the Texas shrimp fishery. Mar. Fish. Rev. 44(9-10):1-4.

Matlock, G.C. 1986. The case against federal preemption. Presented 11th Annu. Mar. Rec. Fish. Symposium, 1-2 May 1986, Tampa, Florida.

Perrett, W.S., J.E. Weaver, R.O. Williams, P.L. Johansen, T.D. McIlwain, R.C. Raulerson, and W.M. Tatum. 1980. Fishery profiles of red drum and spotted seatrout. Gulf States Mar. Fish. Comm. No. 6. 60 p.

REMARKS

LT. THOMAS A. NIES
United States Coast Guard
Fisheries Law Enforcement Branch
Washington, D.C.

I am puzzled by some of Mr. Matlock's statements concerning the Texas shrimp closure. He has pointed out that the Fishery Conservation Zone (FCZ) was closed to shrimping under the Gulf of Mexico shrimp fishery management plan (FMP) in order to improve the effectiveness of the state closure and to ease enforcement difficulties that were hampering it. This year, however, the opening of most of the FCZ has created a situation similar to the years before the FMP went into effect. It will be interesting to see if Texas—no doubt suffering from declining oil revenues—can now effectively enforce the closure. Limited Coast Guard patrols during the last week of the closure noticed numerous violators in the band of the FCZ closed to shrimping.

PART FOUR

Enforcement

More than $220 million were spent by the federal government in FY 1985 to carry out the Magnuson Fishery Conservation Management Act of 1976. Nearly 60 percent of these expenditures were for enforcement of the regulations promulgated under the act. In late 1985, federal fisheries enforcement effort was reduced substantially when the Coast Guard's budget was cut. Sea patrols by the Coast Guard in the Northeast region, for example, were cut in half as a result. At the same time the demands on enforcement resources are growing. The number of fishery management plans (FMPs and PMPs) in place has more than doubled in the last five years. What are the consequences of these developments? How can the enforcement system cope? Clearly, there is a need to improve enforcement efficiency. Novel regulatory and enforcement strategies are needed which are less costly and at the same time sufficiently effective to achieve management objectives.

The three papers in this section discuss some of the most recent developments and thinking about ways to improve enforcement of the MFCMA. The paper by Professor Hennessey and David Kaiser provides an overview of the existing fishery law enforcement system. They also outline a commonly used framework which explains how enforcement policies affect compliance with fisheries law and regulations. Hennessey and Kaiser summarize recent research related to the framework and to ways of improving the cost-effectiveness of the enforcement system.

A key enforcement tool is the use of observers on board fishing vessels. John Dentler describes in his paper the current program and reviews several suggestions for improving it.

The paper by Thomas Nies presents a practical model for significantly improving enforcement and management.   The procedures followed to date for setting regulations often pass down regulations that are unenforceable or very demanding on enforcement resources.   The result too often has been ineffective and costly enforcement and unachieved management objectives.   The model developed by Lt. Nies is of a process for generating management regulations that have reasonable enforcement requirements and that also effectively achieve management objectives.

JON G. SUTINEN
Associate Professor
Resource Economics
University of Rhode Island
Kingston, Rhode Island

CHAPTER 6

Fisheries Law Enforcement:

An Incentive Systems Perspective

TIMOTHY M. HENNESSEY
Professor and Chairman
Department of Political Science
University of Rhode Island
Kingston, Rhode Island

DAVID W. KAISER
Graduate Student
Graduate Program in Marine Affairs
University of Rhode Island
Kingston, Rhode Island

Effective fishery management requires a system which achieves desired levels of compliance with regulations. This paper discusses the existing enforcement system in terms of: 1) the problem of determining compliance; 2) the components of the system and their dynamic interaction; and 3) recent progress in understanding and improving the system.

Compliance objectives and the enforcement modes directed to these ends are important considerations in deciding on alternative fishery management measures. This particular feature was underscored by William Gordon, Director of the National Marine Fisheries Service, in a memo to his regional directors.

> To implement additional fishery management plans without additional resources, we must improve efficiency in obtaining compliance and/or simplify the enforcement requirements and additional strategies and management options need to be developed to reduce enforcement costs without undue loss of management effectiveness. (Gordon 1983)

THE PROBLEM OF COMPLIANCE WITH REGULATIONS

Compliance with regulations is necessary if the benefits of fishery management are to be derived. Therefore, the degree of compliance is usually viewed as an indicator of enforcement performance. Using the approach identified by Sutinen and Hennessey (1986) we view compliance as a problem of choice for individuals subject to regulation. We assume that fishermen facing such constraints have preferences concerning alternative states of the world and are capable of choosing among these. Compliance mechanisms structure the incentives of fishermen as they go about deciding whether to comply with the regulation or not. In an attempt to obtain such compliance, government officials invest in a variety of compliance mechanisms. In doing so they are concerned to determine the mix of mechanisms which will prove optimal in dealing with the set of compliance problems.

The regulatory process attempts to influence the private benefit-cost calculations of the regulated individuals in order to obtain acceptable compliance levels. Questions remain concerning which factors individuals will take into account in making such choices. There are a variety of such factors, but Becker (1968) identifies the following: 1) the probability of violating without being detected; 2) the benefits associated with such undetected activities; 3) the probability of being detected, but avoiding sanctions; 4) the benefits associated with 3; and 5) the probability of being detected *and* sanctioned and the costs of such sanctions. In making these probability calculations, the individual is assumed to compare the expected value of returns from violations with the expected value associated with compliance. Sutinen and Andersen (1985) employ Becker's paradigm in their formal model of fisheries law enforcement.

There are, however, at least two problems with using compliance measures as performance indicators. First, as shown by Sutinen and Andersen, a very high level of compliance is not necessarily desired for a cost-effective enforcement program. Second, as Sutinen and Hennessey (1986:13) note, the extent of overall compliance is nearly impossible to measure and, therefore, is not known. The data measure instead the extent of detected noncompliance which is only a part of overall noncompliance, since a significant proportion of violations will go undetected. If surveillance and monitoring were random, levels of detected noncompliance could be extrapolated to the entire population to provide an estimate of the overall levels of noncompliance. Monitoring and surveillance—especially boardings and inspections—are not random, however. The typical enforcement program focuses its surveillance and monitoring efforts on those vessels they estimate to be violations.

In sum, due to biases inherent in enforcement procedures, the extent of detected noncompliance cannot be used to estimate the extent of overall noncompliance and compliance.

The enforcement system can be operated effectively only if public officials utilize sanctions appropriately. Stigler (1970) argues that public authorities have four basic means to improve compliance: 1) minimize the chances that violations will go undetected; 2) maximize the probability that sanctions will follow the detection of violations; 3) speed up the process from time of detection to assignment of sanction; and 4) make the sanctions large. There is a dispute among experts concerning the best or mix of alternatives among the foregoing. Some scholars have argued that the probability of being sanctioned is more important that the size or magnitude of the sanction (Becker, 1968; Tullock, 1974), while others have argued that making the charging time follow as closely as possible to the detection of illegal behavior is the most important factor in enhancing compliance.

In any case, processing speed and severity of penalty are important criteria to employ in examining the operation of the existing enforcement system. In the section which follows, we will discuss the components of the system and its dynamics with special attention to processing speed and penalties.

AN OVERVIEW OF THE ENFORCEMENT SYSTEM

The U.S. Fishery Management Enforcement System has four main features as depicted in Figure 1. Section I, on the extreme left side of the figure, shows the various players involved at different stages of the enforcement system. These include the representative fishermen and other key actors: the eight Regional Fisheries Management Councils, the Department of Commerce (DOC), the National Oceanic and Atmospheric Administration General Counsel (NOAAGC) of the DOC, the National Marine Fisheries Service (NMFS) of NOAA, the Coast Guard (CG) of the Department of Transportation and the Administrative Law Judge (ALJ).

Section II of the figure depicts the supply of violations, apprehension and charging and various stages through which a violation passes before settlement. When a fisherman is caught violating a fishery management plan (FMP) by NMFS or Coast Guard enforcement officers, the violator will be charged with a violation depending on the evidence. Once charged, a Notice of Violation Assessment (NOVA) is issued by the NOAA General Counsel. The NOVA lawyers decide whether to litigate or settle the case out of court. According to NOAA lawyers, 80 percent of all cases are settled out of court. Of these, 70 percent of the fines assessed are collected. It is important to note in settlement cases that NOAA considers 50 percent of an assessed fine an acceptable penalty.

When the NOAA General Counsel considers the violation to be serious enough to warrant litigation, the full amount of the assessed penalty is sought. If convicted, the violator is expected to pay the full amount of the fine or he or she may appeal to the ALJ on procedural grounds. The ALJ may dismiss the case or uphold NOAA's decision.

Following Becker 1968, Section III of the figure depicts each stage of the enforcement system as viewed by a potential violator as he calculates an expected probability of being caught (P_1), caught and charged $(P_2(1))$, convicted $(P_3(1)(2))$ and payment of a fine $(P_4(1)(2)(3))$. The decision to violate is then based on the expected amount of a fine and the potential profit to be gained through the violation.

Section IV, on the far right of the figure, shows that the effectiveness of the system is influenced not only by the probability of sanctions but also by the time taken to process the case through collection.[1] The less time a violation takes to go through the system, the less time costs are for the NOAA General Counsel in terms of both money and workload. This decrease in time and money spent prosecuting a case increases the effectiveness of the enforcement system.

Problems in Penalty Assessment

The overriding goal of the NOAA General Counsel is to deter further violations. In order to deter potential violations and reduce recidivism, a certain level of compliance with the regulations is necessary. The present enforcement system relies on a schedule of fines for various violations.

The problem is to set a fine amount that will yield a reasonable probability of payment. This should occur in a time span that would be economically "painful" for the fishermen. Figure 2 shows that increasing the fine amount not only decreases the probability of a fisherman paying a fine because the violator has an incentive to drag out the process, but increases the NOAA General Council's workload and time to continue prosecuting the offender.

The problem in finding the fine amount that will be paid in a reasonable time period is illustrated in Figure 3. The preferred position for fishermen who violate is little or no penalty and a long time in which to pay. The preferred position for fishery managers is to levy stiff fines which would be paid in a short time to

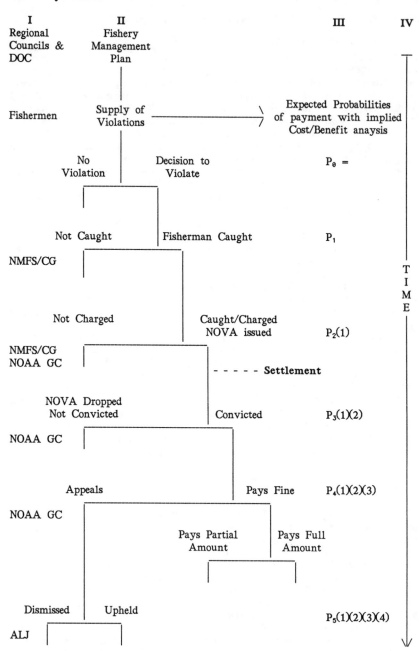

I	II	III	IV
Regional Councils & DOC	Fishery Management Plan		

Fishermen   Supply of Violations ———————→ Expected Probabilities of payment with implied Cost/Benefit anaysis

No Violation   Decision to Violate $P_0 =$

Not Caught   Fisherman Caught P_1

NMFS/CG

Not Charged   Caught/Charged NOVA issued $P_2(1)$

NMFS/CG
NOAA GC   - - - - - **Settlement**

NOVA Dropped Not Convicted   Convicted $P_3(1)(2)$

NOAA GC

Appeals   Pays Fine $P_4(1)(2)(3)$

NOAA GC

Pays Partial Amount   Pays Full Amount

Dismissed   Upheld $P_5(1)(2)(3)(4)$

ALJ

TIME

Figure 1. Desired Situations

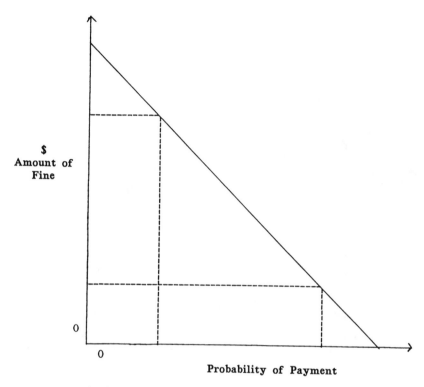

Probability of Payment

An increase in fine amount = a decrease in probability of payment.

A decrease in fine amount = a decrease in GCNE workload and time but also a decrease in the deterrent effect.

An increase in fine amount = an increase in GCNE workload and time which is only valuable if there is an increase in the deterrent effect.

Figure 2. U.S. Fishery management enforcement system.

maximize compliance. The preferred position for NOAA General Council is to achieve a level of fines that will actually be paid by the fishermen, will deter further violations, and will be acceptable to the fishing industry and other political entities whose constituencies are affected by the enforcement system. The differing incentives of the key actors must be taken into account in order to operate the system effectively. But given these theoretical considerations, what can be done to improve performance?

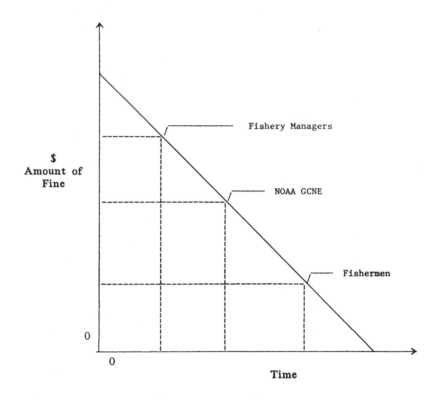

Figure 3.   Probability of payment.

SUGGESTED IMPROVEMENTS TO THE SYSTEM: RESULTS OF THE UNIVERSITY OF RHODE ISLAND WORKSHOP ON FISHERY LAW ENFORCEMENT

In October of 1985 a group of 20 experts from the U.S., Canada, and Denmark were brought together at a Fishery Law Enforcement Workshop at The University of Rhode Island Alton Jones Campus. The results of this conference provide a number of important insights into the operation of and potential improvements in the current system. Several of these improvements will be discussed below.

As we have already noted, measuring the deterrent effect of fishery law enforcement is extremely difficult. Some progress has been made, however, by Canadian researchers Edwin Blewitt, William Furlong, and Peter Toews in their paper "Canada's Experience in Measuring the Deterrent Effect of Fisheries Law Enforcement."

They gathered interview data on fishermen's perceptions of the Canadian Law Enforcement System, the extent of non-compliance and the probabilities of gains and losses associated with fisheries illegalities. In their interviews they attempted to get at fishermen's perceptions of the enforcement system using the following model:

Fishermen's Perceptions

(1) $P_C = P_A * P_{PR/A} * P_{C/PR} * P_{PN/C}$

Where: P_C - overall probability of conviction.

             P_A - probability of arrest.

             $P_{PR/A}$ - probability of prosecution given arrest.

             $P_{C/PR}$ - probability of conviction given prosecution.

             $P_{PN/C}$ - probability of punishment given conviction.

(2) $PEN = (P_{F/C} * F) + (P_{CA/C} * CA) + (P_{GE/C} * GE) + (P_{L/C} * L)$

Where: PEN   - the perceived penalty.

             $P_{F/C}$ - probability of fine given conviction.

             F   - value of fine.

             $P_{CA/C}$ - probability of catch forfeiture given conviction.

             CA   - value of forfeited catch.

             $P_{GE/C}$ - probability of gear forfeiture given conviction.

             GE   - value of forfeited gear.

             $P_{L/C}$ - probability of license suspension given conviction.

             L   - value of lost fishing time.

Source: Blewitt, Furlong and Toews (1985, 5)

Empirical data from the interviews offered strong support for the economic model of criminal behavior discussed in part one of this paper. All of the explanatory variables display the hypothesized effects on violation rates and are statistically significant. As they observe: "The Commission of illegality in the fishery can be effectively controlled by altering the associated gains and losses" (Blewitt, Furlong and Toews, 1986:34). They conclude that the policy instruments leading to severity and likelihood of punishment had a strong deterrent effect on the violations.

Fundamental to the Fishery Law Enforcement System is the enforceability of the regulations associated with the fishery management plans. If these are somehow flawed, then we can expect little in the way of effective enforcement. In their paper, "Enforcement Costs in Fishery Management: The Alternatives," Morris Pallozzi and Steve Springer argue for a careful look at the enforceability of regulations and their costs. They explore alternative approaches to fishery law enforcement and argue that choices among alternatives should consider: 1) compliance and what constitutes a reasonable level thereof; 2) the enforcement modes available to meet selected regulatory requirements; 3) the relative costs of enforcement modes; 4) their effectiveness; and 5) the strategies employed once appropriate modes are established (Pallozzi and Springer, 1985:4).

Based on seven years of fishery management experience, they propose the following strategies: 1) combine two or more enforcement modes into one where possible; 2) change gear restrictions to gear possession prohibitions; 3) eliminate incidental take provisions; and 4) the use of fishing vessel transmit terminals. They conclude that the most desirable enforcement strategy is to pick modes which produce reasonable levels of compliance while keeping costs to a minimum.

The speed and severity of penalties are influenced by the operation of the litigation process which spans the period from detection of a violation to the termination of the case (see Figure 1).

An important aspect of the litigation process is the imposition and collection of reasonable penalties (see Figure 2). Jim Brennan, Deputy General Council at NOAA, argues that setting the penalty at the right level is the key element in establishing a workable penalty system. If the penalty is set too low, the fine becomes an acceptable cost of doing business. If the penalty is set too high, the offender will seek to take advantage of procedural delays to extend the process. He argues that "penalties should be set at a level slightly higher than the profit that an offender would derive from a violation." Rational fishermen would then refrain from violating the act. If the detection possibility is perceived as zero, then, of course, a penalty set at the statutory maximum would not affect the behavior of the fishermen. Thus, it is clear that the probability of detection is a factor that should be included in penalty levels (Brennan, 1985;51).

Maggie Frailey, also of the NOAA General Council's office, argues in her paper, "Problems of Case Management," that we need to speed up the process and make it more effective through: 1) better regulations; 2) better documentation; 3) reducing the problem of collateral changes; and 4) improving collections. The latter is a particularly vexing problem, according to Frailey, with some 200 respondents owing NOAA more than $1.3 million in civil penalties.

Margerite Matera of the NOAA General Council's Staff in Gloucester, Mass. in her paper, "Regional Management of Fisheries Law Enforcement Cases," recommends that the effectiveness of the enforcement process could be enhanced by reliance on A) suspended penalty amounts—a form of probation—to obtain long-term compliance and B) permit sanction. These two changes would appear to have a number of advantages in increasing the effectiveness of the system.

CONCLUSIONS

In this paper we attempted to provide an overview of the fishery law enforcement system which took into account the incentives of the key actors and the operation of the system. We employed a political economy approach to modeling the incentives of a representative fisherman as he went about deciding to comply with regulations or violate them.

We argued that the enforcement system could be improved if public authorities designed processing systems and penalties in light of the rational fishermen model. We noted the fundamental problem of determining levels of compliance and the impossibility of deriving inferences about system effectiveness relying solely upon detected noncompliance.

Finally we turned to the results of the October 1985 workshop in Law Enforcement held at URI. The papers presented there offered considerable support for the incentive systems view of the enforcement process based on a political economy paradigm. The system can be effective if public authorities utilize management programs based on such incentive systems.

NOTES

[1] Collection has to proceed through the U.S. Attorney's Office, where in the Boston office alone, current fishery violation cases have to be added to a backlog of 15,000 existing U.S. Attorney cases.

REFERENCES

Becker, Gary. 1968. "Crime and Punishment: An Economic Approach." *J. Polit. Econ.* 76:169-217.

Blewitt, Edwin; William Furlong and Peter Toews. "Canada's Experience in Measuring the Deterrent Effect of Fisheries Law Enforcement," delivered at the Workshop on Fisheries Law Enforcement, University of Rhode Island, October 21-23, 1985.

Brennan, James. Untitled, delivered at the Workshop on Fisheries Law Enforcement, University of Rhode Island, October 21-23, 1985.

Frailey, Margaret. "Problems of Case Management," delivered at the Workshop on Fisheries Law Enforcement, University of Rhode Island, October 21-23, 1985.

Gordon, William. 1983. Enforcement Problems. NMFS Memo, FCM5:WPA (June).

Matera, Margerite. "Regional Management of Fisheries Law Enforcement Cases: The Assessment of a Civil Penalty," delivered at the Workshop on Fisheries Law Enforcement, University of Rhode Island, October 21-23, 1985.

Pallozzi, Morris and Steven Springer. "Enforcement Costs in Fisheries Management: The Alternatives," delivered at the Workshop on Fisheries Law Enforcement, University of Rhode Island, October 21-23, 1985.

Peterson, A.E., Jr. 1982. Prepared statement in U.S. Congress, House, Committee on Merchant Marine and Fisheries, hearings before the Subcommittee on Coast Guard and Navigation, 97th Congress, 2nd Session (Serial No. 97-26).

Stigler, G. 1970. "The Optimum Enforcement of Laws," *J. Polit. Econ.* 78:526-536.

Sutinen, Jon G., and Peder Andersen. 1985. "The Economics of Fisheries Law Enforcement." *Land Economics* Gl:387-397.

Sutinen, Jon G. and Timothy Hennessey. "Enforcement: The Neglected Element in Fishery Management," in Edward Miles, (ed.) National Resource Management: Essays in Honor of James Crutchfield, Seattle, University of Washington Press, 1986.

Tullock, Gordon. 1974. "Does Punishment Deter Crime?" *The Public Interest,* 36:103-111.

Young, Oran. 1979. "Compliance and Public Authority." Baltimore: Johns Hopkins Press.

Young, Oran. 1981. "Natural Resources and the State." Berkeley: University of California Press.

Young, Oran. 1982. "Resource Regimes." Berkeley: University of California Press.

CHAPTER 7

Improvement In Fisheries Enforcement:

How Do We Get There From Here?

JOHN L. DENTLER
Staff Assistant, U.S. Congress
House Committee On Merchant Marine and Fisheries
Washington, D.C.

I believe this conference is very timely. Congress and the executive branch of the federal government are more and more frequently asking where savings and efficiencies can be achieved. This in turn has brought about greater scrutiny of the Magnuson Fishery Conservation and Management Act of 1978 (MFCMA)—and indeed, more generally, where revenues can be raised. For example, the President's budget submission to the Congress for FY 1987 included a proposal for a federal marine sportfishing license fee. This same proposal has now been woven into the House Concurrent Budget Resolution, directing the Committee on Merchant Marine and Fisheries to report legislation implementing the President's proposal. As another example, during the first session of this Congress, the House Committee on Merchant Marine and Fisheries included, and the House passed, as part of its Budget Reconciliation Act, a measure to increase foreign fishing fees. The ultimate measure worked out between the Senate and the House is conditional in nature and became a part of Public Law 99-272. a third example is reflected by the fact that the authorization level for the MFCMA itself will, in all likelihood remain at the current level for at least the next three fiscal years. These examples underscore what is to become a trend—ways to maintain current programs and to improve the cost-effectiveness of fisheries management.

Before proceeding further, I should point out that much of the impetus for the MFCMA was to restrain the then uncontrolled foreign fishing that was taking place off our coasts. It is not surprising that the act mandates that foreign fishing vessels operating in the U.S. fishery conservation zone (FCZ) carry a U.S. fishery observer—with limited exceptions. Observers play two critical roles: 1) as collectors of critical fishery data; and 2) as a means of monitoring foreign fishing compliance with U.S. fishery regulations.

I have been asked to address the issue of fisheries enforcement and, in particular, to summarize a report on the U.S. Foreign Fishery Observer Program issued by the General Accounting Office (GAO) in response to a 1983 inquiry by the Chairman and

145

Ranking Minority Member of the House Committee on Merchant Marine and Fisheries' Subcommittee on Fisheries and Wildlife and Wildlife Conservation and the Environment.

GAO STUDY

The Congressional request to the GAO centered around the issue of cost and effectiveness of the observer program within these key areas:

- The process by which the NMFS programs costs for budgeting and billing;

- The issue of health and safety conditions on foreign fishing vessels;

- The use of observer-generated data;

- Observer training; and

- The use of contract observers in the Pacific Northwest and Alaska.

CAPITALIZE THE FOREIGN FISHING OBSERVER FUND

The GAO study resulted in several recommendations to the Congress and to the National Marine Fisheries Service to improve the observer program. First, the GAO pointed out that there is a need to capitalize the Foreign Fishing Observer Fund and to initiate an actual-billing process.

The so-called American Fisheries Promotion Act of 1980, among other things, created a revolving Foreign Fishery Observer Fund. This act mandated that fees levied on foreign fishermen were to be deposited into this fund or account and that the receipts were then to be used to operate the observer program. Although the idea of a revolving fund is sound, the administration has never requested nor has the Congress provided working capital in an amount sufficient to pay for observer costs. In addition, in an effort to protect its jurisdictional prerogatives, the Committee on Appropriations has successfully opposed all attempts at removing outlays from the account from the annual congressional appropriations process.

To compensate for these two shortcomings, NMFS operates the program on an advanced billing basis. In order to insure that enough funds are available at the beginning of the year, NMFS has restricted its planned level of observer coverage until sufficient reserve funds have accumulated. The GAO concluded that NMFS regularly over and underbilled foreign fishing nations and did not achieve full observer coverage. Furthermore, they noted that NMFS has spent a great deal of time answering inquiries relating to billing procedures and correcting mistakes. The GAO report noted that NMFS has considered requesting that Congress appropriate the necessary funds to capitalize the account; however, due to budget considerations, such a request has never been included in the President's budget request.

The GAO estimates that an appropriation of $3-7 million would be required in order to capitalize the observer fund. This year as a part of Chairman Jones' recommendation to the Appropriations Subcommittee on Commerce, Justice, State and Judiciary, which has jurisdiction over appropriations for NMFS' programs, a request was made that sufficient funds be made available to capitalize the observer fund. Such a request, if heeded, would allow NMFS to administer the observer program on an actual cost basis rather than the estimated billing process now used, thereby resulting in more accurate billing and better coverage.

ESTABLISH HEALTH AND SAFETY STANDARDS
FOR FOREIGN FISHING VESSELS

The second area investigated by the GAO relates to health and safety conditions on board foreign vessels and how the conditions affected U.S. fishery observers. The FCMA mandates that all foreign fishing vessels operating in the U.S. fishery conservation zone carry U.S. observers unless the duration of the fishing trip is so short that the deployment of the observer is impractical or the conditions on board the vessel are such that the health and safety of the observer is jeopardized. The act does not authorize sanctions to be taken against vessels that are unsafe nor does the act specifically authorize the Secretary of Commerce to develop health and safety regulations. Furthermore, NMFS officials have concluded that currently, the agency does not have the authority to promulgate health and safety regulations.

The National Marine Fisheries Service has been studying the health and safety issue since 1984 and has yet to develop specific health and safety recommendations; however, in the first session of the 99th Congress, the administration transmitted to the Congress draft legislation which specifically authorized the Secretary to impose sanctions against inadequate or unsafe foreign fishing vessels and to issue regulations setting forth the circumstances for imposing sanctions. The administration recognized, as did the GAO report, that the current situation provides a disincentive for foreign fishing vessels to maintain adequate health and safety conditions for observers. If the observer is removed for reasons related to health and safety, the vessel can continue to fish without being observed and without penalty or restriction. Without an observer, there is a greater likelihood for noncompliance with U.S. fishing regulations, the underlogging of landings, and less revenue to the U.S. since poundage fees are collected on observed and reported landings.

Although the administration's recommendation relating to foreign fishery observers was not included as a part of H.R. 1533. the House bill that would reauthorize and amend the MFCMA, Chairman Jones recently introduced H.R. 4897 relating to this issue. This bill would require foreign nations, as a condition of obtaining a foreign fishing permit, to certify that its vessels meet all of that particular nations applicable vessel safety regulations. Second, the bill directs the Secretary of Commerce to promulgate health and safety criteria and to impose sanctions against vessels which do not meet these requirements. The Committee has not taken action on this measure, but it may be included in an omnibus fishery bill that will be brought up on the House floor later this year.

In response to an inquiry by the Chairman of the Committee on Merchant Marine and Fisheries, the Administrator of NOAA presented a summary of a 1985 study related to health and safety conditions on board foreign fishing vessels. The study showed that some vessels lacked items such as lifejackets, emergency position indicating radio beacons (EPIRBs), flares, life boats, radar, and in some cases vessels had no watch officers, were rat-infested, or were structurally unsound. The report showed that 22 percent of the foreign vessels operating in the FCZ have been found to contain health or safety hazards. The following figures represent the percentage of deficient vessels by nation:

Vessel by Nation	Percent of Deficient Vessels per Vessels Inspected
Japan	08%
USSR	20%
Korea	35%
Poland	20%
Spain	58%
Italy	50%
Netherlands	17%
Taiwan	100%
Germany	20%
Portugal	0%

Many of you may be thinking that some of the items listed as inadequacies are items that U.S. fishing vessels are not required to carry, and this, in some cases is true. However, I point out that no one is twisting the foreigners arms to fish in our FCZ and, second, speaking on behalf of the Chairman of the Committee on Merchant Marine and Fisheries, I believe we have an obligation to provide a safe working environment for U.S. fishery observers. I believe that the enactment of the provisions contained in H.R. 4897 would help meet that obligation. In addition, the committee is now in the process of writing legislation on fishing vessel insurance and safety that will, among other things, establish new safety standards, including many of those just mentioned, for U.S. fishing vessels.

MISCELLANEOUS CONCLUSIONS

The GAO report also concluded that he observers play a key role in the collection of fishery data. Fishery managers, researchers and enforcement personnel in NMFS, the U.S. Coast Guard, and members of the Regional Councils all concluded that the observers perform an invaluable function, both in terms of compliance monitoring and in gathering fishery-dependent biological data. The Coast Guard recommended that better coordination between the observers and the Coast Guard could enhance enforcement efforts. The GAO report also recommended that a more uniform observer training program be implemented and that the use of contract observers in Alaska and the Pacific Northwest is questionable in that it violated personnel policy of the federal government.

CONCLUSIONS

I realize that this brief review of the GAO study on the fishery observer program is in no measure a comprehensive review of fisheries enforcement. Nonetheless, I believe that the short review does provide an examination on how a small part of the fisheries enforcement program can and is being improved. As the federal budget for fisheries and other programs come under increased pressure and scrutiny, further efforts will be made to improve the effectiveness and efficiency of fisheries management.

CHAPTER 8

A Simple Model for Fisheries Enforcement

LT. THOMAS A. NIES
United States Coast Guard
Fisheries Law Enforcement Branch
Washington, D.C.

Fisheries law enforcement is only recently receiving attention as an important element of fisheries management. With the initial passage of the Magnuson Fishery Conservation and Management Act of 1976 (MFCMA), enforcement was assumed to be perfect or nearly so. Unfortunately, it is becoming obvious that poor enforcement can contribute to the failure of a management plan. At the same time, a poorly designed management plan can make enforcement difficult or prohibitively costly. It is clear that in designing a management scheme, the successful enforcement of the management measures chosen can be crucial. It is important, then, to realize what steps may be necessary for designing an enforcement system given any management system. A simple model can help analyze enforcement alternatives that may be available.

BUDGET, ENFORCEMENT ACTIVITY AND COMPLIANCE—ALL RELATED

Even without a new management scheme, a careful analysis of the enforcement system may be useful in light of recent budget actions. In October 1985, the Coast Guard reduced fisheries patrols by approximately 50 percent. Put in simpler terms, this means that for much of the summer of 1986, only one high endurance cutter was on patrol in Alaskan waters; the Texas shrimp closure received only limited patrols; and only one ship at a time patrolled the Northwest Atlantic fisheries. Boardings in the Alaska region during the October-February time period dropped from 241 in FY 1985 to 123 in FY 1986—a considerable drop even when the reduction in foreign fishing effort is considered. The effect of this decrease in patrol effort may not be noticeable for some time; in the past, there has been roughly a year's delay between changes in boarding rates and corresponding changes in violation rates. At the same time as patrols are being reduced, however, increasing commitments to high seas salmon enforcement in the North Pacific Ocean have necessitated dedicating already scarce resources to a new patrol.

In discussing this issue, it is difficult to escape the system currently in effect. The use of terms such as "management plan" should not be taken to refer to a fishery management council document approved by the National Marine Fisheries Service, but to the framework for fisheries management generated by responsible authorities. It is easier to use terms that have a specific meaning under current law, but that should not be interpreted as implying the current system is the only alternative.

THE ENFORCEMENT MODEL

The first step is to realize that an enforcement strategy is not created to punish violators of the fishing regulations. The enforcement system should have as its goal the compliance of most fishermen with the regulations. If widespread compliance is achieved, carefully chosen management measures will be able to achieve the goals they were designed for—optimum yield, stock rebuilding, full employment, etc. This attitudinal viewpoint is often difficult for enforcement agencies to maintain when faced with a fishery that has a problem with widespread and frequent violations. The result is an overemphasis on enforcement actions, considered separately from the management issues and goals enforcement is trying to help achieve.

Second, enforcement does not consist solely of the contact between the enforcement agent and the fishing industry. The enforcement system has three major, distinct parts or elements: the drafting and promulgation of regulations, the enforcement contact, and the prosecution or penalty process. Each of these elements can be further subdivided in some systems. In the present U.S. federal system under the MFCMA, for example, the enforcement contact can occur either at-sea or at the dock. The prosecution can follow a civil or criminal penalty process. Even the regulations are a joint effort of the management councils and the National Marine Fisheries Service (NMFS).

Ideally, the three separate elements should be closely related and should provide feedback to each other and to the management plan. Some managers state that enforcement is the responsibility of the enforcement agencies and should not be a limiting factor for fisheries managers. In a limited sense, they are correct. The goal of management is not to create a successful enforcement plan. This approach, however, ignores the fact that enforcement is one element of the management process. All the regulations in the world will not conserve resources if they cannot be enforced. Managers should take into account the limitations of their enforcement agencies, both in capabilities and resources, when constructing the plan. To do otherwise is to court disaster if a fishery is heavily capitalized and fishes on declining stocks.

The regulations, of course, are the direct link between the intentions of the managers and the actions of the enforcement agencies. To a large extent, they will determine the form of the enforcement contact and can subtly influence the performance of the agents, who may not necessarily understand the goals and biology behind the management plan. Enforcement agents can provide valuable information on the ability of the regulations to be enforced. The prosecution process can serve as a check on the activities of the agents, insuring violations are adequately documented and regulations are interpreted correctly. All three elements can have a significant impact on the management plan and can illuminate necessary changes. Deficiencies in any one element can effectively prevent enforcement from succeeding in supporting the manager's decisions. This is forcefully demonstrated by economic analysis of the perceived benefits of violating a regulation[1]—a weak link anywhere in the chain can make effective enforcement impossible.

Enforcement Contact

While each of the three elements is equally important, I intend to concentrate primarily on the contact between agents and the industry. In many instances, this contact can be the most expensive in the process; in FY 1985, the U.S. Coast Guard, for example, spent nearly $67 million on cutter and aircraft patrols. The other two elements will only be mentioned because of their relation to the enforcement act.

The Coast Guard, responsible for numerous peacetime and wartime missions, has created a useful tool for analyzing resource requirements to perform law enforcement missions. Used by the Operational Law Enforcement Division in developing resource requirement estimates for future years, it is based on a common thread that runs through many of these missions. In most cases, Coast Guard units must first detect the presence of a vessel, identify it to determine its activity and status under the law, and then intercept that vessel (if necessary) to conduct a boarding and take law enforcement action.

This model has only been used when discussing maritime patrol resources; but, with some minor modifications, it can be used to analyze a fisheries law enforcement strategy. In order to enforce regulations on the fishing industry, the agent must first *detect* fishing activity (either harvesters or processors). He must then *identify* the vessel or processor and then, finally, make *contact* (intercept) to enforce the regulations. The primary difference in using this model for fisheries management is that, in many cases, the identification phase will be accomplished simultaneously with the detection phase.

Management Considerations

Breaking down enforcement planning into these three phases (detection, identification, and contact) enables managers to quickly compare enforcement schemes for various strategies. It can also be used to evaluate alternatives to a system currently in use. Different methods of accomplishing each one of the elements can be examined and compared to each other. As an example, consider a strict limited entry fishery where authorized participants are allowed complete freedom to fish for any species in any quantity at any time. The enforcement needs are simple: participants must be detected and identified, with contact required only if an unauthorized participant is noted. They can be detected at the dock or at-sea. If detected at-sea, boats or aircraft can be used. If the number of processors are limited (because of economics or regulation) as well as or instead of the number of harvesters, the detection problem can be simplified even further. Changing conditions in the fishery may require a different enforcement strategy; if, for example, illegal participants are transferring catches at sea, the detection and contact phases may have to move offshore.

Which Enforcement Resources?

Once the requirements of the management strategy are clear, the next step would be to determine who can best provide the enforcement resources. This may turn out to be the most difficult part of the whole procedure. Should fisheries managers look solely at the best method to meet their needs, or should they consider benefits to society that may accrue because existing resources are adapted to the enforcement mission? There are weaknesses in each approach. Creating forces that do nothing but fisheries enforcement may unnecessarily duplicate resources already in place. On the other hand, using existing resources may involve compromises in equipment and the setting of priorities by the enforcement agency. The goal with this model, then, should be to choose the resources and methods that will allow for the best accomplishment of the three phases of enforcement.

Some basic truths emerge from experience with current enforcement schemes. Detection and identification are simpler and far cheaper if performed at the dock than if performed at sea. Boats may be localized into fairly distinct areas (known landing ports) and the cost of transportation for the enforcement agent is minimal. Even the contact itself can be simpler: it is easier to determine the size of a catch while watching an offload than to estimate frozen blocks of product, or layers of fish iced down in a hold, while trying to hold on in a seaway. At the same time, however, the contact at dockside can be limited to observing what is brought into port. Fishing operations and practices, as well as the location of the catch, can be difficult (if not impossible) to determine at the pier. The more specific limitations placed on fishing operations, the more difficult and costly the detection and identification phases will be.

As mentioned earlier, the goal of enforcement is not necessarily to catch all violators but to achieve the compliance of the majority of fishermen. When looking at the three phases of a particular management scheme, the compliance of most fishermen may depend on their perception of enforcement rather than on the actual performance of the enforcement agencies. An expensive, covert system of monitoring the fleets may result in numerous convictions that convince remaining fishermen that the regulations should be obeyed. At the same time, a cheaper, highly visible patrol may accomplish the same task if accompanied by sufficient convictions that fishermen realize the enforcement is not just a paper tiger. Publicizing successful enforcement efforts may be a cheap way to influence these perceptions.[2]

The Current System

How does all this work under the MFCMA? First, the current scheme relies on two federal agencies augmented in some areas by state enforcement officials. The National Marine fisheries Service primarily performs dockside contacts while the Coast Guard performs only at-sea enforcement. Coast Guard enforcement is most effective and efficient when used to patrol fisheries that are spaced over a wide area, at-sea, regulated by complex management plans with strict gear, logkeeping, and reporting requirements. In these instances, fisheries managers can take advantage of cutters and aircraft that are already patrolling the open ocean for a variety of reasons. Large boarding parties can inventory catches with a high degree of accuracy. Patrolling cutters can quickly respond to observer reports of possible infractions. Lengthy patrols maximize on-scene time. In the view of the model, the detection, location, and contact phases all benefit from the existence of a trained, experienced force that is already in place. The disadvantage, of course, is that competing missions may limit the time such an agency is willing to devote to fisheries.

Model Caveats

The model described above can be applied to any management system. It can also be used to analyze enforcement alternatives under the current system. There are three issues, however, that should be considered before its application.

First, the tendency of fisheries managers has been to view the industry as having two distinct elements: domestic and foreign. The same approach has been made by enforcement agencies. It is time for a different viewpoint on enforcement issues. As the foreign fleets are phased out of the Exclusive Economic Zone, the domestic fishing industry continues to grow and resemble the fleets being displaced. Large catcher/processors present similar management problems regardless of the flag flown. In the future, it may be necessary for management to borrow some of the same regulatory restrictions that are used effectively with foreign vessels. As an example, domestic groundfish boats in the Bering Sea are now required to submit simple activity reports. On-board observers are being considered in many domestic fisheries. Strict logkeeping requirements may be adopted. Thinking on enforcement should be reoriented to categorize fisheries not by nationality but by the degree of complexity of the regulations that are in place.

Second, the choice of enforcement method should not be made prior to development of the management plan. The decision to use dockside enforcement, for example, can limit the manager to few fisheries alternatives. Limiting enforcement to one potential mode can severely restrict the choices available to the managers. In complex fisheries, some problems—gear conflicts between user groups, discard of undersized or prohibited species, landing limits—may not be easy to enforce if only one mode is used.

Finally, regardless of the management scheme chosen, the real challenge is not to rely on any single enforcement mode, but to integrate all elements into the management plan. Dockside and at-sea enforcement should be used in the instances where each is most effective. Combinations of state and federal agencies should be considered. Prosecution must result in penalties that are timely and deter future violators. Regulations must be carefully written to reflect the plan's intent and be understandable.

CONCLUSION

With these considerations in mind, the enforcement needs of any management plan can be readily developed using the model. Even optimum use of this model, however, will do little to answer many of the questions that currently puzzle fisheries managers. Enforcement costs still must be analyzed, and coordination between the elements of enforcement and the management plan must still be addressed. Even so, the model can help guide managers in developing their enforcement strategies.

NOTES

[1] Blewett, Edwin, Furlong, William, and Toews, Peter (1985). "Canada's Experience in Measuring the Deterrent Effect of Fisheries Law Enforcement," unpublished paper, Workshop on Fisheries Law Enforcement, University of Rhode Island, October 21, 1985, 1985, p. 4.

[2] McGroary, Allan (1985). "Fishery Enforcement Programs of the Massachusetts Division of Law Enforcement," unpublished paper, Workshop on Fisheries Law Enforcement, University of Rhode Island, October 21, 1985, p. 5.

The views represented in this paper are attributable only to the author and do not necessarily represent the views of the Department of Transportation or the United States Coast Guard.

REMARKS

GUY D. MARCHESSAULT
Deputy Executive Director
Chief Scientist
New England Fishery Management Council
Saugus, Massachusetts

I am troubled by the discussion of enforcement here and in other forums. In my opinion, the general discussion of enforcement has not been successful in breaking new ground, particularly in the area of defining alternatives to the status quo. Instead of a careful examination of the overall enforcement structure, with particular reference to its responsiveness and accountability in support of fisheries management, we have engaged in lengthy review of the enforcement structure as it exists today. Fishery managers are repeatedly told that funding for National Marine Fisheries Service and Coast Guard enforcement activities is either fixed or in danger of being reduced. Fishery managers are advised that the proper response to these circumstances is either to make regulations "self-enforcing" or to adopt only regulations that can be enforced shoreside. Having once been only a factor to be considered in balancing the costs and benefits of management options, the costs of enforcement have begun to emerge as the ultimate determinant of what constitutes acceptable fishery management policy. With enforcement costs as an absolute constraint, surely optimum yield is in need of being redefined.

If you look at the last nine years of fishery management activity, you will see that the overall enforcement capability has not kept pace with the demand, at least not in the Northeast. As a matter of fact, there are five-fold the number of domestic regulations in existence today as there were in 1977, and over that same period, it is my understanding that the actual enforcement capability in the Northeast region has either stayed the same or diminished. The problem for the regional councils is that they are only one part of the triad that constitutes the fishery management structure; the councils are joined by NMFS and the Coast Guard in the implementation of council policies and plans. Under the act, the councils were given a clear mandate to develop management programs, but they were not given the responsibility for establishing an effective enforcement capability. The councils' mandate was not qualified by the ability of NMFS or the Coast Guard to fulfill their complementary responsibilities under the act. The councils had no other option but to presume that the responsibility for effective implementation of fishery regulations was accepted by the other parties, and that the means to achieve effective enforcement would follow. Nobody said stop, and the fishery management regulations kept on coming. Regrettably, we now find ourselves in the position of having to question whether any one set of regulations can be effectively enforced with the collective resources that exist today.

That said, the question remains, what is the responsibility of the councils? In my opinion, there can be little doubt that the regulations developed by the councils must be unambiguous and technically capable of being enforced. Information such as the marginal cost of enforcing one regulation relative to another must be considered along with other biological, economic, operational and social factors in determining the preferred management measure. Further, regulations should be balanced so as to not excessively burden any one enforcement sector. Not everything can be enforced shoreside and not everything can be enforced at sea. But notwithstanding this responsibility, it is unacceptable to abandon an entire category of measures just because enforcement is currently weak in that area, particularly if those measures are deemed the most appropriate for achieving the management goals.

So now we must come to terms with reality, and we realize that under the budgetary stringencies that now exist we have but two options. On the one hand, we can begin a thorough process of rethinking the status quo arrangements for fisheries enforcement and find more cost-effective means for enforcing our fishery management programs (and in this process anything and everything is fair game), or we can agree that only one or two fisheries, not five, can be managed in the Northeast because only one or two fisheries are capable of being enforced with the existing resources.

We cannot waste much more time in engaging in nonproductive debate about what takes precedence: the public decisions of the council, the budgetary constraints of an agency or the enforcement priorities of an administration. We must first resolve, collectively, to find solutions to our enforcement problems, given the realities as they exist, and then we must agree and inform the Congress of what the real limitations are on our collective ability to manage the nation's fishery resources. It is then left to the Congress to determine what is in the public's best interest.

PART FIVE

Research Needs

Rethinking research needs in support of fisheries management is a timely and appropriate subject for discussion. Now that the concept of property rights has been extended to encompass living marine resources within territorial limits, as prescribed by Law of the Sea, it is appropriate to consider whether research is to be continued as more of the same, or if a fresh, systemic approach is not a more appropriate means for maximizing management options.

A valuable and a fresh perspective of a Fisheries Management Council senior staff member is provided in the detailed account of research needs in support of fisheries management in a large continental shelf ecosystem by Guy Marchesseault. He stresses the need for defining the population parameters of the biological system producing the fisheries biomass and supporting research on density-dependent effects of recruitment, growth, and mortality of target species including multispecies finfish communities, sea scallops, lobsters, and surf clams. Marchesseault pinpoints the analytical models that will need to be satisfied by appropriate research to improve management of fisheries stocks through fishing gear modification. He emphasizes the need to shape management objectives around the results of economic analyses. Each of his research components allows for a performance feed-back loop to evaluate success of the systems application. His total systems approach requires, in addition to biological and environmental information, economic research of fishery production effort, trade models on marketing, and bioeconomic models to assess impacts of limited entry to the fisheries.

In the thoughtful presentation of Alec MacCall, questions dealing with the why?, how much?, and what? of fisheries research are addressed from an ecosystems perspective. His approach to the new fisheries research strategy is based on considerable experience in studies of the California Current, which is an ecosystem where energetics are driven primarily by upwelling of the water column. He stresses the importance of changes in physical condition on the high biomass of anchovy-sardine that undergoes large-scale shifts in abundance resulting in serious losses to the economies of the coastal states within whose jurisdiction the resources reside.

MacCall emphasizes the utility of systemic ecosystem-oriented research as a critically important investment to be made prior to the posing of resource problems, indicating that, "The information which will be of greatest long-range use in answering management questions will be gained by system-oriented research rather than by routine research devoted to 'fine-tuning' current management." In a summary section on ecosystem modelling, he argues that a systems understanding will be necessary in the future to replace the presently and inappropriately applied static equilibrium yield models.

In planning for fisheries ecosystems research for the year 2000 and beyond, MacCall recommends the establishment of consortia that combine local, federal, and where appropriate—international agencies with academic institutions to pursue coordinated studies in large marine ecosystems (LME). He recommends that the California Cooperative Oceanic Fisheries Investigations could serve as a useful model of a successful LME research consortium.

The new strategies prescribed by Marchesseault and MacCall provide useful examples of how fisheries research can be improved significantly to support the management required in the 1990s.

Introducing these two major addresses are remarks on how both systemic approaches can be integrated in research that will support the conservation and management of fisheries resources within large marine ecosystems.

KENNETH SHERMAN
National Marine Fisheries Service
Northeast Fisheries Center
Narragansett Laboratory
Narragansett, Rhode Island

CHAPTER 9

Fisheries Research Strategies for the 1990s

KENNETH SHERMAN
National Marine Fisheries Service
Northeast Fisheries Center
Narragansett Laboratory
Narragansett, Rhode Island

FISH BIOMASS AS NATIONAL WEALTH

The extensions of national jurisdictions over fishery resources resulting from adoption of the exclusive economic zone (EEZ) concept from the Law of the Sea Treaty by most maritime nations have provided new sources of national wealth from the ocean. Resources that were previously freely shared among nations are now subject to national regulation, licensing, and other restrictions on users. The new "wealth," however, is being subjected to erosion and dissipation from heavy domestic exploitation. On a global scale, the potential losses of fish protein from mismanagement and overexploitation have not been determined. Considerable controversy surrounds estimates of annual global harvesting levels of the marine fisheries. Fisheries projections given in *The Global 2000 Report to the President* indicate that the world harvest of fish is expected to rise little, if at all, by the year 2000 from the level of 60 million metric tons (mmt) reached in the 1970s (Hennemuth and Rockwood, 1980). In contrast, the predictions in *The Resourceful Earth* argue for an annual yield of 100-120 mmt per year of conventional species by the year 2000 (Wise, 1984). This kind of controversy is not unexpected when one considers the meager efforts presently underway on a global scale to improve the data base for estimating fishable biomass, probable levels of annual sustained yields, and estimated losses through mismanagement.

Unfortunately, fishery scientists have been for the most part narrowly focused on variations in contemporary annual yields of stocks as input information to strategic decisions dealing with the conservation and management of traditional fishery resources. This narrow focus has led to the present inability to accurately forecast major biomass flips in species dominance. The flips have occurred widely around the globe, including clupeids of Japan, Chile, Peru, and West Africa. In the 1960s a shift in dominance from pelagic species to demersal species was reported for waters of the North Sea (Hempel, 1978a,b,c). A shift from the dominance of Atlantic herring to sand lance was observed on Georges Bank beginning in 1976 and continuing through the present (Sherman et al., 1981). The causes of these dramatic population shifts are not fully understood by fisheries scientists. In the case of the shift in abundance from pelagic to demersal species in the North Sea, it has been hypothesized that predation of young stages of gadoids by herring, mackerel, and other pelagic species was responsible for maintaining low yields of demersal species in the 1960s. The reduction in population levels of pelagic species, through heavy fishing mortality, in turn released predation pressure on the demersal species. This predator-prey interaction is suspected by some fishery scientists as the principal factor leading to the crash of pelagic species in the early 1960s in the North Sea (Andersen and Ursin, 1977, 1978; Ursin, 1977). This more holistic view of predator-prey relationships among fish species inhabiting large areas of the North Sea has given rise to a new strategy for improving fisheries research in support of the conservation and management of fishery resources within large marine ecosystems.

NEW PRINCIPLES OF CONSERVATION

The new research strategy is based on the recognition that marine fish species have evolved and adapted their reproductive success to geographic areas of unique bathymetry, circulation, biological productivity, and trophodynamic interrelationships among the populations. Most populations of finfish are highly mobile, migrating hundreds to thousands of kilometers within relatively large ocean areas that they inhabit and within which they grow, reproduce, and die. Within the EEZ of the United States, seven such systems have been identified—the East Bering Sea, Gulf of Alaska, California Current, Insular Pacific including the Hawaiian Islands, Gulf of Mexico, Southeast Atlantic Shelf, and Northeast Atlantic Shelf (Fig. 1). Each of these Large Marine Ecosystems (LMEs) extends over a geographic area exceeding 200,000 km² within which unique predator-prey and environmental relationships have developed over the last million years. The samples of fish collected by fisheries scientists represent a slice through evolutionary time in which economically important species such as herrings, mackerels, cods, hakes, and others have evolved spawning, migration, and feeding patterns that are difficult to understand unless observed throughout population ranges of the stocks under investigation.

Increasing attention has been focused, over the past ten years, on the modelling of LMEs as a way forward in understanding recruitment mechanisms and other important biological processes aimed at improving the management of living marine resources from an ecosystem perspective. The most recent example of the ecosystem approach to fisheries conservation and management is the Convention on the Conservation of Antarctic Marine Living Resources (CCAMLR). Article II of the Convention requires that the member nations follow principles of conservation, interpreted as rational use of the marine living resources of the Antarctic ecosystem in accordance with the:

    (a)   Prevention of decrease in the size of any harvested population to levels below those which ensure its stable recruitment. For this purpose its size should not be allowed to fall below a level close to that which ensures the greatest net annual increment;

    (b)   Maintenance of the ecological relationships between harvested, dependent and related populations of Antarctic marine living resources and the restoration of depleted populations to the levels defined in sub-paragraph (a) above; and

    (c)   Prevention of changes or minimization of the risk of changes in the marine ecosystem which are not potentially reversible

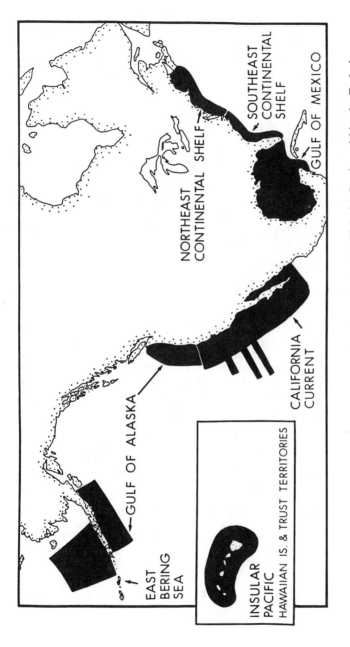

Figure 1. Large Marine ecosystems under investigation by the National Marine Fisheries Service within the Exclusive Economic Zone of the United States.

over two or three decades, taking into account the state of
available knowledge of the direct and indirect impact of
harvesting, the effect of the introduction of alien species, the
effects of associated activities on the marine ecosystem and of
the effects of environmental changes, with the aim of making
possible the sustained conservation of Antarctic marine living
resources.

Among the membership of the convention, are the principal fishing nations of the
globe including: signatory nations—Argentina, Australia, Belgium, Chile, the
European Community, the Federal Republic of Germany, France, the German
Democratic Republic, Japan, New Zealand, Norway, Poland, South Africa, Union of
Soviet Socialist Republics, the United Kingdom, and the United States; and acceeding
nations—Brazil, India, Peoples Republic of China, and Republic of Korea.   In the
decade-and-a-half to the year 2000, it is likely that some of these countries will
adopt these principles for the conservation and management of living resources
within their respective EEZs, particularly in those countries where conflicts may
arise regarding fish catches and their impact on dependent and associated predator
species, including marine mammals.

FISHERIES RESEARCH IN LMEs

Several elements and requirements are basic to the large marine ecosystem
approach to research:

1. LME studies are systemic in nature. That is, they focus on
    the key variables in an ecosystem and seek to explain how
    these variables interact to cause change. This approach
    requires multispecies, rather than single species studies. It also
    requires an understanding of physical, chemical, and biological
    oceanography, weather and fishery-related variables and
    changes (Bakun, 1986). It requires a modeling process within
    which studies take place. (Beddington, 1986).

2. LME studies require long-term data sets. These time-series
    data sets allow eventual understanding of natural variability
    in an LME. They also permit understanding of the magnitude
    and effects of anthropogenic changes.   For example,
    catch-effort fisheries data are required as well as fisheries
    independent surveys (Daan, 1986).   Also, there must be
    monitoring of important pollution discharges into the water
    column and close monitoring of natural environmental effects
    on the ecosystem (Kullenberg, 1986). To accomplish this, data
    must be collected in a standard form and stored in a
    retrievable format to permit their manipulation and analyses
    over the years.

3. Interdisciplinary process studies are required to begin to
    understand and model ecosystem relationships. These studies
    help provide guidance for identification of what data sets
    should be collected (Sherman, 1986).

4. The approach should make use of species which can serve as
    indicators of ecosystem change (CCAMLR, 1986). Often data

on such species are easier to gather than information on the changes which they reflect; and

5. A principal focus of large marine ecosystem studies should be the causes of change in individual species recruitment (annual population renewals) over time. This focus unifies a newly evolving biodynamic theory (Rothschild, 1986) which is applicable in widely divergent types of ecosystems. For example, the most important cause of recruitment variability in the California Current ecosystem is thought to be changes in physical oceanographic parameters (MacCall, 1986) while recruitment in the U.S. Northeast Atlantic Shelf ecosystem seems to be most substantially affected by fishing (Sissenwine, 1986).

As was pointed out in an earlier study (Sherman and Alexander, 1986), large marine ecosystems are tractable units for the conservation and management of fisheries resources on a global scale. There are no legal constraints to marine ecosystems management (Belsky, 1986), and they can be managed to optimize economic yield (Christy, 1986). During the 1990s, new technologies to improve measurement efficiencies of biological production and environmental variables will be available for operational use. By the year 2000, the costs for measuring variability and improving forecasting of trends in the fisheries should be very much reduced from present levels, thereby enhancing the application of fisheries management from an ecosystems perspective.

Adoption of the LME strategy to living resources research on a global scale will provide far more options for optimizing yields from fisheries resources for the next generation than exist for today's fisheries managers.

REFERENCES

Andersen, K.P., and E. Ursin. 1977. A multispecies extension to the Beverton and Holt Theory of Fishing, with accounts of phosphorus circulation and primary production. Medd. Danm. Fisk.-og Havunder. N.S. 7:319-435.

Andersen, K.P., and E. Ursin. 1978. A multispecies analysis of the effects of variations of effort upon stock composition of eleven North Sea fish species. Rapp. P.-v. Reun. Cons. int. Explor. Mer 172:286-291.

Bakun, A. 1986. Definition of environmental variability affecting biological processes in large marine ecosystems. pp. 87-108. *In* K. Sherman and L.M. Alexander (Eds.) Variability and management of large marine ecosystems. AAAS Selected Symposium 99, Westview Press, Boulder, CO. 319 pp.

Beddington, J.R. 1986. Shifts in resource populations in large marine ecosystems. pp. 9-18. *In* K. Sherman and L.M. Alexander (Eds.) Variability and management of large marine ecosystems. AAAS Selected Symposium 99, Westview Press, Boulder, CO. 319 pp.

Belsky, M.H. 1986. Legal constraints and options for total ecosystem management of large marine ecosystems. pp. 241-261. *In* K. Sherman and L.M. Alexander (Eds.)

Variability and management of large marine ecosystems. AAAS Selected Symposium 99, Westview Press, Boulder, CO. 319 pp.

CCAMLR (Commission for the Conservation of Antarctic Marine Living Resources). 1986. Report of the Working Group for the CCAMLR Ecosystem Monitoring Program, Hamburg, Federal Republic of Germany 2-7 July 1986. SC-CAMLR-V3.

Christy, F.T., Jr. 1986. Can large marine ecosystems be managed for optimum yield? pp. 263-267. *In* K. Sherman and L.M. Alexander (Eds.) Variability and management of large marine ecosystems. AAAS Selected Symposium 99, Westview Press, Boulder, CO. 319 pp.

Daan, N. 1986. Results of recent time-series observations for monitoring trends in large marine ecosystems with a focus on the North Sea. pp. 145-174. *In* K. Sherman and L.M. Alexander (Eds.) Variability and management of large marine ecosystems. AAAS Selected Symposium 99, Westview Press, Boulder, CO. 319 pp.

Hempel, G. (Editor). 1978a. North Sea fish stocks—Recent changes and their causes. Rapp. P.-v. Reun. Cons. int. Explor. Mer 172:449 pp.

Hempel, G. 1978b. Synopsis of symposium. Rapp. P.-v. Reun. Cons. int. Explor. Mer 172:445-449.

Hempel, G. 1978c. North Sea fisheries and fish stocks—A review of recent changes. Rapp. P.-v. Reun. Cons. int. Explor. Mer 173:145-167.

Hennemuth, R.C., and C. Rockwood. 1980. Fisheries projections, Chapter 7, Vol. II., pp. 105-115. *In* U.S. Council on Environmental Quality and the Department of State, Gerald O. Barney (Director), The global 2000 report to the president: Entering the twenty-first century. Vols. I-III. U.S. Government Printing Office, Washington, D.C.

Kullenberg, G. 1986. Long-term changes in the Baltic ecosystem. pp. 19-31. *In* K. Sherman and L.M. Alexander (Eds.) Variability and management of large marine ecosystems. AAAS Selected Symposium 99, Westview Press, Boulder, CO. 319 pp.

MacCall, A.D. 1986. Changes in the biomass of the California Current ecosystem. pp. 33-54. *In* K. Sherman and L.M. Alexander (Eds.) Variability and management of large marine ecosystems. AAAS Selected Symposium 99, Westview Press, Boulder, CO. 319 pp.

Rothschild, B.J. 1986. Biodynamics of the sea. International Council for the Exploration of the Sea C.M. 1986/L:25, Ref. G+H, Sess. O.

Sherman, K. 1986. Measurement strategies for monitoring and forecasting variability in large marine ecosystems. pp. 203-236. *In* K. Sherman and L.M. Alexander (Eds.) Variability and management of large marine ecosystems. AAAS Selected Symposium 99, Westview Press, Boulder, CO. 319 pp.

Sherman, K., and L.M. Alexander (Editors). 1986. Variability and management of large marine ecosystems. AAAS Selected Symposium 99, Westview Press, Boulder, CO. 319 pp.

Sherman, K., C. Jones, L. Sullivan, W. Smith, P. Berrien, and L. Ejsymont. 1981. Congruent shifts in sand eel abundance in western and eastern North Atlantic ecosystems. Nature 291(5815):486-489.

Sissenwine, M.P. 1986. Perturbation of a predator-controlled continental shelf ecosystem. pp. 55-85. *In* K. Sherman and L.M. Alexander (Eds.) Variability and management of large marine ecosystems. AAAS Selected Symposium 99, Westview Press, Boulder, CO. 319 pp.

Ursin, E. 1977. Multispecies fish stock assessment for the North Sea. International Council for the Exploration of the Sea C.M. 1977/F:42. 19 pp.

Wise, J.P. 1984. The future of food from the sea. pp. 113-127. *In* J.L. Simon and H. Kahn (Editors). The resourceful earth. A response to global 2000. Basil Blackwell Inc., New York, NY. 585 pp.

CHAPTER 10

Research Requirements for Fishery Management in the Northwest Atlantic: A New England Fishery Management Council Perspective

GUY D. MARCHESSEAULT
Deputy Executive Director
Chief Scientist
New England Fishery Management Council
Saugus, Massachusetts

INTRODUCTION

Regional Fishery Management Councils were established by the Magnuson Fishery Conservation and Management Act (MFCMA) and charged with the responsibility for developing the policies and plans for managing the nation's fishery resources, consistent with the seven national standards contained in the act and associated regulatory statutes. Under the Act, the Secretary of Commerce is charged with providing the councils with the scientific data and information necessary to undertake this management task. The Secretary satisfies this responsibility in three ways:

1) The Secretary maintains a major ocean monitoring and research capability housed within its National Marine Fisheries Service (NMFS) fisheries centers;

2 The Secretary supports marine and coastal research programs in the states through cooperative agreements and funding programs such as P.L. 88-309, The Commercial Fisheries Research and Development Act; and

3) The Secretary supports academic marine research through direct contracts with academic/research institutions and through funded research under the Sea Grant College Program.

Although most councils look to the NMFS fisheries centers to provide data and basic research on most marine fishery resources, the New England Council (Council) has also come to depend on the states and academic institutions to provide critical inputs to management. For example, several New England States have played a key role in undertaking research in support of the management of both the herring and lobster fisheries. The Council has further looked to the universities to provide inputs of a more analytical nature. University analysis of the economic dimensions of the fisheries in areas such as production, demand, trade, marketing and bio-economic decision model development have been a major source of input to the plan development process. In addition, universities have assisted in gear research, survey design, age and growth methodologies, coastal ecology, and organismic studies to examine the growth, fecundity, maturity, feeding and recruitment characteristics of many marine species. Finally, university research has virtually been the sole source of data and information on the socio-cultural nature of the fishery.

The fact is that the data and information upon which the Council depends come from several sources, each of which is uniquely positioned to assist the council in acquiring knowledge of a particular type or specific to a particular level of research. For example:

Federal Fisheries Centers:	Open ocean fisheries resources, large marine ecosystems;
State Fisheries Agencies:	Coastal fishery resources, coastal ecology, critical habitats; and
Academic Research Centers:	Socio-cultural research, methodological research, engineering studies, organismic research.

Whatever the source of the information, it is clear that the funding support comes in large part from the federal government. Funding provided to states and universities, in my view, is highly appropriate to the fulfillment of the Secretary's responsibility to support the marine fishery management process. Monies spent at the state and university levels are typically cost-effective because of such factors as matching funds, lower personnel costs, and lower overhead costs. Moreover, universities are well-positioned to conduct relatively short-term investigations that are vital to an understanding of a natural resource that characteristically fluctuates with a periodicity measured in decades. In practical terms, the breadth of research supported by the federal government represents the best approach to securing information vital to the management of an important natural resource, particularly when viewed in relation to cost-effectiveness, the maintenance of critical expertise, and the ability to co-opt a full range of non-federal personnel, physical, and funding resources into the process.

The purpose of this paper is to discuss some of the more important research projects which should be undertaken to address deficiencies in the current understanding of the dynamics of the commercial and recreational fishing industries and the supporting fishery resources. The discussion of research topics below is not intended to be exhaustive and is very much cast in terms of the Council's near-term requirements for management set in the context of the current regulatory environment. That said, the identification of required new research flows as a logical sequence once management objectives have been established on the basis of perceived biological and socio-economic problems in the major fisheries. Performance indicators, as a series of general data categories that can be used as surrogates for measuring the attainment of the management objectives, are either obtained through established collection mechanisms or require new measurements and methodologies.

BIOLOGICAL RESEARCH NEEDS

A convenient starting point in this discussion of research needs is from the biological perspective. The population dynamics of the renewable exploited resource sets the stage, defining the maximum level of sustainable harvest and the conditions under which any given level of harvest may actually be realized. But the implied equilibrium conditions rarely, if ever, approximate the biological systems. Instead, variable annual recruitment, discounted by losses through natural mortality, result in a constantly changing level of resource abundance. From the short-run perspective, the task of the population dynamicist is to define the parameters in the biological system that describe change. A knowledge of these parameters will aid in evaluation of the long-term effectiveness of alternative management programs in meeting stated goals and assist in assessing the risk of failure within any short-term time period.

Biological research needs are overviewed in Table 1. Across the top of the table are the major fisheries of concern. These are subdivided according to either biological research needs of an analytical nature or operational characteristics of commercial fishing gear. Specific research areas are further detailed below:

Multi-Species Fishery

Gear Research. Typical selectivity curves for various cod-end mesh sizes in otter trawls, by species, are derived from data collected from short-duration research tows and usually describe a symmetrical sigmoid shape. In commercial practice, however, tows are of much longer duration such that the selection characteristics of ordinary diamond mesh is degraded by clogging of the meshes and distortion of the mesh opening, particularly toward the end of the tow. The resulting selection curve operating in a commercial tow may be substantially different from that based on a research tow. Moreover, because of the differing morphology and behavior patterns of the component species within the multi-species complex, each species may be expected to exhibit its own unique selection curve for any given mesh size. The actual operational selection curves, by species, are needed to evaluate selection coefficients for use in more realistic fishery simulation analysis for quantitative estimation of the potential benefits of mesh control.

As a corollary to the preceding discussion, new types of gear need to be developed which have better, and more predictable, selection characteristics under operational conditions. Square mesh cod-ends are viewed as having great potential in this regard, but there remains a substantial amount of work to evaluate its relative effectiveness as compared to traditional diamond mesh.

Under the category of desirable new gear types is included specialized gear for targeting single species in the multi-species environment. The example currently under development is the northern shrimp separator trawl. It may also be desirable to develop gear for particular use in the recognized single-species, small mesh fisheries, such as whiting, to reduce discard mortality on juveniles of the regulated groundfish species.

Analytical Models. Quantitative models in population dynamics employ certain functions and parameters which, once evaluated, are assumed to remain constant over the long-term. Examples include the instantaneous rate of natural mortality and the constants in the growth equation. There is evidence, however, that natural mortality may increase with higher abundances as well as with age. Also, the growth rate probably is reduced with increased abundance. Most importantly, stock-recruitment

Table 1

Biological Research Needs of the
New England Fishery Management Council

	Multi-Species	Sea Scallop	Lobster	Surf Clam
Gear Research	Actual resulting selectivity of otter trawls in commercial operations	Selectivity of alternative configured dredge gear	Assessment of mortality in alternative constructions of pot gear	Assessment of selectivity and induced mortality in hydraulic dredge gear
	R & D of gear with improved selection characteristics	Assessment of mortality rates in commercial operations	R & D for biodegradeable escape panels	
	Comparative selectivity: diamonds mesh vs square mesh	Assessment of by-catches in commercial operations	Assessment of effects of vents on lobster catches	
	R & D gear for single-species fisheries (e.g., shrimp)	Impact of dredge gear on habitat	Assessment of effects of vents on catches of by-catch species	
		R & D new gear with improved selectivity and reduced mortality		
Analytical Models	Density dependent effects on recruitment, growth and mortality	Density dependent effects on recruitment, growth and mortality	Improved age and growth models	Density dependent effects on recruitment, growth and mortality
	Stochastic recruitment models for fishery simulations		Comprehensive stock-recruit model	

relationships are thought to be heavily influenced by density-dependent mortality within the early life history stages. A better understanding of the dynamics would allow formulation of improved models.

Fishery simulations are an important tool for investigation of the consequences of management action. But they are useful only in sensitivity analyses, since the important feedback relationship between stock and recruitment is lacking. Simulation models which include terms describing the expected variability in recruitment would enhance their predictive capability.

Sea Scallop Fishery

Gear Research. Following upon the current enthusiasm for gear modification within the industry as the principle management approach, it is necessary to develop an understanding of the selection properties of the alternative candidate gear configurations. Additionally, it is important to assess the impact of such gear, under conditions of commercial operations, in terms of: 1) induced mortality on scallops; 2) the level of by-catches; and 3) the impact on the habitat of important benthic species.

Analytical Models. It has been speculated that sea scallops may exhibit density-dependent effects on the success of larval settlement. Further, sea scallop growth rate appears to be influenced by temperature as well as depth, and may also be affected by abundances. Finally, the extent to which natural mortality is influenced by density of individuals within scallop beds is unknown but should be investigated. This may have implications regarding optimal harvesting strategies.

Lobster Fishery

Gear Research. Certain recurring themes within the overall subject of gear research on lobster traps are once again at the forefront of discussion. Uncertainties with respect to the effect of escape vents on the catch of black sea bass in trap gear has led to a partial disapproval of amendment #1 to the lobster FMP. Further research is required to: 1) examine the effects of vents on the catch of a wider range of finfish species over a broader range of localities (particularly in the southern New England/mid-Atlantic area); and 2) support or refute the assertion that escape vents increase the efficiency of traps in capturing marketable lobsters. Finally, with the recent developmental efforts to perfect a workable biodegradeable escape panel about to reach fruition in the State of Maine, there is a need to conduct similar studies in more southerly areas. With the increasing use of wire mesh as construction material in lobster traps, the timely development of a workable escape panel is becoming increasingly more important. For the same reason, the assessment of induced mortality in lobster traps constructed of various materials is an important issue.

Analytical Models. No compendium of research needs on lobsters would be complete without citing the need for the development of a technique for the aging of animals. With the latter information, models which account for the discontinuous growth in lobsters could be developed.

In recent years, serious efforts to describe the stock-recruit relationship in lobsters have suggested somewhat contradictory results; preliminary information from studies in the State of Maine may be consistent with significant density-dependent effects whereas data collected by Canadian investigators suggest a more linear relationship between stock and recruits.

Surf Clam Fishery

Gear Research. Hydraulic dredge gear has been alleged to inflict significant mortality on small surf clams, both through breakage and through the stranding of clams on the surface of sediments. The question deserves a series of definitive investigations. In addition, improvement in the selection characteristics of dredge gear might enhance the efficiency of commercial operations and aid in the enforcement of minimum size regulations.

Analytical Models. Two major areas of research are required: 1) factors influencing the success of larval settlement and subsequent recruitment are virtually unknown; and 2) the state of knowledge of growth and mortality in sea clams, particularly in resource areas north of the mid-Atlantic Bight, is still rudimentary.

ECONOMIC RESEARCH NEEDS

In general, economic analysis is necessary to assess the impacts of management measures and helpful to determine what directions fishery management should take in the long-term.

Economic research needs are overviewed in Table 2. Across the top of the table you will see the major fisheries of concern to us, subdivided according to some of the major areas of economic research. It is probably most efficient to first discuss the areas of research, and subsequently highlight the specific application across fisheries.

Production economics is the study of the conversion of many inputs into a saleable output(s). Fisheries present us with some bizarre twists on the standard production of goods. For instance, many normally variable inputs are fixed in fisheries, at least in the short-term, such as crew, gear, and biological abundance, and other inputs become the choice variables such as days at sea and fishing area. Generally, one thinks about production with a standard eight-hour day or forty-hour week, with the number of employees as a variable input. In fisheries the number of crew is fixed, at least for the duration of the trip, and the days at sea are the variable input. Alternatively, one may raise cattle from the same range annually, rather than being required to search for an abundance of fish to catch at a different spot daily. Thus, our production models in fisheries are specified with independent variables like days fished and annual abundance rather than the number of men and winches.

Introducing prices into our production function gives us the supply of fish, which is simply the expected reaction of fishermen to changes in market prices(s) and input prices in terms of their output produced. Further, it is possible to derive the response of fishermen to changes in prices which result in shifts in the proportion of the quantities of inputs used to produce the same output level. For something like a particular fishing area, for which there is no market and thus no market prices, we can use a proxy such as fuel cost for unproductive steaming time to get that area. If the area is then closed for management purposes, e.g., a three-month spawning closure, it is the same as if the fuel cost to that area had become prohibitively high. Fishermen are expected to reallocate their efforts into all other fishing areas which remained open. A short-run supply model would allow us to estimate how many days fished in each of those open areas fishermen would take, based on their historical use of those areas. Such a model is necessary to assess these kinds of reactions in both the multi-species and sea scallop fisheries.

A different approach is needed with a developing fishery like the surf clam on Georges Bank. Historical use data do not exist for this surf clam fishery. Nevertheless, a good deal of helpful information may be provided to assist in an efficient development of the fishery, pointing the way towards daily landings requirements, best landing areas, etc. A linear programming model is necessary to

Table 2

Economic Research Needs of the
New England Fishery Management Council

	Multi-Species	Sea Scallop	Lobster	Surf Clam
Production Economics	Behavioral model to assess redirected effort with closed areas	Behavioral model to assess redirected effort with closed areas		LP model to assess most efficient distribution pathways in the Northeast
Economic Development				Bio-Economic models to assess optimum sized vessels
Marketing	Trade models to assess impacts of imports	Trade models to assess impacts of imports	Demand models to assess impacts of larger size limits	Demand models to assess impacts on Mid-Atlantic market
Economic Policy	Bio-economic models to assess impacts of limited entry	Bio-economic models to assess impacts of limited entry		Bio-economic models to assess impacts of limited entry
Other		Supply model to assess derived demand for modified gear		

perform this task. The most difficult task with this type of fishery model is to collect the most appropriate data for its estimation. For example, it is important to know the location and level of markets in New England which an indigenous surf clam fishery would take over from traditional channels in the mid-Atlantic region. The degree to which these markets are captured will be dependent on the relative cost of supplying surf clams from the traditional mid-Atlantic fishery versus the developing New England fishery. The relative cost data might include vessel fuel costs, crew size, trucking costs, etc. These results may also point to areas for market expansion given a new proximal resource.

Economic development is a subject that is not discussed much in New England's fully exploited fisheries, but is important to a fishery like the surf clam on Georges

Bank.   Bio-economic models which combine the features of market demand and biological production may be used to describe the optimal sized vessel for the surf clam fishery in New England and thereby provide critical information on the level of capitalization necessary to fully exploit the fishery.

Marketing is usually associated with developing fisheries and not thought of in terms of developed fisheries such as the multi-species and sea scallop fisheries. Nevertheless, when the whole world is considered as your markets, rather than the traditional region, there may be room for further development.   Expansion of the traditional demand models for an open economy in the multi-species and sea scallop fisheries involves supply and demand models for major trading partners as well as the rest of the world, and inclusion of many macro-variables such as exchange rates. Separately, in the lobster fishery, demand for different sized lobsters has not been adequately treated, mainly because landings and price data by size have not been collected.   This information is necessary to assess the impacts of increases in the gauge.   A survey for such a purpose should be implemented prior to any amendment to that affect.   Finally, demand models must be developed to determine the effect of the competitive markets in New England on monopoly markets in the mid-Atlantic surf as the clam fishery on Georges Bank grows.

Economic policy must assist in developing overall fishery management policy through the choice of management objectives which are desirable and feasible. Probably the greatest need for economic research lies in the integration of demand, production, and biologic equations into bio-economic models which may provide the optimal levels of fishing effort based on basic relationships such as stock-recruitment, input-output, and supply-demand.   These static equilibrium models should show us the level of landings that can be achieved by each fishery, thus providing an objective goal for which to strive.   Additionally, systems of equations must be developed to indicate the paths which may be taken to achieve these goals.   Using the same basic relationships as above, recursive, dynamic, and stochastic forms must all be estimated to determine which combination best simulates the particular fishery in question.   Only after the costs of the latter transition periods are understood and compared with the present value of static equilibrium models can management decisions be made with confidence.

Finally, the current wave of enthusiasm for gear modification in the sea scallop fishery provides a unique opportunity to study the expected effects of such attempts to impose inefficiencies.   The problem is similar to that of estimating the displaced effort during a closure as described above. Fishermen determine the bundle of inputs to produce the desired output based on the price of the inputs.   When the price of one of those inputs changes, such as when the dredge catches less because of some modification, the fishermen may be expected to shift into more intensive use of now relatively less expensive inputs, using more fuel to make a few more drags for example.   The degree of such shifts and the impact on expected landings is of primary concern to fishery managers, who cannot rely on a simplistic "knife-edge" reduction in fishing mortality.

SOCIO-CULTURAL RESEARCH NEEDS

The New England Council's basic socio-cultural data needs for the development of fishery management plans, particularly for the pan-regional multispecies finfish fishery, are overviewed in Table 3.   Just as the fisheries resource changes over time, so also does the fishing industry change, adapting to the vagaries of resource variability and management efforts, and to new opportunities created by technological developments.   To understand the dynamics of these changes and to predict impacts it is important to be aware of the diversity involved in the fishing industry. Beyond the obvious diversity of boats, gear, fishermen, dealers and processors, the fishing industry includes the diversity of communities that are economically dependent on fishing.

Determination of the socio-cultural impacts of fisheries management plans relies on research that describes the diverse components of the industry and the interrelationships among those components. The components and the relationships are not static, however, so research needs to include in-depth studies of critical parameters and monitoring efforts to measure these parameters over time.

Among the issues with which the council is currently grappling are questions about the potential impacts of such regulatory options as limited entry, the feasibility of forcing fishermen to follow regulations, and problems arising from the competition between fishermen using different gear types. Each of these issues could be illuminated by in-depth socio-cultural studies.

Because regulatory efforts usually have negative economic impacts on some portion of the fishing industry (especially the harvesting sector), opportunities for alternative employment in the community should be monitored. Realistic assessments of opportunities, however, require not only an inventory of alternative occupations in the community yielding similar incomes, but also monitoring of requisite educational levels, existence of special interest groups (e.g., unions), and awareness of ethnicity and kinship relationships that might affect opportunities for alternative employment.

In addition to the socio-cultural characteristics that are clearly associated with economic impacts of management plans, an inventory of important institutions in the community and a monitoring of non-pecuniary values or attitudes yields valuable insights that could, for example, help predict fishermen's compliance with particular regulations.

The data base on the socio-cultural characteristics of the New England fishing industry is incomplete and much of what has been collected is out of date. Without

Table 3

Socio-Cultural Research Needs of the
New England Fishery Management Council

MONITORING:

General Descriptive:	boats, operation, crew, market, income.
Demographics:	age, education, language, ethnicity, kinship, residence, religion.
Interest Groups:	unions, cooperatives, dealers, buyers, processors.
Employment:	alternative fishing related or non-related opportunities.

IN-DEPTH:

Non-pecuniary attitudes and values:	toward management, other users, satisfaction, future goals.

basic information, it is difficult for the council to predict the impacts of their management plans and concomitantly difficult to mitigate negative impacts. These problems can lead to failure of the management plan. Just as biological research needs include monitoring and detailed analyses, so too does socio-cultural research.

CONCLUSION

Some of the research discussed above is currently being undertaken by a combination of federal, state and private entities, including the staffs of the fishery management councils whose informational needs are often immediate. It has to be understood that the development of fishery management plans under the Magnuson Fishery and Conservation and Management Act of 1976 is highly demanding of our ability to understand how the fishery operates, how the resource and the biological system respond, and who will bear the costs or reap the benefits of management decisions over time. In the case of open ocean marine fisheries, we are operating at the cutting edge of management science. Almost all of the available methods and techniques are retrospective; whereas, all of the demands upon our decision-making capabilities are prospective. The data and informational needs of fisheries management are pressing the disciplines of fishery-related science hard, and the councils are relying upon both the diversity of research expertise represented by the scientific community at large, as well as the continuing commitment on the part of the federal government, the states and private entities to fund marine fisheries research, to provide critical information in a timely manner.

As the pressure mounts to cut government spending, and pending Gramm-Rudman-Hollings budget cuts force agencies to prioritize their programs, the question arises as to what is the continuing responsibility of the federal government in support of fisheries research. There can be little doubt that of the research programs cited above, the federal and state governments must be responsible for: 1) resource surveys; 2) environmental assessment; 3) habitat monitoring; 4) ecosystem studies; and 5) fish stock assessment. Arguably, the federal government has principal responsibility for research focused at the marine environment beyond three miles, but the indisputable linkage between open ocean and coastal systems argues strongly for continued federal support for coastal marine research as well.

What then should be the priority of federal funding for operational, economic or socio-cultural research? To understand the desirability of federal funding for operational research, one must first accept that fish mortality occurs in the ocean, not on the dock. Gear is the interface between the fishermen and the fishery resource, and it is here that the most effective efforts can be made to target species, minimize juvenile mortality, and minimize degradation of the habitat. To the extent that gear modifications reduce the cost of fishing, the industry might be expected to finance gear research. Unfortunately, efficient gear and resource conservation do not often go hand in hand, particularly when resources are in decline. Therefore, it is in the interest of conservation that gear research must proceed, and the federal government is the only likely source of funding support to give the councils access to this critical management tool.

The federal statutes that mandate regulatory analysis, i.e., the Regulatory Flexibility Act and Executive Order 12291, are unambiguous in their requirement for sophisticated economic analysis of management alternatives. Management decisions are inextricably linked to calculations of cost-effectiveness and cost-benefit. Unfortunately much remains unknown about the economics of the fishing industry, and the requisite analyses are particularly problematic for complex, multispecies fisheries such as exists off the Northeast coast of the United States. As a consequence of the federal mandate and the incomplete state of our knowledge, it continues to be appropriate for the federal government to support fisheries economics research. To this end, the federal government has recently become less reliant upon academe by increasing its in-house capability to satisfy some of the Council's needs for economic information and analyses. It may also happen that private companies will find it in their best interest to conduct economic analyses on various aspects of the fisheries, but the latter information will not find its way easily into the public domain, and the councils' needs cannot be expected to be satisfied in this manner. Therefore, federal funding support for fishery economics research must remain firm in order to assure well-informed, well-justified management programs.

Lastly, we come to the issue of federal funding for socio-cultural research. This area has perhaps been the most neglected historically, yet socio-cultural impacts should bear importantly upon management decisions. In many instances, fishing communities are culturally homogeneous, with similar values and outlooks, and fishermen have only a limited ability or opportunity to be assimilated into other areas of the work force. Information on these communities helps to frame the initial conditions for proposed change, and guides decisions with respect to, for example, the acceptability and enforcibility of regulations and the socio-economic consequences of rebuilding a fishery resource. The way that much socio-cultural information has entered the Council's decision-making process is through the background and experience of the Council members themselves and the Council's advisors. Other information has come as the result of council contracted studies and independent research funded through sources such as Sea Grant. But this loosely structured approach is ultimately unacceptable because it results in the diminished importance of socio-cultural information relative to other structured, "scientific" information on biological, economic or operational dimensions of the decision environment. The fact of the matter is that less information exists on the socio-cultural character of the fishery than exists in any other area, and without additional governmental support, important information to judge the regulatory impacts of proposed measures will not find its way systematically into the fishery management plan development process.

In conclusion, it appears that continued federal funding of fisheries-related research is vital to the nation's interest in the effective management of its marine fisheries resources. Funding support should continue to be broad-based, effectively utilizing the expertise that exists within the scientific community, fostering the development of refined expertise, and co-opting the physical, personnel and funding resources of the states and private institutions. In these budget cutting times, the issue should not be whether to continue funding, but rather the issue should be how scarce financial resources can be most effectively directed to meet the priority needs of the councils.

CHAPTER 11

Rethinking Research For Fishery

and Ecosystem Management

ALEC D. MacCALL
Fisheries Biologist
Southwest Fisheries Center
National Marine Fisheries Service
National Oceanic and Atmospheric Administration
La Jolla, California

WHY DO RESEARCH?

It is appropriate to preface this discussion with some general comments on the objectives of, or justifications for, fishery or ecosystem research. Probably the most generally accepted justification for research is the prospect of improved management, whether it be for increased yield or value, or perhaps for a predictive capability which decreases risk. The assumption is the more we know, the more closely we can approach our management objectives. Unfortunately, this argument is at times perverted in order to postpone difficult decisions, or to rationalize poor management performance: "We don't know enough about the resource to..."

As we move from consumable resources to those which traditionally are not consumed (for simplicity, I call these "non-consumable"), such as seabirds and marine mammals, research is often justified by legislative mandate. Several U.S. legislative acts, such as the National Environmental Protection Act (NEPA), the Marine Mammal Protection Act (MMPA) and the Endangered Species Act (ESA) require an ecosystem understanding of interactions among species and impacts of man's activities. This category also includes progressive international treaties such as the Convention for the Conservation of Antarctic Marine Living Resources (CCAMLR), which specifically calls for an integrated ecosystem approach to management. To some extent, these mandates include an accounting for indirect effects on consumable resources. For example, contaminants and habitat destruction addressed by NEPA affect both consumable and non-consumable resources. On the other hand, the MMPA includes fishery impacts on the food supplies and mortality of marine mammals, but in its intent of protection rather than management, excludes consideration of those mammals' impacts on fishery values. Importantly, these legislative mandates for management and protection of non-consumable resources have mostly focused on large, visible high-level predators (at least in the marine realm), and that is where most of the attendant research has been directed.

HOW MUCH RESEARCH?

Given the various justifications or motivations for conducting research, the equally important but difficult question remains as to how much research is appropriate. In the case of consumable resources, the value of research is potentially quantifiable. In keeping with the assumption that more information should allow closer approach to optimum utilization, we can draw two important quantitative inferences: First, there is a limit to the value of information, as the resource itself has a limit to the benefits it can provide under ideal management. Second, the value of information conforms to the rule of diminishing returns. Initial information on a resource is valuable in establishing reasonable expectations by management, whereas additional information serves mainly to refine the approach to optimum utilization. It is arguable whether there is a limit to information in the way that there is a limit to fishery value, but in any case, accumulation of useful information also conforms to the rule of diminishing returns as a function of cost.

The relationship between information, its cost, and fishery value is instructive (Figure 1). Given ideal management, maximum net value from a fishery (benefit less cost) is achieved at relatively low levels of information (Figure 1a). Here, ideal management is characterized as low-expectation, low-cost, and robust or self-limiting (low-risk). For example, the fleet size would be limited to that which is able to harvest an amount well short of the estimated maximum sustainable yield, and quota determinations, monitoring and enforcement would be avoided. Ideal management is somewhat of a fiction, but serves mainly to contrast with actual management (Figure 1b). Performance of actual management has been variable, but most often fishery value has been dissipated by excess fleet capacity (so-called "overcapitalization") and excess fishing pressure, placing the fishery on the descending limb of the production curve (i.e. increased fishing intensity leads to decreased average yield). Ironically, actual fishery management often has led to relatively low fishery value partially as a consequence of aggressively but haphazardly trying to maximize that value.

Information costs can be evaluated in terms of fishery economics: research is in effect a form of capital investment, and monitoring incurs an operating cost. From this viewpoint, actual management often tends to overinvest (or "overcapitalize") in information, and this habit has been a further source of dissipation of total fishery value. It is easy to see the forces which cause this problem: managers, researchers, and the various interest groups which vie for allocations of the resource all agree on the need for more information to support their individual arguments or interests. Researchers may claim that their work relates to management even when the connection is negligible—such claims may improve prospects for funding. The cost of the research is seldom a consideration; usually it is not borne by the interest group requesting it or benefiting from it, but rather by government agencies. Private interest groups may add to this total expenditure by hiring consultants to provide them with new information. Furthermore, such expenditures are often matched by the cost of government or opposing interest groups' responses to such efforts.

WHAT SHOULD WE DO?

Unfortunately, the solution is not simply to spend less on monitoring and research. Most present fishery management institutions have locked themselves into policies requiring intensive research and monitoring efforts. For example, most interpretations of the Magnuson Fishery Management and Conservation Act of 1976

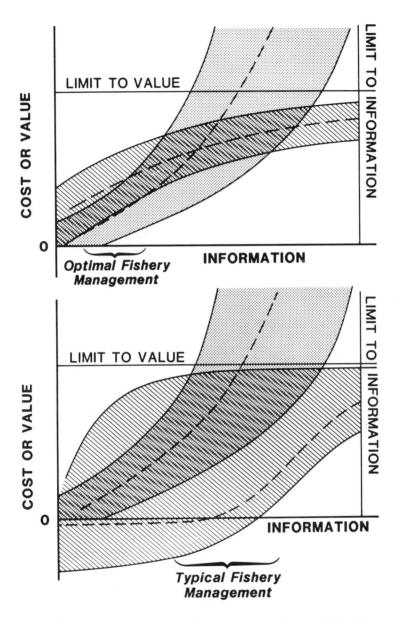

Figure 1. The relationships among information, its cost (stippled region) and its benefit (hatched region) to fishery management a.(upper): "Ideal" management; b.(lower): "Actual" management. Shading represents the range of likely outcomes. Dashed line represents the most likely outcome.

(MFCMA) have required annual setting of harvest limits, quotas or allocations, with associated requirements of information on the status of the resource, harvests and concerns of relevant interest groups. Given the existing management framework, reducing the investment in information would incur substantial risk of further declines in fishery value due to subsequent misinformed or uninformed management decisions.

Within the context of this information model, there are two courses of action which promise to improve the cost-effectiveness of information and management. The first, and less likely of the two, is to change management toward a "low-information" system. The potential value realizable from low-information management is critically dependent on establishing the appropriate management expectations and institutions. I will not go into describing such institutions, except to say that they would be substantially different from those presently governing most U.S. fisheries, and most likely would be perceived to be non-democratic, or at least non-egalitarian, requiring substantial limitation on freedom to participate in the fishery. Some candidates for these management approaches are discussed elsewhere in this symposium.

The second course of action is to keep routine fishery monitoring and research to the minimum level necessary to meet immediate management needs, and to emphasize research aimed at better understanding the workings of the physical, ecological, and human systems surrounding these fisheries. I am defining routine research to be that which follows the existing cost vs. information curve in Figure 1. The alternative, or system-oriented research, is characterized by the potential to *shift*, rather than follow, either of the entire curves: to increase the information obtained at given cost, or to increase the fishery value realizable at a given level of information, opening up new management possibilities within the existing management philosophy. I emphasize the word "potential" in the above definition, as the latter kind of research naturally contains uncertainty as to its eventual utility. If its utility were proven in advance, most likely the research would already have been done.

The distinction between the two kinds of research is not clear. Also, the appropriate level of routine research and monitoring is difficult to determine. Beyond its use in current fishery management, routine information forms an important base for system understanding, further blurring the distinction between the two types of research. Perhaps it is easier to attempt to clarify the distinction by means of examples.

EXAMPLES OF SYSTEM-ORIENTED RESEARCH

Elsewhere in this symposium, I was informed that the Atlantic surf clam fishery is presently opened for a few hours, once a week, when a disproportionately large number of vessels descend on the resource. Accuracy of the details are unimportant to my example: currently the abundance is estimated annually, whereas it was also suggested in the symposium that this routine monitoring could reasonably be reduced to a bi- or tri-annual effort. This would be an improvement in the cost-effectiveness of routine research. However, if we consider a system view of the geography of surf clam productivity, we can hypothesize the following model which stands in contrast to routine homogeneous fishery models. Mobility of the resource occurs only during the planktonic phase, when the spawn diffuses along the coast. Clams are immobile once they settle. The edge of the population is determined by physical or competitive conditions, and clams at the edge of the population contribute very little to the population's productivity—their offspring are mostly lost to uninhabitable locations. Clams at the center of the population have the greatest probability of contributing surviving offspring because they are surrounded by inhabitable locations. This suggests that an unrestricted fishery could be allowed at the edges of the resource, and that the center of the population should be managed for maximum spawn production rather than maximum yield. Because of filter-feeding cannibalism, the density in the center might have to be reduced somewhat to achieve optimality. The point is that research dedicated to developing a geographic understanding of the system could lead to a rather different pattern of fishing within the present management philosophy, with an increase in realized productivity.

Some examples of system-oriented research on ecosystems include study of the cause and biological effects of prolonged changes in physical conditions. Bakun (In press) has shown some striking changes in the physical conditions off Peru (Figure 2). Changes of this kind, though perhaps not always this extreme, occur in all ecosystems. There is little reason to doubt that these physical changes are associated with changes in spawning and survival of fish eggs, larvae and juveniles, and hence sustainable yields. A system understanding will be necessary to replace the inappropriate static equilibrium yield models presently governing fishery management with models which account for these changes. A related type of ecosystem change is the apparent replacement of one species by another, for example, the anchovy-sardine "flips" which have occurred in California and Peru, and the replacement of herring by sand lance in the north Atlantic. To the extent that these replacements are mediated by interspecific competition, there are good prospects for improved, coordinated management; alternatively, if these replacements prove to be the result of largely independent responses to the physical changes described above, management will have fewer viable options.

The increasing concern over the effects of contaminants and habitat loss on fish production is not being answered by current simplistic single-species fishery models. Again, a system-oriented understanding is necessary to address these problems. An adequate model must contain a representation of the temporal and spatial structure of the population or ecosystem in order to estimate the impacts of local perturbations. These models may provide additional information useful to fishery or ecosystem management, as in the case of the surf clam model proposed above.

Another important reason for system-oriented research stems from the way we address management problems. Traditional academic research has a well-known method: after a problem is posed, the researcher conducts research, gaining *new* information by which the question is answered. It is very rare that management questions or problems can be solved by this method. After the management problem is posed, the fishery or ecosystem researcher must sort primarily through information which has *already* been gathered, such as time series of abundances. There is very little in the way of research to collect new information which can help in solving the problem. Thus our ability to answer management questions is constrained by existing knowledge, by the nature and quantity of past research. The information which will be of greatest long-range use in answering management questions will be gained by system-oriented research rather than by routine research devoted to "fine-tuning" current management.

The remainder of this discussion will focus principally on the research (and monitoring) needed to improve our understanding of marine ecosystems, rather than on research specifically intended to support fishery management. Nonetheless, fisheries are clearly elements of these ecosystems, and fishery research remains important to the discussion in several respects. Fisheries have demonstrated the capability to influence the target species' abundance, sometimes to the point of virtual elimination as a functional element of an ecosystem [this has been the case with the Pacific sardine (*Sardinops sagax*) off California]. Also, fisheries are one of the few ecosystem processes which are nominally under man's control. Indeed, fisheries represent ecological "experiments" of extraordinarily large scale, albeit without proper

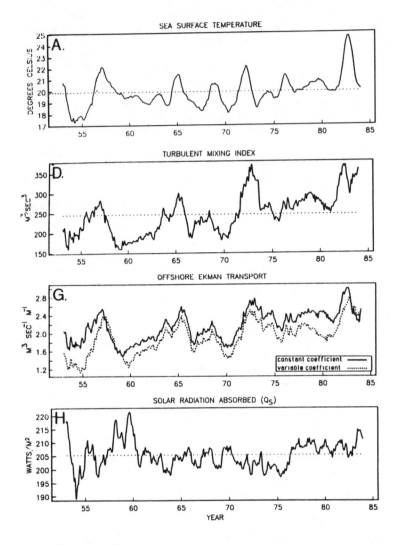

Figure 2. Time series of several physical oceanographic variables off the coast of Peru, showing changes in patterns over time (from Bakun, in press).

experimental controls. Finally, given that a fishery exists, it can be a source of large amounts of information at relatively low cost.

RESEARCH FOR MANAGEMENT OF MARINE ECOSYSTEMS

Ecosystem understanding necessarily requires a foundation of knowledge about the physical setting: physical oceanography, climatology etc. This foundation includes continuity of monitoring. Experience has shown that there are major shifts in physical patterns and associated biological patterns as progressively longer time periods are considered. Moreover, these shifts can be sudden, cannot be anticipated, and are difficult to recognize until well after the fact. Bakun (in press) presents time series of a suite of physical measurements for the Peruvian coast, some of which are reproduced in Figure 2. While the presence of dominant events such as the 1954-55 cold period and the 1982-83 El Nino have highly visible effects at the time they occur, the prolonged changes such as the shift in patterns following 1977 are more likely to cause changes in the structure of the ecosystem. Accordingly, it is important to supplement monitoring and research of the present system with information on the past behavior of the system. These sources include historical archives such as newspapers and journals, and natural chronological records such as tree rings and laminated sediments (Figure 3). It is often the biological information in these records that elucidates the changes that must have occurred in the physical system.

Another aspect necessary to understanding ecosystem functions is an appreciation of the historical development of man's impacts on the ecosystem. It is tempting to

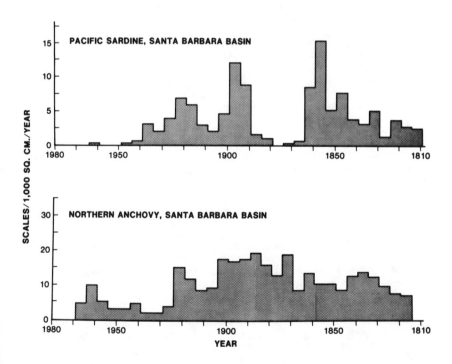

Figure 3. Recent scale deposition rates for Pacific sardine and northern anchovy off southern California (from Soutar and Isaacs 1974).

think of ecosystem impacts beginning with the major industrialization of fisheries in the early 20th century, but substantial impacts may have resulted from low-technology exploitation in the 18th and 19th centuries. For example, nearly all species of pinnipeds on the Pacific coast of the United States were reduced to very low abundances by the fur and oil trades during the last century and by predator control during the early decades of this century (MacCall 1986). Also, many of the large predatory fishes such as the tunas were depleted off California by 1920, when the tuna fleet began moving southward toward tropical waters. Natural mortality rates of the prey fishes must have been below the historical average as industrialized fisheries on these small pelagic fishes were expanding, a supposition which has never been addressed in the single-species fishery analyses and management.

A third area necessary as background to ecosystem research is biogeography. While it lacks glamour and is time-consuming and costly, an inventory of species, abundances and distributions (especially over time) is particularly valuable to multispecies or ecosystem management decision making. Of course the effort put into this work will vary according to species or trophic groups, both due to accessibility and interest on the part of researchers or managers. Government seems to be a necessary agent in this task, either by doing the work itself (e.g., the egg and larva surveys conducted in association with the California Cooperative Oceanic Fisheries Investigations, CalCOFI, Kramer et al., 1972), or by requiring such information to be part of environmental impact statements (EIS) or similar reviews. It is notable that fishery management plans developed under the MFCMA now must contain an EIS to meet the requirements of the NEPA.

Some marine ecosystems are unique, but most have several parallels. For example the eastern boundary currents off California, Peru, South Africa and North Africa contain remarkably similar assemblages of pelagic fishes, suggesting functional similarities in key oceanographic processes (Parrish et al., 1983). Comparative oceanography and biology of equivalent ecosystems not only provides insight into the workings of those ecosystems, but comparative history of exploitation may provide a rough replication of the massive fishery "experiments" mentioned above.

ECOSYSTEM MODELS

The value of constructing formal ecosystem models is debatable. As a tool to improve understanding of an ecosystem, the exercise often has been of greatest benefit to the builder himself. Unfortunately, this improved understanding has not easily been transferred to non-participants. As a tool to aid managerial decision-making, complicated ecosystem models tend to produce output which is too complicated to assimilate, especially if effects of random variability are included. Also, these complicated models tend to be sensitive to assumptions, such as the functional forms used to represent non-linear relationships. An example of this kind of uncertainty is the assumed form of the stock-recruitment relationship. Two popular stock recruitment models are the Ricker curve and the Beverton-Holt curve. These two curves are shown in Figure 4, which is taken from two well-known publications. Our uncertainty is demonstrated by the fact that two well-respected fishery experts have independently based these curves on the same data! While the two curves are about equally reasonable fits to these data on North Sea plaice, the corresponding anticipated patterns of population growth and stability are quite different. For management purposes, accurate and easily interpreted analyses usually are best produced by a much less complex model which is designed specifically to address the particular issue. Of course there are some issues, such as ecosystem stability and reversibility of species declines, which may require very large and complicated models; accordingly, definitive answers should not be expected. Beddington (1986) provides a useful discussion of this problem.

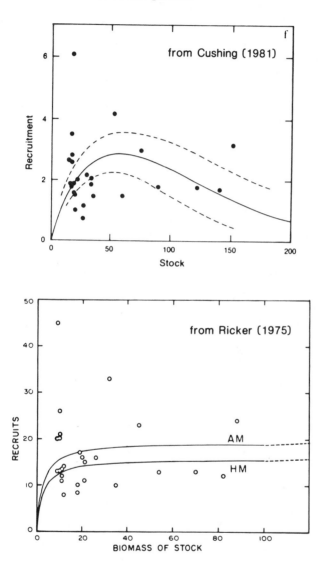

Figure 4. Demonstration of uncertainty in functional relationships: Independent fitting of two different stock-recruitment relationships using the same data on North Sea plaice.

The two most successful (or at least the most ambitious) marine ecosystem models have been Laevastu's Bering Sea model (Laevastu and Larkins 1981), and Ursin's North Sea model (Andersen and Ursin 1977). The two models represent rather different approaches to the problem, and require somewhat different kinds of background research and input data. The Bering Sea model is a compartmentalized accounting model, whereas the North Sea model is constructed of simultaneous differential equations. Thus the Bering Sea model emphasizes information on states while the North Sea model emphasizes information on rates, although the two models overlap substantially in their requirements. These large models have tended to be opaque to outside observers, and the extensive "tuning" of parameters which is required to obtain reasonable model behavior can hide serious deficiencies in our knowledge. Both of these models have had the advantage of portraying relatively closed, landlocked ecosystems, unlike the open systems found along continental coastlines or in mid-ocean. A satisfactory structure for ecosystem models of open marine systems has yet to be developed.

A much less ambitious model consists of a static input-output budget for various trophic components of an ecosystem. This would seem to be a minimum requirement for ecosystem understanding, forming the basis for estimating fluxes and perhaps carrying capacities for individual trophic levels or groups. Given the biomass in each trophic category, inputs can be calculated from information on energetics or food consumption, while outputs can be calculated from mortality rates. The matrix can be constructed on the basis either of inputs or of outputs, but can be considered satisfactory only if the two approaches agree, which seldom has been the case even for individual trophic categories. Bergh (1986) developed a trophic budget for the Benguela Current system off South Africa (Figure 5), based on a Delphi method survey of experts' opinions. A severe difficulty, which is common to the study of all marine ecosystems, was his inability to obtain reliable estimates of abundance and rate parameters for the squids, which by any account must be a major element in the system.

A common problem in these models is an apparently insufficient supply of prey. Green (1978) attempted such a budget for the California Current, as a starting point for modeling the effects of fisheries on the carrying capacity of marine mammals, but found that estimated fish and squid production could not meet estimated predator needs.   Given that many of those predators, especially pinnipeds, have steadily increased in abundance, she concluded that the imbalance was erroneous, and that current knowledge could not support the modeling effort.   Hunter and Lynn (Southwest Fisheries Center, in prep.) have estimated total anchovy (*Engraulis mordax*) predation by mackerel (*Scomber japonicus*) in southern California, and again, estimated anchovy consumption by this predator nearly exceeds the total abundance of anchovies.   It is clear that substantial uncertainty exists in all three quantities appearing in each cell of the matrix—abundance, consumption (input rate) and mortality (output rate)—but the consistent direction of the imbalances is disturbing. Hunter and Lynn suspect that the mackerel obtained from fishery catches are more likely to have been feeding on anchovies than the average mackerel in the population, thus biasing the samples. In the past, similar discrepancies were perceived for lower trophic levels (e.g., zooplankton vs. phytoplankton, phytoplankton vs. carbon fixation), but these are now being resolved (R. Eppley, Scripps Institution of Oceanography, pers. comm.). The keys to improved understanding have been better knowledge of rate processes, and better accounting for spatial and temporal patterns of variability. Spatial distributions of most marine organisms are characterized by a high degree of contagion (patchiness); trophic interactions must be similarly patchy, and trophic rates may be influenced as much by the spatial variance as by the mean of a species' density.

SOUTHERN BENGUELA SYSTEM
(Tonnes Carbon x 10^3. yr^{-1})

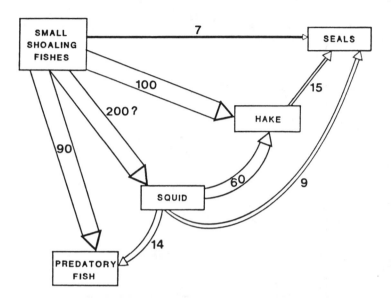

Figure 5. A trophic budget for the Benguela Current (from Bergh 1986).

OPERATIONAL CONSIDERATIONS

The expense of ecosystem research requires that surveys and sampling be planned for efficiency, but with emphasis on multiple purpose activity. These two objectives can conflict, as can be seen in the contrast between pelagic fishery landings, which tend to include few species but are conveniently centralized, and landings by demersal fisheries, which often include many species but are geographically diffuse (Figure 6). Another barrier to multiple purpose activity is institutional jurisdictions. For example, the National Marine Fisheries Service has responsibility for marine fishes and marine mammals, but not for seabirds, which are the responsibility of the U.S. Fish and Wildlife Service. Even within agencies, there may be psychological barriers between traditional fishery researchers who subconsciously promote consumptive uses of fish, and marine mammal or seabird biologists who stress the role of fish as forage.

An interesting possibility for low-cost ecosystem monitoring is the use of "indicator species." The reproduction or physiological state of some predators may be closely tied to the availability of prey. For example, the reproductive success of brown pelicans (*Pelecanus occidentalis californicus*) in southern California closely tracks the abundance of northern anchovy, its primary forage (Anderson et al. 1982, Figure 7). Similarly, changes in guano production by seabirds in South Africa and

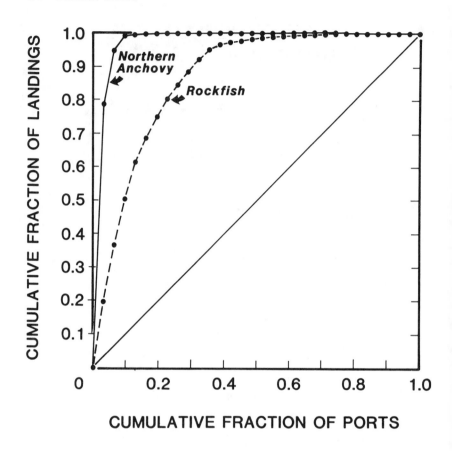

Figure 6. Comparison of relative geographic dispersion of landings of a pelagic fish (northern anchovy) and a groundfish species complex (rockfish, *Sebastes* spp.) in California in 1975.

Peru have reflected changes in abundance of pelagic fishes (Crawford and Shelton 1978). Monitoring of penguins and pinnipeds in the Antarctic has been proposed as a source of information on the abundance of forage species, including krill. Inexpensive (relative to the cost of seagoing surveys) monitoring of these "indicator species" could provide information, albeit imprecise, on changes in forage populations including a variety of forage species such as squids which have not been sampled effectively by existing methods.

Drawbacks to the use of indicator species include the difficulty of interpreting the information without verification or calibration. Use of indicator species as as a source of information for fishery management is unlikely not only because of imprecision, but because of the reluctance of fishermen to allow their fishery harvests to be governed by the performance of a competitor. In contrast, indicator

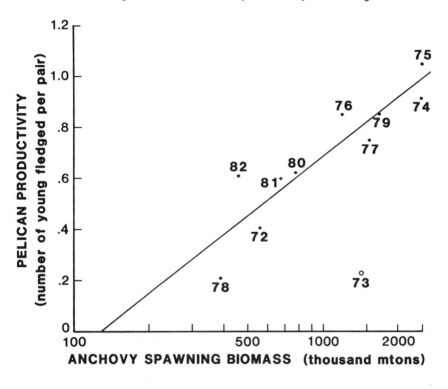

Figure 7. Relation between brown pelican productivity and anchovy spawning biomass off southern California (from MacCall et al. 1983).

species could be used quite effectively in the "low-information" management I described earlier.

WHO WILL DO THE WORK?

Fishery and ecosystem research is costly in time, money and manpower. For this reason alone, we must expect severe limitations on the amount of research which can be accomplished. There are additional barriers and impediments which render the work even more difficult. Areas of ecosystem research are divided into a bewildering number of jurisdictions and funding sources, with no single entity being responsible for coordination or integration. Further difficulties arise in large ecosystems which span international boundaries, where various nations may have very different policies toward research and management. The best hope for ecosystem research may lie in formation of consortia similar to CalCOFI on the Pacific coast (Baxter 1982, Reid 1982) which unite local, federal and perhaps international government agencies with academic institutions in pursuing and coordinating ecosystem studies. In the absence of incompatible goals (as might arise from implementation of the MMPA or the MFCMA) the mutual benefits should foster a strong and effective cooperative effort.

REFERENCES

Anderson, D., F. Gress and K. Mais. 1982. Brown pelicans: influence of food supply on reproduction. Oikos 39:23-31.

Anderson, K. and E. Ursin. 1977. A multispecies extension to the Beverton and Holt theory of fishing, with accounts of phosphorus circulation and primary production. Meddr. Danm. Fish.-og Havunders N.S. 7:319-435.

Bakun, A. In press. Monthly variability in the ocean habitat off Peru as deduced from maritime observations, 1953-1984. In: D. Pauly and I. Tsukayama (eds.) The anchoveta and its ecosystem. International Center for Living Aquatic Resources Management (ICLARM), Manila.

Baxter, J. 1982. The role of the Marine Research Committee and CalCOFI. CalCOFI Rep. 23:35-38.

Beddington, J. 1986. Shifts in resource populations in large marine ecosystems. pp.9-18 In: K. Sherman and L. Alexander (eds.) Variability and management of large marine ecosystems. AAAS Selected Symposium (99): 319p.

Bergh, M. 1986. The value of catch statistics and records of guano harvests for managing certain South African fisheries. Ph.D. Diss., Univ. Cape Town, South Africa. 335 p.

Crawford R., and P. Shelton 1978. Pelagic fish and seabird interrelationships off the coasts of South West and South Africa. Biol. Conserv. 14:85-109.

Cushing, D. 1981. Fisheries biology. Univ. of Wisconsin Press. 295p.

Green, K. 1978. Ecosystem description of the California Current. U.S. Marine Mammal Comm. Final Rep. Contract No. MM7AC-026. 73p.

Hunter, J., and E. Lynn. In prep. Consumption of northern anchovy (*Engraulis mordax*) by the mackerel *Scomber japonicus*. Southwest Fisheries Center, La Jolla, CA.

Kramer, D., M. Kalin, E. Stevens, J. Thrailkill, and J. Zweifel. 1972. Collecting and processing data on fish eggs and larvae in the California Current region. NOAA Tech. Rep. NMFS CIRC-370:38p.

Laevastu, T., and H. Larkins. 1981. Marine fisheries ecosystem: its quantitative evaluation and management. Fishing News Books Ltd., Farnham.

MacCall, A. 1986. Changes in the biomass of the California Current ecosystem. pp.33-54 In: K. Sherman and L. Alexander (eds.) Variability and management of large marine ecosystems. AAAS Selected Symposium (99):319p.

MacCall, A., R. Methot, D. Huppert, and R. Klingbeil. 1983. Northern anchovy fishery management plan. October 24, 1983. Pacif. Fish. Management Council, 526 S.W. Mill St., Portland OR 97201.

Parrish, R., A. Bakun, D. Husby, and C. Nelson. 1983. Comparative climatology of selected environmental processes in relation to eastern boundary current pelagic fish reproduction. pp. 731-777 In: G. Sharp and J. Csirke, (eds.) Proceedings of the expert consultation to examine changes in abundance and species composition of neritic fish resources. FAO Fish. Rep. 291(3):557-1224.

Reid, J. 1982. An oceanographer's perspective. CalCOFI Rep. 23:39-42.

Ricker, W. 1975. Computation and interpretation of biological statistics of fish populations. Fish. Res. Bd. Canada, Bull. 191:382p.

Soutar, A. and J. Isaacs. 1974. Abundance of pelagic fish during the 19th and 20th centuries as recorded in anaerobic sediment off the Californias. Fish. Bull. U.S. 72:257-273.

REMARKS

ILENE M. KAPLAN
Department of Sociology
Marine Studies Program
Union College
Schenectady, New York

An ostensibly straightforward comment concerning the need for further research based on the abundance of existing questions was directed to the Research Needs panel. But this seemingly innocent remark only scratched the surface of an issue which needed to be addressed at this session but was not.

The abundance of questions is not, in and of itself, an indication of the need for research. Many questions may be asked, but a large number of them may not be very useful. The asking of questions and the pursuit of answers is indicative, however, of a *process* which orchestrates, and thereby controls, the directions in which our knowledge can be enhanced. The process itself is rather complex and generates its own set of uncertainties.

Who, What, and How of Fisheries Research

Of paramount importance to this process are the ways in which questions are shaped. To begin with, we must ask *whose* questions will be pursued and thus serve as guidelines for research on fisheries—those of fishermen, consumers, fisheries managers, government officials or scientists? It should be fairly obvious that the common interests of each of these groups in United States (and very often foreign) fisheries by no means suggests that the concerns are the same. Each group has its own set of priorities and self-interests which motivate behaviors and structure beliefs. Yet depending on *whose* questions will guide investigations on fisheries and their management so will be influenced the focus and emphasis of future policies.

What will be done to implement fisheries studies is another important and politically laden facet of research, especially when it comes to funding considerations. Funding for fisheries management projects, including maintenance programs, seems to be on the lean side, particularly when one compares the allocations made to other marine programs. It has already been strongly asserted that fisheries management expenditures and allocations for scientific endeavors together receive less than one third of possible marine oriented fundings (see R. Gutting's paper, this conference).

And finally, *how* research is to be conducted is in many ways the most complex and difficult issue to be raised. Scientists must always be aware of the pitfalls of ethnocentrism in designing research projects. Each of us, because of our backgrounds, our experiences, and our training brings a particular orientation which not only shapes the questions we ask, but the particular framework which influences the way we approach the questions that are eventually decided upon as the focus of research. As such, the "how" component of research in fisheries studies is, in many ways, the umbrella and key factor in determining the directions in which we are heading.

In the crucial area of fisheries management, these are only some of the questions of particular concern when we discuss the pursuit of research. We are dealing, not just with theoretical constructs to guide research, but with the anticipation of ultimate policies that will affect precious natural resources.

PART SIX

Privatizing the Fisheries

This session will deal with the merits of "privatizing" the fisheries. For some, this is a euphemism for assigning property rights to the fishery. The fishery resources of the United States should be held in trust for the benefit of the nation and the rights to use the resource should be sold or assigned like timber or mineral resources—that's one interpretation of "privatization."

To others, "privatization" refers to the debate over what is the proper role of government. Regarding fisheries, what is the proper role of the National Marine Fisheries Service and which of its functions might better be transferred to the private sector or shared with regional bodies and the states?

I'm glad to see this subject addressed.

KENELM W. COONS
Director
New England Fisheries Development Foundation
Boston, Massachusetts

CHAPTER 12

Fisheries Management: Another Option

S. FRED SINGER
Visiting Eminent Scholar
George Mason University
Fairfax, Virginia

A PROBLEM OF SEMANTICS

It is important that we get things straight in terms of definitions otherwise we may spend much of our time arguing without effect about the meaning of words, rather than about the important issues. So, let's see if we can get rid of ambiguity and agree on certain definitions for "management," "limited access," and "privatization."

I will try, though I may not succeed, in *not* using the word "management." In the fisheries business the word "management" means different things to different people. For example, to some people the word "management" means or includes the setting of TACs (total allowable catch), OY (optimum yield) or ABCs (allowed biological catch), or whatever you wish to call it. To me that is not "management." Let's call that the "setting of TAC." It is a subject which should be done on the basis of the available scientific data. Knowing that data are imperfect, knowing that the science is imperfect, one tries to do the best job one can. There are differences of opinion; there is a grey area within which the TAC may move. But I would like, for the purpose of our discussion here, to assume that whenever we set a TAC, it has been arrived at on the basis of "best scientific judgment." If I were a lawyer I would say: let's *stipulate* the TAC's. Let's assume they have been set by perfect human beings who have tremendous insight, foresight, perspicacity, and wisdom. These people are not ordinary mortals. They know; they understand fish; they know how to set the TAC.

HARVESTING THE TAC: EFFICIENCY V. TRADITION

What we are really talking about in "management" is another issue. And that is, how should this TAC be harvested? How is that portion of the fish stock which the scientific group permits us to catch, in a particular season, in a particular area, to be collected? That is not a scientific problem; that is a socio-economic problem. But that is the real management problem of the fishery.

There are two ways to approach this. From the point of economic efficiency, one should harvest the TAC as economically as possible, using up as few resources as possible, as few boats as possible, as few crews as possible, and as little fuel as possible. Keep the cost of harvesting down—that is what a farmer does. He will try to minimize his harvesting costs. That is what a fisherman would do if he owned the fishery resource, i.e. if he owned the rights to harvest the stock. That is the point of view that I will take.

The other point of view, diametrically opposed but equally valid, argues for full employment in the fisheries industry, particularly among the harvesters. We do not worry so much about the processors for some reason. Processors seem to work on the principle of economic efficiency; those who cannot meet the standard don't survive and go out of business. But in the harvesting part of the fisheries business there is this point of view that we should protect the employment of fishermen, perhaps even allow more fishermen to enter into the industry—with the result, of course, that their livelihood becomes smaller and smaller. That point of view I don't agree with, but it does have some important constituents—first of all, a certain fraction of the fishermen themselves.

I would argue that if we had this point of view of full employment in another harvesting industry, namely agriculture, then we would still have 80% of the population of the United States engaged in farming. However, over the years we have reduced the percentage of the active farm population from 80% to 4%, a factor of twenty. We are living better, eating better, have cheaper food, and a greater variety than we have ever had. I use this analogy because I believe that inevitably we will be moving towards an era where because of technology advances there will be fewer fishermen and fewer boats catching the same amount of fish—since the TAC is ultimately limited. I agree that there are some unexploited fish species, but that is a side issue that I don't want to get into here. Obviously, the unexploited species will some day be fully exploited, so we really are just postponing the matter by a few years.

TRADITION

Let me talk about the second viewpoint first, that of full employment. The way to put that into effect is by providing something which can be called "limited access" to the fishery. You limit the access of fishermen to certain hours of the day, certain days of the week, or so many days a month, or what-have-you. You set up all kinds of rules and regulations which reduce the efficiency of fishing. There are examples of this—the surf clam and oyster fishery. Granted, this will increase the number of persons employed; but it leads to a waste of resources.

You could do the same thing in agriculture. I am old enough to remember wheat being harvested with scythes and threshed on the threshing floor. That is a great way of keeping lots of people employed, but a poor idea from an economic point of view. The result of this is that the wheat is very expensive, if you pay full wages; or if wheat is priced competitively, it means you pay the workers a pittance. You can't have cheap wheat and full wages. And the same with fish. You can't have cheap fish that the housewife can buy and pay full wages to a multitude of fishermen. If you want to compete with fish from abroad, with other kinds of protein (chickens, catfish from ponds, or whatever), you have to do one of two things, you have to pay fishermen a pittance or you go out of business. Another alternative is to institute protective tariffs to keep out the cheaper foreign fish. But then people will not buy fish, because it is expensive. I can still buy imported whiting, frozen, for 65 cents a pound. I don't know of any cheaper fish at the moment that you can buy at supermarkets. But that's still more expensive than chicken.

ECONOMIC EFFICIENCY

Let me go back to the first option, the one I prefer. How do you make fishing an economic enterprise? The answer is "privatization," which means transfer of the property rights from the U.S. government, which owns the fishery resource, to the fishermen. How should this transfer be accomplished? There are several ways to do it. The important thing however, is to make sure that private people, not the government, own property rights to the fish, and most importantly, make sure that these property rights are transferable.

Transfer of Property Rights

It does not matter much how the property rights are assigned to the fishermen, but there are three likely methods:

1) A "grandfather" clause. Anyone who is fishing now can get property rights. That is not very fair, and that is what many call a "limited access;"

2) A lottery. That is sometimes done with mineral leases. Whoever is lucky wins the rights;

3) An auction. I think it is the fairest method. The highest bidder gets the rights. You can, if you wish, limit the number of rights that can be bought by any particular individual, but that is a detail.

The basic idea is to transfer the rights from the U.S. government to private individuals who then own the rights and can do whatever they want with them.

The analogy that I like to use is the oil and gas resource offshore. There is no question that the resource is owned by the government. Nobody in his right mind would dream of giving this resource away to the oil companies. We auction off the leases, and the highest bidder gets them. The highest bidder doesn't have to be a big oil company; it can be a coalition of small companies. Once the rights are acquired they could either be exercised, they could lapse (that would be a foolish thing to do) or they could be resold and transferred.

I would suggest that the same be done for the fishing rights. Once the TAC has been established, a number of rights would then be auctioned off, representing, in total, the amount of the TAC for that year. The successful bidders would acquire the rights. They can exercise them by harvesting that amount of the TAC which is represented by their rights. Or, they do not exercise them, let the rights lapse and lose their money. Or, they sell their rights to some other fisherman for whatever they can agree on. Once the rights have been auctioned off to private indivduals, the free market sets their price.

Limited Access

It may turn out that a few fishermen or fishing companies will buy up the rights of others. My answer is: so be it. It is not unfair. Even if the larger companies buy up the individual fishermen's rights, at least the fishermen end up with money in their pockets. Sometimes they are better off with money in their pocket having sold their rights, than out there fishing against competition and making nothing. In other cases, you may have fishermen out there, each one exercising his own right. This is not "limited access." What I've seen of limited access is a basic protectionist measure to keep out the foreigner, or (in Alaska) the non-Alaskans, or to keep out those not from your locality.

THE GOVERNMENT ROLE

The outcome of this scenario would be that the resource would be harvested in the most efficient manner, with the least expenditure of resources. It will avoid both overcapitalization and pressure to raise the TAC. In other words, it would avoid the political pressure which leads to overfishing. Once the TAC has been divided up in this way, there will be less pressure on the people who have set the TAC. It's sold: the rights have been transferred.

I would think that conservationists would be in favor of privatization since they want to preserve a continued fisheries resource. Fishermen should favor this scheme that preserves the resource and allows them to earn a decent wage for the time put into fishing. I'm sure the Congress would be in favor of it if it raises revenues. People who would like to see the government get out of the fishing business would favor it; the government would do little else except to conduct an auction.

It seems to me that the TAC can be set, without government intervention, by the presently constituted fisheries councils. The role of the government then might include only biological research in fisheries. It is possible that even this aspect be financed by the fishing industry, which benefits from the research. Then again, it might be a proper function of the federal government. After all, there is the Department of Agriculture, which has a publicly financed research program, all for the benefit of the farmers. So you might say, why not have it for the fisheries.

Then there is the matter of inspection. It is possible that self-policing will work better than having the government do the policing. After all, once the fishermen have property rights in the resource, they will want to protect these rights. To protect your own rights you should be willing to pay to have them policed.

RESULTS

Privatization would result in the most efficient type of harvesting we can think of. It should lower the cost of fish on the market and allow us to compete on better terms with imports. Imports are cheaper only because they are harvested more efficiently by fewer boats, fewer fishermen, and perhaps fishermen not paid as well. The latter comparative advantage exists in world trade in many areas, be they textiles, shoes, fish, food resources, and so on. We have a geographic advantage in the United States in that we are closer to our own fishing grounds, which should give us an important edge over foreign fishermen.

I hope that these remarks will help toward an open discussion of the various issues that come under the heading of "privatizing the fishery," "limited access," and "management."

SUMMARY

In summary, I feel we can stipulate the following when discussing my definition of privatization:

1)   The United States government is the ultimate owner of fishing resources in the EEZ (Exclusive Economic Zone).

2) Long-term conservation of the fish stocks is a desirable goal, yielding benefits to fishermen, consumers, and the USG.

3) Conservation requires that annual limits be set on catches of different stocks in different locations, based on the best available scientific knowledge.

4) The management system should allow fishermen who practice the harvesting trade to make a decent living by being allowed to catch a substantial fraction of the yearly quota.

5) Consumers should be able to buy fish at lower prices, competitive with other low-cost protein food.

The key to achieving these objectives is a system of transferable rights for fish. Those who purchase rights from the USG, whether by auction, fees, or some other method, should be permitted to sell their rights if they do not want to use them. The end result will be greater economic efficiency: Fewer but higher efficiency boats will be operating the catch, instead of many boats, each operating near the subsistence level. Knowing in advance his permitted quota, each fisherman can optimize his harvesting program. Foreign fleets operating in the EEZ do so now; they use the minimum number of boats and crews to take their allotted quota (which they know in advance).

As much as we may yearn for the traditional mode of fishing, the development of technology, in the presence of finite stocks, is driving us in the direction of privatization, away from a common property resource. When one boat can do the fishing of a hundred, thanks to radar, helicopters, satellites, etc., we should not try to reduce the efficiency of each boat to 1% by regulation that institutes noneconomic methods. After all, U.S. farm population has gone from 80% to less than 5% without long-term dislocations and with great benefits to the consumer in terms of cheaper food.

CHAPTER 13

Parsing Privatization Proposals

DANIEL A. REIFSNYDER
Foreign Affairs Officer
Office of Fisheries Affairs
Bureau of Oceans and International
  Environmental and Scientific Affairs
Department of State
Washington, D.C.

PRIVATIZATION: NOT SYNONYMOUS WITH LIMITED ENTRY

I am pleased to be here to discuss privatizing the fisheries. Ambassador Wolfe has asked me to convey his regret that he could not be here with you. Let me also say that my remarks are entirely personal and should not be taken to reflect the views of the Department of State.

If anyone is wondering what someone from the State Department might have to say about privatization, you are not alone. The topic for me has involved enormous struggle. I confess that my first effort in dealing with it involved trying to find someone else to deal with it.

As in other things, first efforts are not always successful. I am here and I will try to make the best of an issue which to me had seemed to lack an international dimension. On reflection, I think I have found one, but I ask your indulgence if it takes me awhile to reach it.

If "publicize" were a proper antonym of "privatize," there would be a certain irony in the publicity privatization has recently brought to the fisheries. Perhaps not since Vatican II reconsidered fish on Fridays have fish attracted such attention. Ironically, too, confusion of the issue may have done little more for the fishing industry.

The problem, I think, is that two currents of contemporary thought have been run together under the rubric of "privatization" when, essentially, they are separate and distinct. On the one hand, there is the issue of "limited entry." On the other, there is the issue of "privatization." They are not synonymous.

Limited entry is a method of regulating fishing by limiting the entrants or participants in a fishery. One way of limiting entry is to confer property rights in fish. It is largely this that Professor Singer has advocated as a means of avoiding the so-called "tragedy of the commons." That tragedy is described as too many people maximizing individual advantage by catching increasing amounts of a finite resource, resulting ultimately in its depletion and their impoverishment. It is argued that, without property rights in fish, there are inadequate incentives to conserve.

Privatization, I believe, is altogether different. Privatization is an effort to define and clarify the respective roles of government and the private sector. Privatization is rooted in the principle that the competitive enterprise system, characterized by individual freedom and initiative, is the primary source of national economic strength. It also holds that, in the process of governing, the Government should not compete with its citizens.[1] Even more fundamentally, privatization asks, "How much government do we need?"

Confusion arises between these two currents of thought because advocates of property rights in fish have advocated "privatizing" the fisheries. By this use of the term, they do not mean that Pt. Judith fishermen should perform research cruises because they can catch fish more efficiently than Woods Hole scientists. They mean, instead, that participants in a fishery should be limited by creating property rights in fish and by making these rights freely transferable.

MUTUAL COERCION MUTUALLY AGREED UPON

If you will accept this distinction, I trust you will also accept that I have been asked to talk about privatization, not property rights and not both. In this I am fortunate, since it is not clear that creating property rights in fish would equate with privatization of the fisheries. The reasons are fairly obvious. Presumably government would create these property rights, lease or sell them, and realize the profit. But even before asking what then, what exactly would the government lease or sell, and how much of it? Would it be ocean space as with off-shore oil and gas leases, or rights to operate as with radio and television stations, or allocations of fish as some have advocated selling to foreign fleets? If ocean space, the answer as to what is sold is simple—the answer as to what is bought is not. Every fisherman knows that sometimes fish are where you think they are and sometimes they are not.

If the government were to sell rights to operate a fishery, defining the right becomes more complicated. The right will be meaningful only in relation to the resource available and the number of rights sold. And since one fisherman might use his right to operate a tired gillnetter and another to run a new stern trawler, something more than a simple right to go fishing might be required in order to assure that the rights leased or sold could be equated and that no more than the available resource were harvested.

If instead allocations are sold, problems similar to those with ocean space may arise. Many are the foreign captains who will affirm that an allocation does not always equate with fish in the hold. Weather, environmental conditions, mechanical problems, etc., all conspire at times to defy the alchemist.

More important, perhaps, to the issue of privatization, would the government simply walk away after leasing or selling the rights created and let fishermen catch everything within their assigned areas, or operate as mentioned with any kind of gear or vessel, or find their allocations wherever and whenever they choose? It seems to me that, notwithstanding their leases, licenses and permits, oil companies are rather heavily regulated in their operations, as are radio stations, as are foreign fishermen.

My point is that creating property rights in fish would not necessarily reduce government involvement in the fisheries.

Would property rights in fish avoid the tragedy of the commons? Perhaps, but recall that Garrett Hardin, who is credited with first describing that tragedy, did not advocate property rights so much as coercion.

Social arrangements that produce responsibility, Hardin suggested, are arrangements that create coercion. "The man who takes money from a bank acts as if the bank were a commons," he said. "How do we prevent such action? Certainly not by trying to control his behavior solely by a verbal appeal to his sense of responsibility." "Rather...we...insist that a bank is not a commons [and] seek the definite social arrangements that will keep it from becoming a commons."[2] The social arrangement he advocated in this instance was not property rights for bank robbers but outright prohibition.

Hardin also suggested that temperance, as opposed to prohibition, could also be created by coercion. He pointed out, for example, that downtown shoppers can be kept temperate in their use of parking space by introducing parking meters for short periods and traffic fines for longer ones.

In other words, the commons and its tragedy can be avoided by a variety of coercive devices, from prohibition to taxation. Property rights are only one such device. They are coercive only to the extent that others are denied access to that which is privately owned.

The only kind of coercion Hardin recommended, however, was what he termed "mutual coercion, mutually agreed upon by the majority of the people affected."[3]

It seems to me that 'mutual coercion, mutually agreed upon by the majority of people affected' is essentially the goal sought by the fishery management councils in developing fishery management plans. In some instances, mutual coercion results in gear restrictions and closed areas, in others it results in quotas and trip limits. If the coercion mutually agreed upon is insufficient to protect the resource, other forms of mutual coercion obviously may be necessary.

The point is simply that the tragedy of the commons is to be avoided by restrictions on what can be removed from or placed in it, not exclusively or even preferably by selling off pieces of it. And selling off pieces of it, as I've suggested, does not necessarily promote privatization.

PRIVATIZATION: HOW MUCH GOVERNMENT?

How much government do we need is an ancient, perhaps timeless, question. In preparing for this conference, my research took me back well beyond the 20th century, and even the Revolution to Plato and to Aristotle. I only stopped there because of the poverty of my library. I would like to read a few lines from *The Politics*. In it, Aristotle said:

> ...those which are ineffective without each other must be united in a pair. For example the union of male and female is essential for reproduction since each is powerless without the other; and this is not a matter of choice, but is due to the desire, implanted by nature in both animals and plants, to propagate one's kind. Equally essential is the combination of ruler and ruled, the purpose of their coming together being their common safety.

Common safety, or what we nowadays call the national defense, has ever been considered a legitimate function of government, although views of what this might involve have changed considerably over time. It will be remembered that the authors of the *Federalist* devoted some pages in responding to criticism of the new Constitution that it did not prohibit the establishment of a standing army.

My point is that even accepting certain activities as the legitimate function of government, views will vary over time and among people as to how much or how little is required. With your permission, being in New England, I would like to quote a New Englander on this score. In his "Essay on Politics," Emerson said:

> In dealing with the State we ought to remember that its institutions are not aboriginal, though they existed before we were born; that they are not superior to the citizen; that every one of them was once the act of a single man; every law and usage was a man's expedient to meet a particular case; that they all are imitable, all alterable; we may make as good, we may make better. Society is an illusion to the young citizen. It lies before him in rigid repose, with certain names, men and institutions rooted like oak-trees to the centre, round which all arrange themselves as best they can. But the old statesman knows that society is fluid; there are no such roots and centres, but any particle may suddenly become the centre of the movement and compel the system to gyrate round it; as every man of strong will, like Pisitratus or Cromwell, does for a time, and every man of truth, like Plato or Paul, does forever. But politics rest on necessary foundations, and cannot be treated with levity. Republics abound in young civilians who believe that the laws make the city, that grave modifications of the policy and modes of living and employments of the population, that commerce, education and religion may be voted in or out; that any measure, though it were absurd, may be imposed on a people if only you can get sufficient voices to make it a law. But the wise know that foolish legislation is a rope of sand which perishes in the twisting; that the State must follow and not lead the character and progress of the citizen; the strongest usurper is quickly got rid of; and they only who build on Ideas, build for eternity; and that the form of government which prevails is the expression of what cultivation exists in the population which permits it. The law is only a memorandum.[5]

Only a memorandum. In the fisheries we have come to accept fairly extensive government involvement, especially since the mid-1970s. This involvement increased as the nation asserted new jurisdiction over the area known as the exclusive economic zone and over the fisheries within it. Government's responsibilities increased as we took on the responsibility of stewardship for these resources. In other words, government increased in direct response to domestic decisions and priorities.

Over the last decade, however, we have also come to question whether the government we have is the government we need. We have sought to define and clarify the respective roles of government and the private sector. Recently, for instance, the Administrator of the National Oceanic and Atmospheric Administration called for defining the minimum level of federal involvement in the fisheries. He suggested that the federal role should be confined to research and enforcement and that the federal government should not be in the business of developing fish products or marketing.[6]

These are domestic decisions regarding the proper role of government. Such decisions fall along a continuum. At one extreme is the current level of government involvement; at the other, perhaps, is no government at all. Somewhere in between is normally where we end up, although the precise point at which we find ourselves at any particular time is often a little bit higher or lower on the continuum than where we were a moment ago. As Emerson said:

> The statute stands there to say, Yesterday we agreed so and so, but how feel ye this article to-day? Our statute is a currency which we stamp with our own portrait; it soon becomes unrecognizable, and in the process of time will return to the mint.[7]

PRIVATIZATION: INTERNATIONAL DIMENSION

A similar kind of continuum exists with regard to privatization in its international dimension. Depending on our domestic priorities and decisions, there is greater or lesser government involvement in the international arena. For example, there are extensive efforts underway to restore Atlantic salmon to New England rivers. These involve private, state and federal initiatives. Because of them, the United States has been instrumental in establishing the North Atlantic Salmon Conservation Organization to enlist foreign cooperation in conserving the salmon produced by our domestic programs. Because of the domestic decision to restore Atlantic salmon, we have an international dimension requiring government involvement.

Similarly, because of domestic decisions regarding the annual specifications in various fisheries, we either have an international dimension or we do not. That dimension, when it exists, is known as joint venture processing and the total allowable level of foreign fishing. Domestic decisions give birth to the international dimension as well as shape and define it.

A further example is that of fisheries trade. If we could market all our seafood domestically, we would have little interest in foreign markets. However, because of prices, exchange rates, consumer preferences, distance to markets and so forth, it is often more advantageous to sell abroad. Domestic decisions to sell some of our production overseas create an international dimension and often require government involvement to assure that U.S. producers are not objects of unfair treatment or discrimination.

To the extent that we decide domestically that access to foreign fishing zones or foreign markets are important, or that we require the cooperation of other nations to conserve our fishery resources, we will have an international dimension. Under our Constitution, involvement in the international arena is uniquely the province of government. But the answer to how much government we need even in this arena is largely determined by domestic priorities and decisions. As Emerson said, "The State must follow and not lead the character and progress of the citizen."[8]

This, then, is the international dimension to privatization. It is a continuum based on a continuum. It expands and contracts in direct relationship to domestic priorities, and it cannot exist but for them.

NOTES AND REFERENCES

[1] Executive Office of the President, Circular No. A-76 (REVISED) on "Performance of Commercial Activities," August 4, 1983

[2] Garrett Hardin, "The Tragedy of the Commons," reprinted in *Exploring New Ethics for Survival/The Voyage of the Spaceship Beagle*, Penguin Books (1973), pp. 260-61

3   *Ibid.*

4   Aristotle, *The Politics*, Penguin Books (1962), p. 26

5   Ralph Waldo Emerson, "Essay on Politics," in *Selected Essays, Lectures and Poems of Ralph Waldo Emerson*, Washington Square Press (1965), pp. 317-18

6   Remarks of Anthony J. Calio, Administrator, National Oceanic and Atmospheric Administration, at the 11th Marine Recreational Fisheries Symposium, Tampa, Florida, May 1, 1986.

7   Emerson, "Essay on Politics," p. 318

8   Emerson, "Essay on Politics," p. 317

CHAPTER 14

Views on the Issue of Privatizing

MYTH OF PRIVATIZATION

JAMES D. O'MALLEY
Shoreside Company
Boston, Massachusetts

A CHANGE IN THE FISHERY

When we talk about "privatizing" the fisheries, I think it is useful to keep in mind that we are really talking about changing the way that the fisheries are privatized, not instituting some totally new concept. After all, every time a fishing vessel heads out to the grounds, it is beginning the process of privatization. The fish gets caught, it is possessed by the person who caught it, and quite thoroughly privatized. So what we are talking about here is a change in the style of how and by whom the resource is privatized. Instead of an individual making that decision on his own, the change proposed is that the process will be pre-empted by the assignment of ownership rights, before the fact of possession, by a governmental body.

Should we require that this change usher in an age of perfection in the fisheries? Not at all. But we ought to have at least a reasonable expectation that this change will be for the better. It has been said several times during this conference, quite rightly, that there are no guarantees in fishing, only opportunities. In discussing this question, we ought to satisfy ourselves that we are at least creating the opportunity for improvement by altering the present system of privatization. We ought to keep uppermost in our minds the question of why we are contemplating this change, and remember that the answer that we all share is "to make things better" than they are now.

THE SUPPOSED BENEFITS

Several arguments have been put forth in defense of the proposed change, and I think we ought to examine some of them.

The first is conservation, the avoidance of the so-called "Tragedy of the Commons." But there is a fundamental misunderstanding—or misapplication—of that phrase, especially as it might or might not apply to the fisheries. Garrett Hardin's thesis, essentially, is that overpopulation has no technological solution, and that the "freedom to breed will bring ruin to all," as growing numbers of people consume finite resources like air and water. He makes a passing remark about fisheries, specifically condemning maritime nations who adhere religiously to the "freedom of the seas." (Keep in mind that this was written in 1968.) He goes on to say that, as responsible human beings, we seek those social arrangements which prevent the tragedy of the commons from occurring.

The social arrangement, in this case, is extended jurisdiction. Human activity is subject to regulation and restraint. The fisheries are simply no longer the commons, and no longer subject to that tragedy. You may not like that idea, because it cuts a lot of ground out from under the position that access must be restricted. But it is a fact. The old concept, usually represented by the yield curve that dips sharply downward as more vessels enter a fishery and hammer the stocks, has no validity under extended jurisdiction. Conceptually, the "curve" levels off and simply continues on to the right, no matter the number of participants.

If there is a quota (if you are firmly committed to that odious system), the number is set; if the fisheries are regulated by methods like mesh sizes, the number is discovered after the fact: there have been so many fish caught under these conditions. In either case, the number of participants is irrelevant to the purpose of conservation. In what other ways might the assignment of property rights lead to an improvement in circumstances, if not in conservation?

The next argument usually offered is the promotion of economic efficiency. Some fishery managers seem to suggest that the tragedy of the commons is not only the destruction of the resource, but the dissipation of rents.

I don't happen to agree with that, and I think that Garrett Hardin would feel that his position was being misstated, perhaps deliberately, but that's beside the point. We have seen that the conservation argument doesn't hold up, what about the economic one? Bromley[1] has pointed out that firms enter any industry until total industry costs equal total receipts and rents are dissipated. Speaking of the fisheries specifically, he goes on to say that restricting entry into an industry so that group receipts are held above group costs is to deny that the competitive equilibrium results in the most efficient use of social resources. Is that right or wrong for the fisheries?

Given an omniscient and incorruptible administrator (whether a person, agency or commission) not subject to the human failings of pettiness, greed, parochialism, laziness, empire-building, we can theoretically envision a system wherein a government agency would determine the appropriate level of an industry's production and then make the consequent decisions on inputs. But why confine this to fisheries? Theoretically, this could be done for any industry. The answer is simple: we recognize, as a society, that production decisions are best left in the hands of those whom the marketplace holds accountable, and we have not made the somewhat fantastic leap of faith that puts those decisions in the hands of a bureaucracy which must be irresponsible. And I use that word in a very precise sense, not a perjorative one. The bureaucrat has no real accountability, and therefore is truly irresponsible, or perhaps "not responsible" would be a gentler choice of words.

I wanted to keep my remarks to a discussion of principles, but in at least one place we have to talk about practicalities and operations. This theoretical administrator would have to make production decisions, because he would either have to decide the amount to be produced, or decide the number of inputs. Herein lies an enormous trap in the marketplace. If, for example, a quota or input level were set to produce 10,000 tons of a resource, and there were really 20,000 tons available, the marketplace (the consumer and industry together) is cheated out of 10,000 tons. Revenues will be too low at exactly the same time that prices are too high. If the administrator, however, errs in the other direction and sets the quotas too high,

10,000 tons might do some real damage to a resource. Information is the essence of this process, and unfortunately, fishery science is not yet predictive. Cycles, fluctuations, and pure anomalies continue to confound the assessment community, the managers, and the industry. The industry shrugs and accepts it as the nature of the resource.

But even if our knowledge of ecosystems were to give us the ability to make fisheries biology a predictive science, and such a system were put into place, there would still be errors. The errors would sometimes be on the lower side out of concern for the resource, sometimes too high in response to political pressure. It really is a question of knowledge, and the proposed system would always be in a brutal catch-up situation. Such is the nature of the resource.

Would we be better off? I think it is extremely doubtful, overall. Remember, we are not talking about conservation here, but about central planning. That is what this discussion is all about. If you have the confidence that there should be some authority which decides how many shoe stores there ought to be, how many television sets ought to be manufactured, you are welcome to that point of view...and I think I know what your occupation is. Parenthetically, has anyone considered that the present allocation process and the madness of quotas is perhaps a type of privatization, with the councils forced to act as the owners? But that is a topic for another conference.

THE TAX PAYER/GOVERNMENT INVOLVEMENT

So we know that the fish don't care and the marketplace is likely to be worse off. Who else is involved? The taxpayer, the government?

Let's talk about that. Are the fisheries subject to government disposition for the purpose of extracting economic rent? I would argue that they are not. Ownership derives from occupation, from possession, from dominion and control, from investment. Government does not possess those fish, does not exercise even the shadow of control, has made no investment in that resource, did not create it. When we speak of privatizing, the fisheries are a lot different from a public airport. Tax money built it, and if the community decides to sell it, well and good. But it is pure fantasy[2] to speak of owning free-swimming fish. I will be the first to acknowledge that this could change, but it hasn't yet. The clearly-stated will of the Congress is that the relationship of government to fish remain that of trustee, not owner. The MFCMA restricts fees to administrative costs, and the levies on foreign fleets do not even begin to approach the uncaught market value of the allocations. Frankly, I would like to leave it that way. I think that the declaration of ownership without the traditional criteria of possession, occupation, control, is a very dangerous thing in terms of defining the relationship between a government and its citizens. We constantly seek to minimize government involvement in our lives, in our daily decisions, because we don't trust its competence or its intent, and we are correct. When we tolerate its intrusion, we demand justification, we want to know by what right the intrusion takes place.

Finally, when we speak of the goals of privatization, we are usually implying that an owner will make more rational investments, take better care of the property involved, and be generally more responsible and thoughtful because he wishes to protect his interests. All laudable goals. All dependent on single ownership. In the case of fisheries, no one is proposing that the resource be turned over to a single entity. That would carry with it all the attendant problems of monopoly, monopsony, price fixing, dead weight loss, and all the other ills that we associate with concentration.

So the fisheries will be turned over to an exclusive multiplicity of individuals and interests. They will still compete for the best catch rates, still create externalities, still have to be kept off the spawning grounds, still have to be constrained in many ways for the protection of the resource...

In short, they will be doing the same things they do now, and have to be regulated in exactly the same fashion. Whatever benefit we imagine from privatization simply cannot accrue in the fisheries. Again, the fisheries are not an airport.

SUMMARY

The fisheries are already under a regime of privatization; for government to usurp that authority confers no conservation benefit and puts production decisions into a bureaucracy with all the attendant drawbacks. The extraction of economic rent makes a claim of ownership that is without merit. The very goals that we associate with privatization cannot be met in the fisheries.

So I would ask that regulations be developed which do protect the resource, letting fish grow and reproduce. Enforce those regulations, and let the businesses and individuals who run them do the best job they can. They will—for themselves, the resource, and for you.

NOTES

[1]   Bromley, D.W. 1969. *Economic Efficiency in Common Property Natural Resource Use: A Case Study of the Ocean Fishery.* Bureau of Commercial Fisheries, Division of Economic Research

[2]   *Douglas v. Seacoast Products.* This reaffirmation by the Supreme Court of government's trusteeship, rather than ownership, of the fisheries resources, took place on May 23, 1977—months after the MFCMA was enacted.

IF THE SHOE DOESN'T FIT, STRETCH IT

RICHARD B. ALLEN
Vice President
Atlantic Offshore Fishermen's Association
Newport, Rhode Island

DEFINING PRIVATIZATION

When I was asked to address the pros and cons of privatization, the first thing I had to ask, of course, was "What is privatization?" After reading Mr. Singer's article, the question became, "Why are we calling limited entry privatization now?"

I have felt for some time that limited entry is not a useful term anymore. As someone said in the first session, it is a blanket term that covers schemes as different as limited transferable licenses and taxes on landings. Limited entry has been such a controversial topic that seldom do we get beyond the broad concept to talk about the specifics.

So now we call it privatization, which may not create the immediate inflammatory reaction that limited entry does but in my mind is no more specific or useful a term. So why are we calling limited entry privatization? Where did the term originate? Who started using it and what did they mean by it?

As far as I know, the present administration started using the term to describe the process of turning back to the private sector certain government functions that might be carried out better by the private sector. I believe Carol Ballew said that it included a desire not to compete with the private sector.

Now, the English language is known for both its internal inconsistencies and its subtle nuances. If we go to a scenic overlook, do we overlook the scenery, or do we look over the scenery?

The most important contribution we can make here is to answer the question whether privatization as it is being used as a substitute for limited entry is actually an accepted part of administration policy, or whether the proponents of limited entry have simply used some subtle semantic skullduggery to hoodwink the administration into believing that limited entry fits into its overall privatization philosophy? Certainly privatization seems like a valid term to substitute for some forms of limited entry. But if we look at privatization as the creation of property rights, is this really what the administration means by the term, when they suggest cutting down on government and reducing the role of government in the market place?

We are talking about allocating the right to fish and at present the market allocates the right to fish. No rational person assumes that we are going to sell off the right to fish and the government is then going to walk away from the problem, never needing to bother with it again. There should be no doubt in anyone's mind that privatization, or limited entry, will require a *new* bureaucracy, with with *more* national standards, *more* guidelines, *more* paperwork, *more* regulations, *more* enforcement, and *more* litigation. Rather than turning to the market to allocate the right to fish, therefore, we will be abandoning the market in favor of a larger and more intrusive role for the federal government. Isn't this exactly the opposite of the administration's policy? And yet, by playing these word games, and by continuing to deal only in broad generalizations, the proponents of limited entry make it seem that their philosophy fits right in with the overall plan.

Aside from its compatibility, or lack of compatibility, with administration policy, one of my greatest frustrations in dealing with the question of limited licenses, individual transferable quotas, or taxes and fees, it the superficial level at which the proponents of these measures plead for them. I believe there is a conscious attempt to avoid talking about the specifics in order to gain widespread acceptance for something that can be made to appeal to everybody until you actually design it and put it into practice. If you attempt to be specific, you start to lose supporters who thought you were talking about a different form or a different variation on a form.

If we wanted to critique Mr. Singer's article in detail, or the paper by Mike Orbach that Bill Gordon had published in *National Fisherman,* I think we could find many inconsistencies and contradictions that arise from the mix-and-match approach that the proponents have adopted. Take one attribute from limited licenses, mix with one attribute from stock certificates, add a dab from taxes and fees, and match with the constituency you are attempting to convince.

Perceived Problems

I don't want to continue what I see as a major failing of the opponents of limited entry, however, and that is a failure to recognize that a lot of people think there is a problem that needs to be addressed. Given the political system, when enough people think there's a problem, they'll try to get a solution to it. If limited entry is the only solution that's been proposed, it will win by default. I would also hope not to adopt the methods of the proponents of limited entry, however, by proposing one broad solution for all the perceived problems.

What are the perceived problems that attract people to limited entry? "Free-for-All Fishing Depletes Stock," the headline says, so conservation is obviously one perceived problem. Limited entry has not been shown to solve conservation problems, and Mr. Singer says that "setting the correct amount every year for each fishery is not a point at issue here: determinations will continue to be made by scientific experts." So, while Mr. Singer implies that conservation will be served by privatization, he states that conservation is not the issue.

But conservation is a perceived problem that will be used effectively, if not legitimately, by the proponents of privatization if it is not dealt with to the satisfaction of those who are concerned with it. The use of "The Tragedy of the Commons" is just such an appeal to those people.

But if we are going to quote Garrett Hardin in what I might term a sort of rabble-rousing way, shouldn't we look a little closer at what Hardin had to say in his essay? Hardin's main concern in the essay was overpopulation, and he concluded that "the freedom to breed is intolerable." He did not, however, suggest that we sell off all potential breeders at puberty, or even that we auction off the right to have children.

Hardin does suggest that we create "social arrangements" to produce responsibility, responsibility in his words being "mutual coercion mutually agreed upon." I would suggest that the Magnuson Fishery and Conservation Act of 1976 and the fishery management councils are such social arrangements. If we are not totally satisfied with the job they have done, it is appropriate to ask why. Does part of the answer lie with individuals who see the success of the management council system as taking away from the impetus for limited entry? We can achieve conservation without limited entry, and we must do so if we do not want to see the conservation issue used, however illogically to generate support for limited entry.

What's the other big problem that attracts people to limited entry. For the fisherman, there's not much question in my mind that he is seeking protection from competition—"we just keep splitting the pie up in smaller and smaller pieces," some say. Which pie, we should ask, the fish pie or the dollar pie? And when did the pieces start getting smaller? Are they really smaller, or aren't they growing as fast as they were? Would they be happy with a constant piece of the pie? How do they want to divide the pie up? Who do they want to divide the pie up? Do they want to be limited to taking a guaranteed slice from their pie, no matter how the pie expands and contracts, or do they want to be free to take a slice from somebody else's pie if their pie seems to be dwindling? Will their net piece of the dollar pie really be larger if they have to amortize an expensive license, or pay for a share of the pie, or pay use taxes on the slice of the pie they take?

Mr. Singer suggests that the federal government has operated on the fallacy that you can get something for nothing. I would suggest that fishermen who advocate limited entry think that they are going to get something for nothing. This is another result of the proponents of limited entry dealing only in generalities that do not dispel that myth. Even though Mr. Singer's main problem with the current system seems to be that "fishermen are charged nothing for the right to fish," he leaves open the possibility that these rights could be allocated on the basis of prior right. It's difficult for me to see how much value would attach to a right that expires at the end of one year, as Mr. Singer proposes, but Mr. Singer also insists that the rights must be transferable so that fishermen could buy and sell them. A fisherman who sees himself as qualifying for a prior right that he can then sell, therefore, thinks he is going to be given something of value for a price that he has already paid (that of being in the business) and for which he did not expect to get any additional value. The federal government would really be in the position of giving fishermen a bonus, although it would not come out of the treasury.

Another fallacious argument that is used to generate support for privatization is that of the high price of fish. With a limited resource, it should be apparent that the cost of harvesting does not determine the price to the consumer. The price is determined by the demand in relation to the supply, which is limited by availability. High prices are brought about by a large demand for a scarce product, not by the cost of production.

After first crediting fishermen with the power to set the price of fish, and discounting the role of consumers in setting the price of fish, Mr. Singer finally gives the consumer the ultimate power to stop the cycle (of higher prices for fish attracting more entrants whose costs eat up their potential profits) by refusing to buy higher-priced fish. He apparently views consumers' buying habits as a limit switch that has been set too high, rather than the automatic cushioning device that the demand curve might be more traditionally viewed as. After ascribing this power to solve the problem to the consumer, that is, the market, however, he continues to call for government intervention in the market place through the privatization of the fisheries.

It's as easy to say that the argument over the high price of fish is a fallacy as it is to say that the price of fish is caused by there being too many fishermen. But what do the facts show? The average ex-vessel price of most major species of fish in New England, when adjusted for inflation, declined during the period from 1978 through 1984. Yellowtail flounder, for example, declined from $.57 per pound in 1978 to $.43 in 1984. Whiting dropped from $.12 to $.08, hake from $.17 to $.09, pollock from $.16 to $.10, winter flounder from $.43 to $.41, cod from $.23 to $.22. Lobster dropped from $1.73 to $1.50 per pound. Redfish showed a small increase, and only haddock and sea scallops showed significant gains, $.30 to $.41 for haddock, and $2.36 to $3.26 for scallop meats. If we looked at scallops today, I think we would find that they've taken a drastic drop in true price in the last two years. Just as the first session pointed out that we are mistaken to look to the councils to discover the cause of the high cost of fisheries management, I think it is clear that we are mistaken to look to the fisherman to discover the high price of fish.

Mr. Singer also decries the fact that foreign fishing rights are determined by politics, rather than economics, and thus "used for mischief." I don't know Mr. Singer, but from his credentials I would certainly hesitate to call him naive. I don't know what else to call it, however, if he believes that a system in which "foreign fishermen would submit bids or purchase fishing rights from the U.S. owners of such rights" would be free of political and foreign policy considerations.

I also find it difficult to believe that Mr. Singer is confident that such a system would be free from economic shenanigans. Rather than a system that automatically, with no opportunity for manipulation, distributes both the right to fish and the revenue from fishing, Mr. Singer proposes an entirely new industry based on speculation in fishing rights. Not on fish, but on the right to fish. The lessons that Mr. Singer urges us to learn from Alaska evidently include that of an original member of Alaska's Limited Entry Commission who apparently soon learned that the business of brokering fishing rights was more profitable than either fishing or serving on the Limited Entry Commission.

To get back to the "tragedy of the commons," from which Mr. Singer steps directly to the statement that the "fairest way to limit access is by establishing transferable property rights," I think we should see what Hardin has to say about property rights. Hardin states that "we must admit that our legal system of private property plus inheritance is unjust..." By contrast, the open access system of fisheries management leads automatically to Hardin's suggestion "that those who are biologically more fit to be the custodians of property and power should legally inherit more." Open access insures that those who are more fit to harvest the resource will be allowed to while those who are not suited to the productive harvest of the fisheries will not be insulated from the workings of the economy by their wealth, either earned or inherited, or by their inheritance of "property rights" to our fisheries.

It has become popular to compare fisheries to other industries, and particularly resource industries, to make the case for privatization. For those who think that oil and gas, timber rights, water rights, and grazing rights are allocated by an "equitable and efficient method," I can offer some references to continuing litigation and legislation that indicates otherwise. These programs sound good until you see how they really work, hardly free from the troubles that cause us to look to limited entry.

A particular example that intrigues me but I have never seen explored except on "Sixty Minutes" a few years ago, is that of licenses to grow peanuts. It used to be popular to use agriculture as a shining example of what property rights could do for the fisheries. Clem Tillion was fond of asking why a loaf of bread was so cheap. It was all due to property rights, farmers owning their land.

But the case of the peanut growers makes clear the distinction between owning the means of production and the rights to production. As a little known leftover from the depression and the second World War, a limited number of individuals possess the right to grow peanuts. Do these people also own farms, and use this combination of physical and legal resources to produce peanuts most efficiently? Not according to Sixty Minutes. Most of the license holders rent out their rights and sit back and profit from this government intervention in the free market.

My understanding of the San Francisco herring fishery is that it is similar, where a license holder need not own a boat, he just hires out with his license to a boat owner who needs him if he is to participate in the fishery.

The Outcomes of Limited Entry

Once you start talking about the specifics, there is no end to the problems you can find with limited entry. What I would hope is clear, however, is that:

1. Calling limited entry privatization is a semantic trick, whether intentional or not, that is intended to gain support from the administration for something that is opposite to its overall policy;

2. Limited entry will not bring about conservation;

3. Limited entry will not lower the price of fish;

4. Limited entry is not the fairest way to allocate fishing privileges;

5. Limited entry will not insure the financial well-being and economic efficiency of our fishing industry; and

6. Limited entry will not remove foreign fishing allocations from the political and foreign policy arena.

Limited entry *will* result in a new bureaucracy, more regulation, and greater interference by the government in the private sector and the free market economy.

OTHER SOLUTIONS

There are problems with our current fishery management system, but there are solutions to these problems that are not based on limited entry. Among the easy ones that I believe most fishermen will agree with Mr. Singer on are the elimination of many of the programs that act as incentives to investing in the fishing business. As we become more concerned with overcapitalization, we must take a harder look at fisheries development programs, which quickly cross some poorly defined and invisible boundary into overcapitalization.

These solutions will only be available to us to the extent that we look for them and consider them, in the same way that we are being urged and directed to consider limited entry. The proponents of limited entry, who happen to be primarily the fishery managers who are in a position to influence strongly the direction that management takes, must be as openminded about the alternatives to limited entry as they are asking us to be about the imposition of limited entry.

PRIVATIZATION SCHEMES: OPPORTUNITY AND CONTROVERSY

WALTER T. PEREYRA
President
ProFish International, Inc.
Seattle, Washington

Economists have long admonished the fishery administrators for the manner in which they manage our fishery resources. They have argued that, because of the common property nature of our fishery resources, we cannot permit uncontrolled entry into the fisheries without fishermen and our nation suffering dire economic consequences. The overcapitalization in certain fully utilized fisheries such as the west coast troll salmon fishery and the New England groundfish fisheries have been cited as examples of the problems created by allowing unlimited entry in our marine fisheries.

As traditional approaches to fisheries management (utilizing such measures as time/area closures, quotas, and gear restrictions) have failed, resource managers have begun to seriously consider more efficient output control models for managing our fisheries. These attempts to control, or more efficiently manage fishing effort in our fisheries, are in reality a means to privatize a public resource.

Such resource allocation schemes have been used successfully in managing harvests of other publicly-owned resources such as our national forests and some privately-owned sedentary marine species such as clams and oysters. There is reason to believe that transferring ownership in some manner to the private sector in certain domestic finfish fisheries could: result in a more orderly and efficient allocation of our limited fish resources; facilitate management; and bring greater benefit to our nation.

PRIVATIZATION SCHEMES

The three principle ways in which we might privatize our fisheries are license limitation, individual resource quotas, or individual resource shares. While the three approaches differ in their functional application, they all basically are designed to eliminate excess capitalization and thereby allow for more efficient utilization of scarce, common property resources.

License Limitation

License limitation, or limited entry, has been the more widely-used scheme to reduce or prevent the dissipation of net economic rent in certain fully-developed fisheries. Most distant-water fishing nations control the growth or size of their fleets through license control. License limitation has also been widely used in Alaska for managing entry into the salmon and herring fisheries. Procedures have been established for determining who is eligible to receive licenses. Limitations are placed on the types of vessels and fisheries for which the licenses are valid. In most cases, the vessel licenses are transferrable and become a valued property right in themselves.

While the limited entry schemes have been successful in reducing effort in these fisheries, the programs themselves have not been universally accepted nor have they been completely satisfactory in allowing the emergence of the most cost-effective harvesting arrangements. Some have argued that the licensing schemes themselves are too mechanistic and unresponsive to the economic interests of the resource users.

Individual Resource Quota

In New Zealand where certain groundfish fisheries are underdeveloped, a resource quota system has been instituted for managing these emerging fisheries. This quota management system, which has operated successfully for several years, is based upon individual transferrable quotas (ITQs). These quotas, which are given for different species to certain operators based on their historical catch and investment in the industry, are valid in perpetuity. The ITQs are transferrable harvest rights that can be sold or traded "at the market." Thus, market forces rather than regulatory interference determine the manner in which the fisheries are prosecuted.

The government becomes involved in providing adjustment assistance, the charging of resource royalties and rentals for the use of this public resource, and quota trading. The harvest right itself is denominated as a specified tonnage of quota with the government adjusting the total allowable catch (TAC) through the buying and selling of quotas. The government has reserved to itself the right of compulsory acquisition of quotas, subject to arbitration on price paid for such quotas if necessary.

Resource Shares

Another approach for controlling entry to our fisheries has been the allocation of resource shares directly among the participants with a resource share being some percentage of the TAC. This approach is being successfully employed in the offshore fisheries of eastern Canada under an enterprise quota system. Under this system, as the TAC rises or falls due to changes in resource abundance, the absolute amount of quota represented by the percentage resource share likewise rises and falls proportionally. An advantage of such a scheme is the non-involvement of government in the buying and selling of quotas to adjust TAC as is done in New Zealand.

In the resource share system, resolution of the by-catch problem might be simplified by requiring that fishermen have sufficient resource share to cover their by-catch needs. For example, in a multi-species fishery, like a trawl fishery, an individual shareholder could be required to own or have access to an appropriate share of the by-catch species in order to exercise his target species share. Depending upon costs of the by-catch share, this would encourage the operator to adjust his by-catch in order to maximize his economic return from the directed fishing operation.

While on the surface the resource share approach would seem to have merit, concern has been expressed as to how the shares themselves would be apportioned among various interested parties. The simplest scheme might be to allocate the resource shares through a lottery or auction system with expired shares reverting back through some central resource agency for reallocation. Again, appropriate royalty or rent could be applied to the resource share to ensure that the nation receives fair compensation for this public resource.

THE PRIVATIZATION CONTROVERSY

The implementation of privatization schemes in our fisheries has not been without controversy. There have been strong arguments put forth both in support and against the concept of privatization of our fisheries. Some of the arguments in favor of the privatization approach have included:

- Privatization would result in a more efficient utilization of our nation's resources;

- The costs and problems associated with managing our fisheries would be greatly reduced. Furthermore, we would begin to move away from the "crisis management" approach common in our fisheries today;

- The role of government in resource allocation would be greatly reduced or even eliminated. This, in turn, would allow fishery management bodies to devote their attention to critical conservation and management issues rather than trying to manage the private sector;

- We would eliminate over capitalization in our fisheries with concomitant reductions in social costs;

- We would come closer to extracting the net economic rent from our national fishery resources rather than having it dissipated in excessive costs as occurs at present;

- We would have a more even flow of higher quality finished products to the consumer at potentially lower costs;

- There would be a reduction in conflicts among resource users as fishing effort and gear is more evenly distributed over the year;

- With fishing effort spread out over a longer fishing season, the likelihood of overfishing would be reduced. Moreover management response time would be lengthened;

- Our fisheries would be safer as each fisherman would have greater latitude in deciding when to fish for his share;

- With improved profitability fishermen would have sufficient funds to allow them to modernize existing vessels, build new ones, or install newer fishing gear;

- Investment risk associated with resource availability would be reduced, thereby encouraging long-term investments in our fisheries; and

- Once harvesters own rights to the resource, they should be in a much stronger position to negotiate long-term supply contracts with willing buyers.

Some of the principal arguments put forth in opposition to privatization of our fisheries include:

- Many American fishermen feel that the imposition of some limited entry or reduced access program in our fisheries would remove an important God-given freedom of choice;

- Power might be concentrated in the hands of a few large corporations to the detriment of the small, independent vessel owner and fisherman;

- Foreign nations could gain control of our strategic fishery resources by buying up resource shares to the long-term detriment of our domestic fisheries and fishermen;

- New entrants would experience increased difficulty coming into the fishery unless they were willing to pay large sums of money. Thus, a fisherman's dream of his son having the opportunity to enter a fishery in a small boat and build himself up over the years through hard work and the application of his own skills and ingenuity would be compromised;

- It will be difficult or impossible to reduce effort in a fair and equitable manner in fully-developed fisheries;

- Total employment in the fisheries would be reduced; and

- Development of under-utilized species might be retarded since historically over-capitalization in one fishery has forced fishermen to innovate and expand into new and under-developed fisheries.

For any scheme to be successful the following factors must be taken into consideration and resolved.

- All fisheries with commonality should probably be included in any privatization scheme. A piecemeal, one-fishery-at-a-time approach will only lead to accelerated dislocation and over-capitalization in those fisheries and on those species not privatized. A good example of this is the situation which occurred in the North Pacific following salmon license limitation when excess vessel capacity shifted over to other fisheries such as halibut, which allows unlimited entry. This contributed to the over-capitalization problems in another fishery.

- Any rights, whether they be licenses, resource shares, or individual quotas, must be treated as private property rights which can be sold, traded, or passed on through an estate.

- Some nominal royalty, or rent should be charged to the share or license so that the nation receives proper compensation for use of the public resource.

- There should be minimal restrictions on season or manner in which a share or license holder chooses to exercise his harvest rights.

- Historical participation of participants in the fisheries on the species being privatized should be taken into consideration.

- Some maximum limit should be placed on the amount of a resource controlled by any one participant in the fishery. Furthermore, foreign control of our fishery resources and the domestic fishermen extracting these resources should be minimized by requiring that more than 50 percent of the equity of any vessel engaged in the U.S. fisheries, as defined by the Magnuson Fishery Conservation and Management Act of 1976, be owned by citizens of the United States.

Regardless of the privatization scheme employed, the resource shareholders individually or collectively should decide on the harvesting scheme desired to take their share of the resource. As opposed to the first-come first-served chaos of today, under a privatization approach, it would be in the interests of the involved participants to apply fishing effort judiciously to ensure perpetuation of the resource and their greatest long-term net economic gain. Collectively, the harvesters operating in their own best interests will also bring the greatest economic benefit to the nation. Furthermore, we should see the creation of a competitive and positive climate for resource development and a more stable management environment, thereby ensuring conservation.

CONCLUSION

As a consequence of our establishment of a 200-mile exclusive economic zone, an enormous economic opportunity is waiting offshore for our domestic fishermen and our nation. Whether or not we fully realize this potential will be largely dependent upon the manner in which we manage our fishery resources. Allowing unrestricted entry into our fisheries has resulted in a chaotic situation in certain fisheries and a no-win situation for resource managers. Furthermore, our nation has not derived the maximum economic benefit from the exploitation and utilization of our vast fishery resources.

For these reasons it would appear to be reasonable to consider some type of privatization scheme in certain fisheries as an alternative to the unlimited entry allowed in most of our fisheries today. Some change in management structure should be taken under serious consideration in the near future to protect and improve the gains made by our domestic fishermen since extended jurisdiction. If we do not make fundamental changes in our approach to allocating certain of our scarce common property fishery resources, we will see one fishery after another become overcapitalized with concomitant adverse social and economic consequences and increasing difficulties in our management regimes. Now is the time to begin a national debate on this important issue and once and for all devise a more rational resource allocation scheme to apply to our nation's fisheries. Our nation, our fishermen, and our fishery resources deserve nothing less.

REMARKS

LEE G. ANDERSON
College of Marine Studies
University of Delaware
Newark, Delaware

While the economic theoretical thrust of Dr. Singer's comments are, for the most part, correct (the only exception being that the price of fish will not fall with a privatization program given a fixed total allowable catch) his rather doctrinaire call for privatization in all fisheries at all times is at best naive. His comments show an ignorance of real world fisheries biology, fisheries industry structure, and the difficulties of policy implementation and enforcement. He ignores the extreme variability of many stocks, biological and technological interrelationships between harvest of different species, and the cost of enforcement procedures. Economists have been discussing limited entry (or privatization) in fisheries for over 20 years because of the potential of private property to improve overall efficiency in the fishery and in the economy as a whole. However, it is generally agreed that it is impossible to have rational discussions on limited entry policy without a detailed analysis of the specific fishery and the specific type of limited entry to be used so that the benefits and costs of implementing the program can be compared with no management and with alternative forms of regulation. Without such information, policy discussions usually default to alternating monologues which usually do not address the same specific issues. There has been much of that here today. Singer's comments would have been much more valuable if he had done more than repeat well-known generalities and instead focused on a real world fishery.

PART SEVEN

Conference Summary

As noted in the preface to these proceedings, the conference was structured around a set of basic questions. Specifically, the objectives of the conference were to critically assess the current system of fisheries management under the Magnuson Fishery Conservation and Management Act (MFCMA), to explore how and whether privatizing the fisheries should be realized, to evaluate the potential for increasing the role of state governments in fisheries management, to learn from management experience in other natural resource fields, and to identify novel approaches to fisheries enforcement and research. The following is an attempt to summarize the wealth of material presented at the workshop as it related to the basic questions. By necessity, this summary has had to overlook several valuable contributions contained in the papers and discussion. There is no satisfactory substitute for reading the entire volume.

CRITICAL ASSESSMENT OF THE CURRENT SYSTEM

There appeared to be widespread agreement on the criteria used for assessing fisheries management. The Reagan administration seeks a system which: (1) interferes as little as possible in private business decisions; (2) reduces the costs of federal fisheries management; and (3) increases government revenues. Other obvious criteria were protection of fishery stocks and development of the domestic fishing industry.

The current system of regional councils, with involvement of all interested parties, is viewed as basically sound, though not perfect. The system has successfully facilitated development, especially of fisheries formerly dominated by foreign fleets. Overall, domestic landings and productivity in the EEZ are up. But these improvements are due to developments in the lower valued fisheries. The system has failed to protect some high valued fishery stocks, especially those traditionally exploited by domestic fleets. Several high valued fisheries have experienced declines in landings and productivity. The current system has not adequately restrained fishing pressure. Over capitalization has been allowed, if not induced, by many management measures.

Too much government intervention and of the wrong kind was a common criticism. Regulations under the current system have led to less efficient production practices and less flexibility in the industry. Furthermore, federal efforts are perceived as often duplicating actions by councils and states.

PRIVATIZATION

There was considerable debate over the meaning of "privatization." Some equated it with conferring private property rights or limited entry measures. Others equated it with reducing or eliminating government involvement in areas more appropriately performed by the private sector.

One of the more substantive issues here is whether limited entry measures require less government involvement. One discussant argued more government involvement will result, whereas another discussant argued less will occur. Both are members of the fishing industry.

INCREASING STATES' ROLE

State fishery management officials from three regions of the U.S. discussed the prospects for increasing the role of state governments in fisheries management. Alaska and Texas clearly desire more authority and less federal interference in their efforts to manage fisheries. Both states perceive a role for federal authority in fisheries management but one that is largely separate from state management efforts.

The smaller State of Massachusetts, on the other hand, faces very limited prospects for expanding its role in fisheries management. A more feasible alternative, at least on the Atlantic coast, would be to provide regional bodies with greater regulatory authority.

LESSONS FROM OTHER FIELDS

The practices and procedures used in the management of other resources appear to offer some desirable alternatives to those used in the current fisheries management system. Among several discussed were: the bidding procedures for allocating exploitation rights used in forestry and minerals management; the use of private property rights measures in rangeland management and pollution control; and the procedures used to manage the exploitation of the transboundary and migratory resources of water and birds.

ENFORCEMENT

Enforcement under the current system is very costly. Also, while reliable measures are lacking, there are numerous reports of ineffective and insufficient enforcement. Improving the cost-effectiveness of enforcement will contribute greatly to improving fisheries management in the U.S. One valuable suggestion for enhancing the cost-effectiveness of enforcement is to directly involve management authorities in enforcement planning and involve enforcement authorities in management planning. The current system has failed to invoke such involvement to a meaningful degree.

RESEARCH

The current research programs to support fisheries management are perceived to be basically sound. There is strong justification for these programs under both the existing system and most feasible alternative management systems. The primary issue in this area is how to allocate scarce research funds among the many competing needs. No definitive answer to this proverbial problem was forthcoming.

Our hope is that these proceedings will contribute in some small way to improved fisheries management and ultimately achieving the objectives set out by the MFCMA.

JON G. SUTINEN
Conference Chairman
Associate Professor
Resource Economics
University of Rhode Island
Kingston, Rhode Island

Rethinking Fisheries Management
June 1-4, 1986

Louis Agard
Western Pacific Fishery
   Management Council
1164 Bishop St., Rm. 1405
Honolulu, HI   96813

Richard Agnello
Economics Department
University of Delaware
Newark, DE   19711

Khamiss S. Al-Bulushi (student)
ICMRD Training Group
University of Rhode Island
Kingston, RI   02881

Lewis M. Alexander, Director
Center for Ocean Management Studies
University of Rhode Island
Kingston, RI   02881

Linda Gunn Alexander (student)
405 Mohegan Avenue
New London, CT   06320

Hamed S. Al-Ghilani (student)
ICMRD Training Group
University of Rhode Island
Kingston, RI   02881

Ali Saleh Al-Harrasi (student)
ICMRD Training Group
University of Rhode Island
Kingston, RI   02881

Richard B. Allen
Atlantic Offshore Fishermen's Assn.
P.O. Box 3001, 221 Third St.
Newport, RI   02840

James L. Anderson
Resource Economics
University of Rhode Island
Kingston, RI   02881

Lee G. Anderson
College of Marine Studies
University of Delaware
Newark, DE   19716

Bob Ballou (student)
University of Maine
192 Stevens Avenue
Portland, ME   04102

Carol Ballew
Budget Officer
Office of Management and Budget
New Exec. Office Bldg., Rm. 9215
Washington, D.C.   20503

Richard R. Banks
Sea Fish Industry Authority
10 Young Street
Edinburgh, EH2 4JQ
United Kingdom

Anant Bharabwaj (student)
ICMRD Training Group
University of Rhode Island
Kingston, RI   02881

Thomas E. Bigford
National Marine Fisheries Service
NOAA
2 State Fish Pier
Gloucester, MA   01930-3097

Peter Boehmer
Seafood Soundings
Box 127
Monhegan Island, ME   04852

Raquel Boehmer
Seafood Soundings
Box 127
Monhegan Island, ME   04852

Lourival Bomkim
Sudere-Se-Brazil
Aracaju-Se, Brazil

Priscilla M. Brooks (student)
Dept. of Resource Economics
University of Rhode Island
Kingston, RI   02881

R. H. Burroughs
Graduate Program in Marine Affairs
University of Rhode Island
Kingston, RI   02881

Sally J. Campen, Consultant
Japan Fisheries Association
7512 Ambergate Place
McLean, VA   22102

Kathleen Castro (student)
ICMRD Training Group
University of Rhode Island
Kingston, RI   02881

Philip Coates
Mass. Division of Marine Fisheries
100 Cambridge Street
Boston, MA   02202

Kenelm W. Coons, Director
New England Fisheries
   Development Foundation, Inc.
280 Northern Avenue
Boston, MA   02210

Chris Cornell
National Fisherman Magazine
21 Elm Street
Camden, ME   04843

James Costakes
Seafood Producers Association
17 Hamilton Street
New Bedford, MA   02740

Brian Crawford (student)
ICMRD Training Group
University of Rhode Island
Kingston, RI   02881

Hamid Dahman (student)
ICMRD Training Group
University of Rhode Island
Kingston, RI   02881

William D. Davies
Fisheries Department
Auburn University
203 Swingle Hall
Auburn University, AL   36849

Moustapha Deme (student)
Dept. of Resource Economics
University of Rhode Island
Kingston, RI   02881

John L. Dentler
Merchant Marine & Fisheries
   Committee
U.S. House of Representatives Staff
House Annex II, Room 545
Washington, D.C.   20515

Joel Dirlam
Professor Emeritus
Economics and Resource Economics
University of Rhode Island
Kingston, RI   02881

William R. Dolan
Political Science Department
Salem State College
Salem, MA   01970

Mohsin Ahmed Eidroos (student)
ICMRD Training Group
University of Rhode Island
Kingston, RI   02881

Salim B. Fadhil (student)
ICMRD Training Group
University of Rhode Island
Kingston, RI   02881

Ben Ferguson
Department of Fisheries & Oceans
Centennial Tower, 200 Kent,
  Rm. 1106
Ottawa, Ontario
Canada K1A OE6

Eugene Fritz
National Sea Grant Office, NOAA
6010 Executive Blvd.
Rockville, MD 20852

Richard P. Gale
Professor
Department of Sociology
University of Oregon
Eugene, OR 97403

Rashid Hamed Ghafiry (student)
ICMRD Training Group
University of Rhode Island
Kingston, RI 02881

Louis Goodreau
New England Fishery
  Management Council
Suntaug Office Park, Rt. 1
Saugus, MA 01906

William G. Gordon
National Marine Fisheries Service
NOAA
3300 Whitehaven Street, N.W.,
  Rm. 400
Washington, D.C. 20235

Clifford A. Goudey
Center for Fisheries
  Engineering Research
MIT Sea Grant
Bldg. E38-376, 292 Main Street
Cambridge, MA 02139

George C. Grant
Assistant Director
Virginia Inst. of Marine Science
Gloucester Point, VA 23062

Walter J. Gray
Director
Division of Marine Resources
University of Rhode Island
Narragansett Bay Campus
Narragansett, RI 02882-1197

Stephen Greene
Canadian Consulate General
Three Copley Place, Suite 400
Boston, MA 02116

Wade L. Griffin
Texas A & M University
Agricultural Economics Dept.
College Station, TX 77843

Thomas A. Grigalunas
Professor
Dept. of Resource Economics
University of Rhode Island
Kingston, RI 02881

Richard E. Gutting, Jr.
Vice President
Government Relations
National Fisheries Institute
1101 Connecticut Ave., N.W.
Washington, D.C. 20036

Lynne Carter Hanson
Executive Director
Center for Ocean Management Studies
University of Rhode Island
Kingston, RI 02881

William J. Hargis
Virginia Inst. Marine Science
William & Mary College
Gloucester Point, VA 23062

Timothy Hennessey
Professor
Political Science
University of Rhode Island
Kingston, RI 02881

Carol Dryfoos Hunter
Coordinator
Center for Ocean Management Studies
University of Rhode Island
Kingston, RI 02881

Angela M. Ivanovici
Australian National Parks &
  Wildlife Service
GPO Box 636
Canberra, ACT 2601 Australia

Lawrence Juda
Professor & Chairman
Geography and Marine Affairs
University of Rhode Island
Kingston, RI 02881

Jeffrey H. Kaelin
Executive Director
Maine Sardine Council
470 N. Maine St., P.O. Box 337
Brewer, ME 04412

David Kaiser
Graduate Program in Marine Affairs
University of Rhode Island
Kingston, RI 02881

Ilene M. Kaplan
Department of Sociology
Director, Marine Studies Program
Union College
Schenectady, NY 12308

Karl Wm. Kieninger
Hydrographer/Marine Consultant
7002 Boulevard East
Guttenberg, NJ 07093

John A. Knauss
Dean and Vice President
  of Marine Programs
Graduate School of Oceanography
University of Rhode Island
Narragansett Bay Campus
Narragansett, RI 02882

Richard Langton
Maine Dept. Of Marine Resources
Marine Resources Laboratory
West Boothbay Harbor, ME   04575

Alec D. MacCall
Southwest Fisheries Center
National Marine Fisheries Service
NOAA
P.O. Box 271
La Jolla, CA 92038

Melvin Makaiwi
Western Pacific Fishery
  Management Council
1164 Bishop St., Rm. 1405
Honolulu, HI 96813

Guy D. Marchessault
New England Fishery
  Management Council
Suntaug Office Park, Rt. 1
Saugus, MA 09106

Douglas G. Marshall
Executive Director
New England Fishery
  Management Council
Suntaug Office Park, Rt. 1
Saugus, MA 09106

Gene S. Martin
College of Marine Studies
University of Delaware
Robinson Hall
Newark, DE 19716

Gary C. Matlock
Texas Parks & Wildlife Department
4200 Smith School Road
Austin, TX 78744

Thomas A. Nies
Operational Division
U.S. Coast Guard
2100 Second Street, S.W.
Washington, D.C. 20593

Dennis Nixon
Assistant Professor
Graduate Program in Marine Affairs
University of Rhode Island
Kingston, RI 02881

Bruce W. Norman
Fishery Management Study
National Marine Fisheries Service
NOAA
14th & Constitution Avenue N.W.
Washington, D.C. 20235

John D. O'Connell (student)
Dept. of Resource Economics
University of Rhode Island
Kingston, RI 02881

James O'Malley
Shoreside Company
P.O. Box 1070
Boston, MA   02205

Joseph Pelczarski
Coastal Zone Management Program
100 Cambridge St., 20th Floor
Boston, MA   02202

Walter T. Pereyra
ProFish International, Inc.
657 N. 34th Street
Seattle, WA   98103

Daniel A. Reifsnyder
OES/OFA
Department of State
Washington, D.C.   20520

Gerald D. Rhodes
Chief
Branch of Development & Production
Minerals Management Service
Reston, VA   22090

Ed Richardson (student)
Resource Economics
University of Rhode Island
Kingston, RI   02881

Alison Rieser
Marine Law Institute
University of Maine
246 Deering Avenue
Portland, ME   04102

Bruce Rogers
Blue Flag Farms, Inc.
61 Switch Road
Hope Valley, RI 02832

Christopher Rogers
College of Marine Studies
University of Delaware
Robinson Hall
Newark, DE   19716

Pamela B. Rothstein (student)
ICMRD Training Group
University of Rhode Island
Kingston, RI   02881

Peter N. Rowe
Smith College
Department of Government
Wright Hall 214
Northampton, MA   01063

Justin Rutka
Economist
Western Pacific Fishery
   Management Council
1164 Bishop St., Rm. 1405
Honolulu, HI   96813

Henry Sakuda
Western Pacific Fishery
   Management Council
1164 Bishop St., Rm. 1405
Honolulu, HI   96813

Richard H. Schaefer
Acting Regional Director
Northeast Region
National Marine Fisheries Service
NOAA
Gloucester, MA   01930

Francis Schuler
National Sea Grant Office, NOAA
6010 Executive Blvd.
Rockville, MD   20852

Kenneth Sherman
Laboratory Director
National Marine Fisheries Service
NOAA
R.R. 7A, Box 522A
Narragansett, RI   02882

Armand Silva
Professor
Ocean & Civil Engineering
University of Rhode Island
Kingston, RI   02881

Maynard Silva
Marine Policy & Ocean Management
Woods Hole Oceanographic Institution
Woods Hole, MA   02543

S. Fred Singer
George Mason University
Fairfax, VA   22202

Robert A. Skillman
National Marine Fisheries Service
NOAA
2570 Dole Street
Honolulu, HI   96822-2396

Eric M. Smith
Connecticut Department of
    Environmental Protection
Marine Fisheries, P.O. Box 248
Waterford, CT   06385

M. Estellie Smith
WHOI (SUNY)
Swift House
Woods Hole, MA   02543

Janet Smoker
National Marine Fisheries Service
NOAA
P.O. Box 211012
Auke Bay, AK   99821

Barbara Duer Stevenson
Otonka, Inc.
Rt. 2, Box 91A
Dagsboro, DE   19939

Jon G. Sutinen
Associate Professor
Resource Economics
University of Rhode Island
Kingston, RI   02881

Gil Sylvia (student)
49 Wheatfield Cove Road
Narragansett, RI   02882

Hiroyuki Takagi
Japanese Fisheries Association
2505 Wisconsin Ave., N.W.,
    Suite 510
Washington, D.C.   20007

Guy Thornburgh
Alaska Department of
    Fish and Game
P.O. Box 3-2000
Juneau, AL   99802

Gerald R. Visgilio
Connecticut College
Box 1511
New London, CT   06320

Ingrid Wendt (student)
Agriculture & Resource Economics
University of Massachusetts
213 Draper Hall
Amherst, MA   01003

Daphne Milbank White
National Marine Fisheries Service
NOAA
Office of Fisheries Management
Washington, D.C.   20235

James R. Wilson
Marine Policy & Ocean Management
Woods Hole Oceanographic Institution
Woods Hole, MA   02543

Gail Wing (student)
Graduate School of Oceanography
University of Rhode Island
Narragansett, RI   02882

Center for Ocean
Management Studies

Annual Conference Proceedings

1. U.S. Coastal Belt: Conflict, Resolution, and Promise
   June 20-21, 1977

2. Formulating Marine Policy: Limitations to Rational Decision-making
   June 19-21, 1978

3. Comparative Marine Policy
   June 18-20, 1979

4. Impact of Marine Pollution on Society
   June 23-25, 1980

5. The U.S. Fishing Industry and Regulatory Reform
   June 22-24, 1981

6. The Newest Federalism: A New Framework for Coastal Issues
   June 21-23, 1982

7. The United States Without the Law of the Sea Treaty: Opportunities and Costs
   June 12-15, 1983

8. Antarctic Politics and Marine Resources: Critical Choices for the 1980s
   June 17-20, 1984

9. The Continental Shelf: Resources, Boundaries and Management
   June 16-19, 1985

10. Rethinking Fisheries Management
    June 1-4, 1986

For information on ordering, contact:

Center for Ocean Management Studies
University of Rhode Island
19 Upper College Road
Kingston, RI 02881
(401) 792-2145